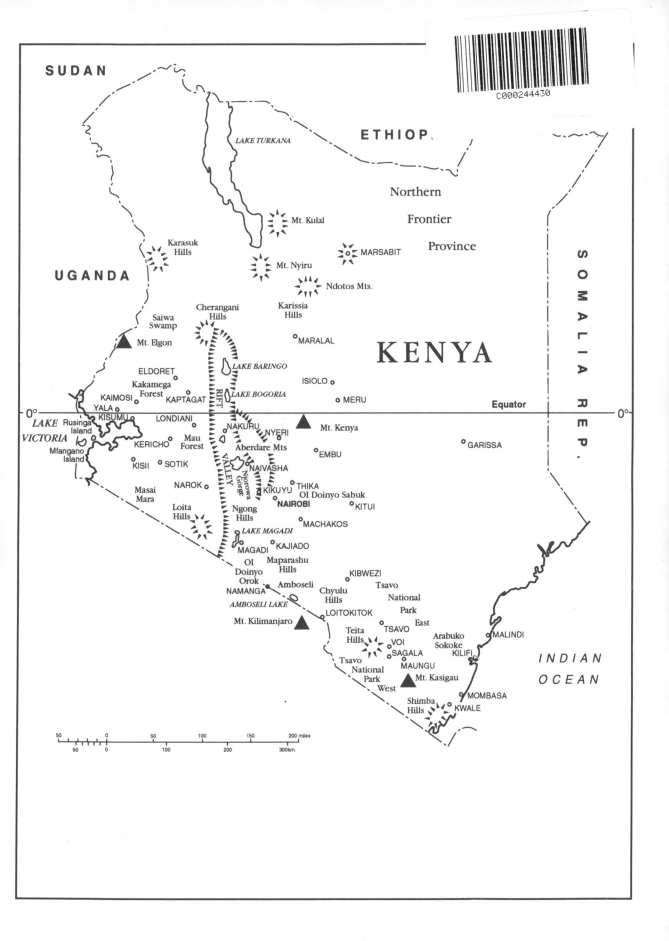

Orchids of Kenya

Orchids
of
Kenya

Joyce Stewart

With photographs by
Bob Campbell

SPONSORED BY
THE KENYA ORCHID TRUST
AND
THE KENYA ORCHID SOCIETY

St Paul's Bibliographies
Winchester

First published by St Paul's Bibliographies, West End House, 1 Step Terrace, Winchester SO22 5BW, UK in 1996.

Published in North and South America by Timber Press Inc., 133 S.W. Second Avenue, Portland, Oregon 97204 in 1996.

A catalogue record for this book is available from the British Library

Frontispiece
Aerangis brachycarpa: epiphyte below tree canopy.   BOB CAMPBELL

ISBN (UK) 1 873040 28 8
Printed in Hong Kong

Contents

The Author and Publisher would like to record their grateful thanks to the Chairman of the Board of Trustees of the Kenya Orchid Trust, Manu Chandaria, and to the other Trustees, Pat Danahy, Ingeborg Gonella, Alexandra Kontos, George McKnight, Dylis Rhodes and Mervyn Vincent; also to past and present members of the Kenya Orchid Society for their generous assistance in contributing funds, photographs and information towards the compilation of this book.

Preface

I went to live in Africa in 1960. Travelling around Kenya with my husband who was setting up a research unit for the Game Department, I tried to learn about the wild flowers, especially the orchids. The epiphytic species we saw on a fishing holiday at Kaptagat were particularly fascinating. Finding orchids in their wild habitats was relatively easy at that time. Finding their names, details of their distribution and other information was much more difficult. An illustrated checklist that recorded 212 orchid species for Kenya was published by the East African Natural History Society in their journal in 1964. It was extremely helpful, but using it made me realise that a book with many coloured illustrations would be ideal.

Before I left Kenya in 1971, Bob and Heather Campbell had collaborated with me to produce a book which introduced African orchids to the world of orchid growers. *Orchids of Tropical Africa* was amazingly successful and soon went out of print. Many people pressed us to write another book and, with this aim in view, Bob continued to photograph the plants that Heather grew as they came into flower. In the meantime, I put together all the information I could find and published a new checklist in 1973. It recorded 247 orchid species for Kenya.

In Natal, where I lived for the next 10 years, I became interested in the orchids of South Africa. I began to collaborate with colleagues from the University of Cape Town, and our book *Wild Orchids of Southern Africa* was published in 1982. Many readers were delighted with that book. We were fortunate to be able to borrow transparencies from many photographers and orchid lovers so that all except a few of the 433 species were illustrated in colour. The designer arranged the photographs of each species immediately adjacent to the relevant text. This made it extremely easy to use, especially for identifying new discoveries.

Kenya Orchid Society members who saw the book on South African orchids were keen to have a similar one for Kenya. They suggested that I should write the text and Bob Campbell agreed, once again, to take photographs. In 1984 I received a grant from the Leverhulme Trust to complete the work needed for the book. I flew to Nairobi and am most grateful for the hospitality and help that I received then. Manu Chandaria lent me a car for two weeks. Heather and Bob arranged my visit, looked after me and took me to the Mara river area. Hermann and Ria Meyer took me for a memorable drive in the Ngong hills. Christine Kabuye gave me working space at the East African Herbarium and welcomed my visit.

On returning to England, I started writing the final text of *Orchids of Kenya* and began to look for a publisher. The Kenya Orchid Trust raised money to help to pay for the costs of colour printing of what they hoped would be a very attractive book, soon to appear! But the next ten years were not successful. Many commercial publishers were approached and persuaded, but each one took some time to investigate the possibilities and then regretfully declined. The situation seemed hopeless. And then in 1995 Robert Cross contacted me. He had heard from his son Edward, in Mombasa, that a book on the orchids of Kenya was being prepared. It was not the kind of book his company, St Paul's Bibliographies, usually published, but because of its Kenya connections he was interested to know more about it. Negotiations proceeded and with the help of Ingeborg Gonella, who was Chairman of the Kenya Orchid Society at the time, were successful. The writing was completed and 280 species are currently recorded. It is certain that this number will soon be surpassed, with the interest in Kenya orchids that is again increasing.

So, finally, I am pleased to present this book to the members of the Kenya Orchid Society, and to everyone interested in African orchids. In its content and design it is the book I wish I had had when I started growing and writing about orchids in Kenya such a long time ago. I hope that it will prove useful to present and future enthusiasts for this fascinating plant family.

The Kenya Orchid Trust
wishes to dedicate this book
to the memory of Hermann Meyer (1934–1989)
in recognition of his enthusiasm for the project
and to
the Kenya Orchid Society
and all its members past and present
who have enjoyed
the orchids of Kenya

Acknowledgements

My interest in orchids and orchid growing in the 1960s was encouraged by several members of the Kenya Orchid Society. Of those who have since died, I remember especially Dr Frank Piers, Brian Perkins, Pat Scott and Donald Wilcock in Nairobi and Marjorie Tweedie of Kitale with whom I had many interesting discussions. Heather Campbell, who joined the Kenya Orchid Society with me in 1964, has been a great supporter for more than 30 years. Philip Archer made many interesting discoveries and sent me all his records after he moved to Tasmania. Botanists at the East African Herbarium were also a major influence. I am grateful for the interest of the late Peter Bally, Jan Gillett and Peter Greenway, and of Bernard Verdcourt, Grenville Lucas and Roger Polhill all of whom are now at Kew.

Many people have helped me during the long gestation period of this book. I would particularly like to thank the present members of the Kenya Orchid Society who have continued to send me information about new records, and flowers and photographs to identify. I hesitate to list their names for fear of leaving out someone, but they know who they are and I am most grateful to them all. They will be glad to know that their discoveries have increased the number of species known in Kenya by more than 30. At the same time I am extremely grateful to the Kenya Orchid Trust which the Society set up to raise and administer funds for use in printing the kind of book they wanted.

At the East African Herbarium (National Museums of Kenya), Christine Kabuye and her staff were most cooperative and helpful during my visit in 1984. I send my special thanks to her and also to Benny Bytebier and Tim Pearce for the chapter they contributed on Orchid Conservation in Kenya in 1995, which brings this book right up to date. I am most grateful to the Leverhulme Trust whose research grant made possible my work in Kenya in 1984.

In England, I extend my warmest thanks to Sir Robert and Lady Sainsbury, whose generosity to Kew made it possible for me to hold a Fellowship there for almost ten years. Work on this book was completed during that time. I thank the Director, Royal Botanic Gardens, Kew, for permission to study the collections there. In the Orchid Herbarium, Peter Hunt, Peter Taylor, Phillip Cribb, Jeffrey Wood and Sarah Thomas have been extremely helpful, over the years, and I thank them sincerely for all that they have done. I am fortunate that the account of the Orchidaceae for the *Flora of Tropical East Africa* was completed at Kew in 1989, and it has been an important reference during the preparation of the descriptions in this account.

The photographs are an essential part of this book. Without them it could certainly not have appeared. Many thanks are due to Bob Campbell, who took most of them, and to all the people in Nairobi, but especially his wife Heather, who supplied the plants for him to focus on in a state of flowering perfection. For those species that Bob did not have the opportunity to photograph, I am most grateful to Eric la Croix for the use of his transparencies. Hermann Meyer was seeking the rarer species to photograph before his untimely death, and several other members of the Kenya Orchid Society (K.O.S.) also generously loaned transparencies.

A special word of thanks is due to Robert Cross for his faith in the project and his tremendous efforts to make it succeed. Myra and Malcolm Givans have given invaluable help in the editorial and production stages and I offer them my warmest thanks.

Finally, I should like to record that it was my husband Donald who took me to an exciting new life in Kenya, only two weeks after we were married in 1960, and most thanks are due to him for providing so many of the opportunities from which this book has emerged – the journeys, holidays, collections, orchid houses, and time to study and write – and unfailing support in so many ways.

Joyce Stewart
Dorset
August 1995

Introduction to Kenya and its Orchids

The Republic of Kenya is approximately 569,258 sq. km (219,789 sq. miles) in extent and is situated astride the Equator. On the eastern side it reaches nearly 5°N and touches the Indian Ocean at 2–3°S. It is narrower on the western side and reaches only 1°S on the shores of Lake Victoria. Longitudinally, it stretches from approximately 34°E to 41°E.

From the white sands of the tropical beaches along the coast to the snow-capped Mt Kenya that reaches 5194 m (17,058 feet) above sea level, there is a tremendous variety of scenery, land surface and vegetation. Well known for its abundance of wildlife, particularly large mammals and birds, Kenya is also one of the most beautiful countries in Africa. The wide altitudinal range and its accompanying changes in temperature are the basic reasons for the great variety of vegetation types and plants.

The complex rainfall pattern is another contributory factor to plant and scenic diversity. The rainfall varies between 125–2540 mm (5–100 inches) per year and falls in either one or two distinct seasons, both of which are somewhat unpredictable. Nearly three-quarters of the country have less than 500 mm (20 inches) per year, and this amount is extremely unreliable from year to year. Humidity is high in the daytime in the coastal belt and in the area around Lake Victoria, both of which are heavily populated. The natural vegetation in which orchids grow has changed greatly and they are now much harder to find. Elsewhere in the country there are many places where conditions are not ideal for orchid growth. It is surprising how many species (280 in 50 genera) have now been recorded in this rather small country. Only 100 genera are recorded for the whole of Africa and the number of species is estimated at about 1200. Thus Kenya provides a home for half the genera and nearly a quarter of the species that are known from the entire continent.

Natural vegetation

East African Vegetation by Lind & Morrison (1974) is a good ecological account of the plants of the region with special sections that describe parts of Kenya and list the major plants. So much has changed since that book was written. Orchids are now much harder to find, especially the terrestrial kinds. Collecting together the photographs for this present book has proved extremely difficult. It is noticeable that many of the terrestrial kinds are not illustrated here. This is quite simply because the plants have been so hard to find.

Above 3000 m the vegetation on the Aberdare Mts, Mt Kenya and Mt Elgon is still fairly well protected. Mostly it comes under the protection of National Park status, or has some kind of forestry protection. The orchids in these montane grasslands can still be found by those prepared to hike in rough terrain and often in poor weather.

Forests in Kenya are of several kinds depending on their location. They cover little more than 2 per cent of the total land area and are decreasing in extent all the time. The Mau forests still cover an appreciable area west of the Rift Valley, but the tree cover is decreasing annually. Coastal forests are reduced to small remnants. Perhaps the best areas to look for epiphytic orchids are the small patches of forest on isolated hills throughout the country, but particularly the hills which catch rain-bearing winds in areas that are largely dry.

More than 75 per cent of the land surface would naturally be covered by woodlands, bushlands and savannah. Much of the woody vegetation in these areas has been removed for grazing, fire wood or building purposes. Orchids have always been relatively few in these habitats.

Grasslands cover the remaining areas, but many of these have been heavily grazed, ploughed up or built over. In many of the inhabited rural and urban areas there is very little natural vegetation at all.

When I first began work on this book, I prepared a series of 100 maps showing the distribution of orchids in Kenya. They were based on a study of all the specimens in the East African Herbarium and at Kew that had been collected in Kenya over the last 100 years. The maps have not been included in this publication, however, because I realise that they would show where orchids have been collected in the past, not where they grow now. The maps have been left out, but perhaps some more accurate ones will be produced in due course, in conjunction with the database of information that now exists at the East African Herbarium and plans for further studies there.

Publications on orchids of Kenya

It may be useful to summarise details of the publications in which information on orchids of Kenya has appeared to date.

1897
In the *Flora of Tropical Africa*, R.A. Rolfe, botanist at the Royal Botanic Gardens, Kew, described 811 species of orchids in 46 genera. Kenya was scarcely known at that time and only 43 orchid species in 14 genera were listed from Nile Land. This area was bounded on the west by the 26th meridian of East longitude; to the east by the Red Sea and the Indian Ocean; and to the south by the Congo Free State (now Zaïre) and German East Africa (now Tanzania).

1943
Mr and Mrs R.E. Moreau, who lived at Amani in northern Tanzania, published an introduction, key to genera and checklist of the epiphytic orchids of the East African territories, including Uganda, Kenya, Tanganyika (now Tanzania), Nyasaland (now Malawi), Northern Rhodesia (now Zambia) and Zanzibar. Their list included 41 species of orchids in 18 genera from Kenya.

1964
Collaboration between Gwen Copley, Marjorie Tweedie and a forest officer, E.W. Carroll, resulted in the publication of a key and checklist to Kenya orchids in 1964. Illustrated with line drawings, this account included 212 species in 38 genera. It was the first attempt at a complete list of the orchids known at the time and is an invaluable record.

1968
Dr Frank Piers' book *Orchids of East Africa* did not attempt to be complete, but drew attention to some of the more spectacular orchids to be found within the region. He described 177 species in 39 genera from Kenya, the area which he knew best, as well as other species with beautiful flowers from Uganda and Tanzania.

1968, 1984, 1989
These years saw the publication of the account of the Orchidaceae in the *Flora of Tropical East Africa* (FTEA) produced by botanists at Kew with collaborators in Kenya and edited by Victor S. Summerhayes (Part 1) and Phillip Cribb (Parts 2 and 3). For every genus and species there is a very detailed description and examples of the specimens studied are cited. Records are provided of every region in which each species occurs.

For Kenya, the species recorded and described are shown below (with the total for the Flora in parentheses).

	Genera in Kenya (in East Africa)	Species (in East Africa)
Part 1	11 (17)	89 (248)
Part 2	14 (25)	53 (178)
Part 3	22 (30)	104 (251)
Total	47 (75)	246 (677)

1974, 1994
Whilst at the University of Nairobi, the botanist Andrew Agnew and his wife Shirley produced the book *Wild Flowers of Upland Kenya*, with the help of various contributors including the present author. This book is restricted to all those species that have been recorded above an altitudinal limit of 1000 m (3000 ft) above sea level. A second edition, with updated information, appeared at the end of 1994. The accounts of the Orchidaceae include:

| 1974 (edition 1) | 37 genera | 206 species |
| 1994 (edition 2) | 42 genera | 215 species. |

1996
For the sake of completeness, and to save readers the chore of counting, perhaps I should record that this book contains descriptions of 280 species in 50 genera. Thus it also shows an increase in genera and species compared with all previously published accounts. I hope it will encourage Kenyan people to continue to travel to remote places, to find new plants, to photograph them and write about them.

View from the Isuria escarpment towards Mara river: forest and grassland.   BOB CAMPBELL

List of orchid genera now recognised in Kenya

To make this book easy to use, the descriptions in Parts I, II and III are presented in alphabetical order by genus and within each genus. The following list shows the genera in systematic order. It may be helpful in trying to identify new discoveries because it shows which are the close relatives of each genus. The classification is based on that of Dressler (1974), which I used in a previous book where a review of African orchids was presented (Stewart & Hennessy, 1981).

Tribe	Subtribe	Genus	Species in Kenya
Neottieae	Limodorinae	*Epipactis*	1
Cranichideae	Goodyerinae	*Platylepis*	1
		Cheirostylis	1
		Zeuxine	1
Epipogeae		*Epipogium*	1
Orchideae	Orchidinae	*Cynorkis*	4
		Habenaria	44
		Bonatea	4
		Platycoryne	2
		Roeperocharis	1
		Holothrix	6
		Brachycorythis	6
	Disinae	*Disa*	9
		Brownleea	1
		Satyrium	11
	Coryciinae	*Disperis*	8
Gastrodieae	Vanillinae	*Vanilla*	4
	Pogoninae	*Nervilia*	4
Arethuseae	Bletiinae	*Calanthe*	1
Dendrobieae	Bulbophyllinae	*Bulbophyllum*	12
		Chaseella	1
		Stolzia	1
Malaxideae		*Liparis*	2
		Oberonia	1
		Malaxis	1
Vandeae	Sarcanthinae	*Acampe*	1
	Angraecinae	*Angraecum*	13
		Jumellea	2
	Aerangidinae	*Aerangis*	10
		Microcoelia	10
		Solenangis	3

TRIBE	SUBTRIBE	GENUS	SPECIES IN KENYA
		Diaphananthe	12
		Margelliantha	1
		Bolusiella	2
		Chamaeangis	3
		Rangaeris	2
		Ypsilopus	2
		Cyrtorchis	4
		Calyptrochilum	1
		Sphyrarhynchus	1
		Triceratorhynchus	1
		Angraecopsis	3
		Cribbia	1
		Tridactyle	10
		Nephrangis	1
Polystachyeae		*Polystachya*	31
Cymbideae	Cyrtopodiinae	*Eulophia*	31
		Oeceoclades	4
		Pteroglossaspis	2
	Cymbidiinae	*Ansellia*	1

Part I Epiphytic Orchids

Orchid plants are always perennial and usually herbaceous, but they have several different ways of growing. For the newcomer to a tropical country, the epiphytic habit is the most intriguing. An epiphyte is a plant that uses another plant to perch upon. Its roots creep over the surface of a branch, twig or trunk of a tree or bush. They rarely penetrate the bark, and never extend into the living tissues beneath, so they are not parasites. They are simply using the surface of another plant as a place on which to grow. The word epiphyte comes from two Greek words *epi* (upon) and *phyton* (plant).

About half of the orchids recorded in Kenya are epiphytes. Because of their dependence on other

Tridactyle bicaudata: monopodial growth with many stems.

Microcoelia koehleri: one of the epiphytic orchids that never bears green leaves.   BOB CAMPBELL

plants they are much less common today than formerly. Some are specific about the kind of tree on which they will grow, perhaps because certain kinds of bark are inimical for the germination of their seeds. Others are apparently not at all choosy. But very few have ever been found on exotic plantation trees, gums, wattles or pines. It is the indigenous trees on which they prefer to grow. Some epiphytes will also grow on rocks. The bare surface appears to provide a suitable place for germination and seedling attachment, particularly if it is shaded from the hot sun. Sometimes these orchids are described as lithophytes, from the Greek words *lithos* (rock) and *phyton* (plant).

The epiphytic orchids in Kenya exhibit two different patterns of growth. Many species are monopodial in habit. This means the stem bears leaves, often in two opposite rows, and goes on growing at its apex getting longer and longer every year. *Aerangis*, *Angraecum* and *Tridactyle* are good examples of genera in which the plants have this habit. Often there is only a single stem, but sometimes branches appear and an old plant may eventually form a large clump. The inflorescences are borne laterally, usually in the axils of the leaves. The roots also arise from the stem and may be extremely extensive, sometimes forming large tangled masses that are completely aerial. Many of these aerial roots turn green when they are wet because they contain abundant chloroplasts. In some orchids, such as the genus *Microcoelia*, green leaves have disappeared, and the roots are able to photosynthesise as well as providing anchorage and absorbing water and mineral nutrients into the plant.

Other epiphytic orchids demonstrate a sympodial habit of growth. The plant consists of a creeping rhizome that remains more or less in contact with the substratum. Upright stems grow from this rhizome every year. *Polystachya* and *Bulbophyllum* species behave like this. The growth of each stem is limited to a single growing season. When complete it bears one or several leaves. It often flowers at the apex, as in *Polystachya* and *Ansellia*, or an inflorescence arises from its base, as in *Bulbophyllum*. The individual stems are often swollen to form structures called pseudobulbs, because they may be shaped like a bulb. Pseudobulbs are close together on the rhizome, forming a tuft of stems, or far apart. Sometimes the rhizome grows in a straight line, but often it branches repeatedly and a dense mat of stems develops.

Most epiphytic orchids grow on the branches and twigs in the canopy of trees where they catch

Aerangis thomsonii: epiphyte in heavy shade.   BOB CAMPBELL

the sunlight but are shaded during the hottest and brightest parts of the day. Others prefer deep shade, and these can be found on trunks as well as the larger branches, often quite near the ground. Many *Aerangis* species are deep shade growers. Orchids grow quite slowly, so they are more likely to be found on old host trees than young ones. Isolated old trees may seem like good places to search for orchids, but often they are disappointing because such trees soon become unsuitable habitats when the branches are exposed to wind or fluctuating temperatures. Likewise, the orchid plants on trees that have fallen in the forest will soon die because the light and humidity they require is drastically changed. Orchids will not survive long if their environmental conditions become adverse.

Look for epiphytic orchids in old established trees and bushes that have not been disturbed. The key that follows provides a means of identifying them. If the plant you have found does not appear to be one of these, try the key for terrestrial orchids instead (page 91). Certain species of *Cynorkis*, *Disperis* and *Brachycorythis kalbreyeri* can sometimes grow on trees as well as on the ground and rocky banks in the forest. The genus *Vanilla* grows as a vine, both epiphytically and over rocks, so that is also included in this key.

Key to the genera of epiphytic orchids

1   Growth sympodial, stems terminated by pseudobulbs.   2
  Growth monopodial, stems continuing growth indeterminately, pseudobulbs absent   7

2   Inflorescence terminal, arising from the apex of a recently formed pseudobulb   3
  Inflorescence lateral, arising from the base of a recently formed pseudobulb.   6

3   Flowers twisted so that lip is lowermost   4
  Flowers untwisted, lip on the upper side. . . . . **Polystachya**

4   Flowers solitary . . . . **Stolzia**
  Flowers several or many in an inflorescence   5

5   Flowers large, yellowish with dark markings . . . . **Ansellia**
  Flowers small, green or dark red . . . . **Liparis**

6   Pseudobulbs bearing 1–3 leaves at the apex . . . . **Bulbophyllum**
  Pseudobulbs bearing 6–11 leaves at the apex . . . . **Chaseella**

7   Plants climbing, stems several metres long, leafless or with large ovate leaves . . . . **Vanilla**
  Plants epiphytic with short or long stems, usually less than 50 cm long   8

8   Green leaves absent   9
  Green leaves present.   10

9   Stems short, roots densely clustered . . . . **Microcoelia**
  Stems elongated, roots emerging all along the stem . . . . **Solenangis**

10   Leaves laterally compressed, overlapping at the base, on elongated stems or forming a small fan   11
  Plants with leaves not laterally compressed   12

11   Flowers white, in racemes from the old leaf axils . . . . **Bolusiella**
  Flowers yellow or brownish, in an apical raceme . . . . **Oberonia**

12   Lip white, fleshy and papillose on its inner surface; pollinia 4 . . . . **Acampe**
  Lip similar to tepals, smooth; pollinia 2   13

13   Column deeply indented at the apex below the anther cap.   14
  Column not deeply indented, usually prolonged into an elongate rostellum below the anther cap.   15

14   Lip ovate to heart shaped, enclosing the column at its base . . . . **Angraecum**
  Lip lanceolate, narrow at the base where it is inserted below the column . . . . **Jumellea**

15   Sepals and petals pure white, or white
        tinged with pink or pale green   16
     Sepals and petals pale green, bright
        green, yellow or brownish, not white . .   24

16   Anther cap bright green, flowers
        pearl-shaped . . . .   *Margelliantha*
     Anther cap white   17

17   Lip similar to the tepals . . . .   *Cyrtorchis*
     Lip different from the other tepals   18

18   Lip 3-lobed   19
     Lip simple, not 3-lobed   23

19   Plants pendent below the branches,
        leaves grass-like . . . .   *Ypsilopus*
     Plants upright, or if pendent then leaves
        not grass-like   20

20   Spurs slender, more than 5 cm long   21
     Spurs short and geniculate, less than
        2 cm long . . . .   *Calyptrochilum*

21   Leaves flat; lip 3-lobed in the upper part . . .
        . . . .   *Solenangis*
     Leaves conduplicate, lip 3-lobed near the
        base   22

22   Roots hairy . . . .   *Angraecopsis*
     Roots smooth . . . .   *Rangaeris*

23   Lip similar in colour to the rest of the
        flower . . . .   *Aerangis*
     Lip with dark green central streak . . . .
        . . . .   *Sphyrarhynchus*

24   Leaves very small, less than 5 cm long . .   25
     Leaves various, always more than 5 cm
        long   27

25   Stems elongated . . . .   *Solenangis*
     Stems very short   26

26   Inflorescence pendent, flowers close
        together . . . .   *Angraecopsis*
     Inflorescence erect or spreading, flowers
        well separated . . . . . .   *Triceratorhynchus*

27   Lip 2- or 3-lobed   28
     Lip entire, not 3-lobed   30

28   Plants pendent below branches, stems
        short . . . .   *Ypsilopus*
     Plants upright or pendent, stems often
        greatly elongated   29

29   Lip 3-lobed, often with basal auricles,
        similar in colour to the rest of the
        flower . . . .   *Tridactyle*
     Lip 2-lobed, white, rest of the flower pale
        brown . . . .   *Nephrangis*

30   Lip wider than long . . . .   *Diaphananthe*
     Lip longer than wide   31

31   Flowers borne in whorls of 2–4 along the
        inflorescence . . . .   *Chamaeangis*
     Flowers borne singly along the
        inflorescence . . . .   *Cribbia*

Acampe Lindley

The rigid stems and thick fleshy flowers of all the plants in this genus make them instantly recognisable. The name is derived from the Greek word *akampes* (rigid) and presumably refers to the rather brittle flowers. The plants have a monopodial habit of growth and bear two rows of leathery leaves along the upright, elongating stem. The flowers are in various shades of yellowish green and white and are borne close together on short, often branching inflorescences.

There are about 10 species of *Acampe*, many of which are widely distributed in Asia; only one species is now recognised in Africa. In Kenya it is found near the coast, often very near the sea, on rocks and as an epiphyte. It has long been known as *Acampe pachyglossa* and has been described under this name in the *Flora of Tropical East Africa*, Part 3 (Cribb, 1989). However, it is very similar to *Acampe praemorsa*, which is found in central and southern India and Sri Lanka, and may be conspecific with that species. Cribb (1992) lists *A. pachyglossa* as a synonym of *Acampe rigida*.

Acampe pachyglossa   BOB CAMPBELL

CULTIVATION

Easily maintained in cultivation provided the plants are kept in a warm and humid environment and in bright light. They can be grown in a pot or basket with an open, free-draining compost, or mounted on a piece of hardwood or cork oak bark.

Acampe pachyglossa Reichenbach f.

Plants erect, epiphytic or lithophytic, often branched and growing in large clumps. Stems rigid, bearing leaves in two rows in the upper part and clothed in old leaf bases lower down, with many thick roots except near the apex. Leaves thick, ligulate, straight or curved, bilobed at the apex with a little mucro between the lobes, 10–25 cm long, 1.5–2.5 cm wide. Inflorescences borne above the leaves, one or more at each flowering, simple or branched with flowers close together. Flowers about 2 cm in diameter, sweetly scented, thick and fleshy, yellowish green with red spots or streaks and a white lip; sepals ovate-oblong or ovate-elliptic, obtuse, 10–12 mm long, 5–6 mm wide; petals spathulate, falcate, 8–10 mm long, 3–10 mm wide; lip 3-lobed, saccate at the base, side lobes small, erect, midlobe thick with a papillose surface.

On trees and rocks in deciduous forest and coastal bush, sometimes in association with *Ansellia* plants; sea level to 900 m; flowering from August to December.

Widespread along the eastern side of Africa from Kenya to South Africa (NE Natal and Transvaal). Also recorded on many of the islands of the western Indian Ocean including Madagascar.

Aerangis Reichenbach f.

The name *Aerangis* was coined from two Greek words *aer* (air) and *angos* (vessel), probably referring to the spur at the base of the lip which contains nectar. Specimens of this genus are among the most attractive and highly sought-after of the white flowered epiphytes of Africa. All the plants have dark green leaves on upright or dangling stems. The flowers are graceful, white or cream, and sometimes tinged with green or pinkish brown. Usually there are many flowers on each raceme and often several flowering stems on each plant. The flowers may appear at any time of the year but are most common during the rainy seasons in April and May or October and November.

There are 10 species of *Aerangis* in Kenya, restricted in distribution to the forests, or areas where forest and bushland were formerly present. Elsewhere, the genus is widespread in tropical Africa and the islands of the western Indian Ocean, although the plants are rarely common. Twenty-nine species have been described from continental Africa and nearly as many from Madagascar and the islands of the western Indian Ocean. One species has been described from both Kenya and elsewhere along the coast of East Africa, and from Sri Lanka.

CULTIVATION

All the species are easily maintained in cultivation. The species from higher altitudes need cooler conditions than those that occur at or near the coast. They all grow well mounted on a piece of bark or timber that is suspended in deep shade, usually in high humidity. Well-rooted plants will also grow well in pots in any kind of compost that is suitable for epiphytic plants.

Key to the species of *Aerangis*

1   Flowers with spur more than 10 cm long. .   2
     Flowers with spur less than 8 cm long. . . .   6

2   Lip pandurate, 8–15 mm wide, with 2 raised ridges or crests at its base and in the mouth of the spur . . . . *A. kotschyana*
     Lip oblong, obovate, apiculate or acuminate, smooth at the base and in the mouth of the spur   3

3   Leaf venation markedly reticulate, darker coloured and raised above the upper surface of the leaf; tepals oblong, acute; column short and thick, not more than 5 mm long   4
     Leaf venation not conspicuously coloured; tepals narrowly oblong, acute or acuminate; column slender at the base, 6–9 mm long   5

4   Leaves greyish green; dorsal sepal not more than 10 mm long . . . *A. somalensis*
     Leaves dark green; dorsal sepal at least 13 mm long, usually 15–20 mm long . . . . *A. coriacea*

5   Woody stem usually more than 15 cm long; leaves the same width throughout and more or less parallel sided; dorsal sepal arching forward over the column, acute . . . . *A. thomsonii*
     Woody stem usually less than 15 cm long; leaves wider in the upper half; dorsal sepal upright or reflexed, acuminate . . . . *A. brachycarpa*

6   Lip narrow and elongated, at least three times as long as wide   7
     Lip wide or narrow but not more than twice as long as wide   8

7   Sepals, petals and lip of equal length, the lateral sepals reflexed at first, then curving forwards . . . . *A. confusa*
     Sepals longer than petals and lip, all the perianth parts spreading . . . . *A. kirkii*

8   Lip more than 7 mm wide, obovate; petals obovate or broadly oblanceolate . . . . *A luteo-alba* var. *rhodosticta*
     Lip less than 6 mm wide, oblong or lanceolate, acute or acuminate; petals narrowly elliptic, acute   9

9   Spur 10–25 mm long; column 2 mm long . . . . *A. ugandensis*
     Spur 3–7 mm long; column 1 mm long . . . . *A. hologlottis*

Aerangis brachycarpa (A. Richard) Durand & Schinz

Syn. *Aerangis flabellifolia* Reichenbach f.

Stem woody, upright or pendent, up to 20 cm long but usually much shorter. Leaves 4–12, alternate, 5–12 mm apart, obovate or spathulate with an unequally bilobed apex, dark green and often black-dotted, up to 25 cm long, 2–6 cm wide near the apex. Inflorescences axillary, arching or pendent racemes up to 40 cm long with 2–12 white flowers in two rows. Flowers slender, elegant, usually pale green at first and with a pinkish tinge when mature; tepals all narrowly lanceolate, acuminate, 20–45 mm long, 4–8 mm wide near the base; dorsal sepal erect, lateral sepals and petals becoming sharply reflexed within a few days of opening; lip deflexed, 20–45 mm long, 5–10 mm wide near the base, narrowing abruptly to a long slender acumen, margins often reflexed, spur straight or slightly flexuous, 12–20 cm long; column slender, terete below, 6–8 mm long.

In dense shade, usually rather low down on tree trunks, branches, or in the forking bases of bushes in highland forests and forest remnants; recorded

Aerangis brachycarpa   BOB CAMPBELL

from Karissia hills, Mt Kenya, Nyeri district, and Narok district; 1500–2300 m; flowers April to July, occasionally in November.

Also known from highland forests in Ethiopia, Uganda, Tanzania, Zambia and Angola.

This is a rather variable species, both in the shape of its leaves and their apical lobes, and in the size of the flowers. In the past it was often misidentified as *Aerangis friesiorum*, which is now known to be a synonym of *Aerangis thomsonii*. Two closely related species have been described in Malawi, *Aerangis splendida* and *Aerangis distincta*, which were not recognised as distinct from this species until recently.

Aerangis confusa J. Stewart

Stem woody, upright or curved with the tip upright, up to 10 cm long. Leaves 3–12, 5–10 mm apart, obovate or oblanceolate, widest near the unequally bilobed apex, dark green with minute black dots, 5–24 cm long, 1.5–5.5 cm wide. Inflorescences axillary, spreading or pendent, with 4–10 pinkish or greenish white flowers in two rows. Flowers erect or curving forwards, 1–3 cm apart; dorsal sepal arching forward over the column, lanceolate-elliptic, 15–25 mm long; lateral sepals reflexed near the base, the tips curving forwards, lanceolate, 18–26 mm long; petals strongly reflexed, lanceolate and acuminate, 15–22 mm long; lip elliptic or lanceolate, margins recurved, 15–23 mm long, spur narrow, 4–6 cm long; column slender, terete below, 6–8 mm long.

In shady places, usually rather low down on the trunks of small trees and bushes, often on

Akocanthera, usually in warmer and drier localities than *Aerangis brachycarpa* which it closely resembles when not in flower; recorded from Mt Kulal, Maralal, Rift Valley, Mua hills and hills in Masai district; 1600–2100 m; flowering rather variable, usually in April to June and October. Hybrids with *A. brachycarpa* have been reported.

Quite common in a restricted altitudinal range in the central and southwest parts of Kenya; elsewhere known only from the northern part of Masai District in Tanzania.

Aerangis coriacea Summerhayes

Stem usually short but may attain 40 cm in length in old specimens, woody. Leaves in two rows, 4–many, ligulate or oblanceolate-ligulate, with two unequal, rounded lobes at the apex, dark green with tranverse veins in a darker colour, up to 22 cm long, 2–4.5 cm wide. Inflorescences axillary, arching racemes bearing 4–22 flowers. Flowers white, or tinged with pink or green, 1–3 cm apart, 3–4 cm in diameter; dorsal sepal erect, lanceolate-elliptic, margins recurved, 13–17 mm long; petals reflexed, oblanceolate-oblong, margins recurved, 13–17 mm long; petals reflexed, oblanceolate-oblong, margins recurved, 13–17 mm long; lip lanceolate or oblong-

Aerangis coriacea   BOB CAMPBELL

Aerangis confusa   BOB CAMPBELL

lanceolate, acute at the reflexed apex, margins recurved in the middle, 14–18 mm long, spur pendulous, flexuous, narrowly cylindrical but widened and somewhat flattened in the apical half, 11–17 cm long; column thick, up to 4 mm long.

In shady places, often near rivers, usually rather low down on trunks or larger branches of trees in the highland forests east of the Rift Valley; 1500–2300 m; flowers in March through to June, usually in May.

Elsewhere, this species is known only from the forests surrounding Mt Kilimanjaro and Mt Meru in northern Tanzania.

Aerangis hologlottis (Schlechter) Schlechter
Stem short and woody, up to 5 cm long in old specimens. Leaves 2–6, close together, linear or narrowly oblong-ligulate, often falcate, unequally bilobed at the apex, dark green, 5–9 cm long, 7–18 mm wide. Inflorescences one to several racemes, arising below the leaves, erect, spreading or pendent, and bearing 6–15 small white flowers. Flowers 5–8 mm apart, up to 10 mm in diameter; dorsal sepal narrowly elliptic, apiculate, 6–7 mm long, lateral sepals similar but narrower; petals narrowly obovate-elliptic, apiculate, 5–6 mm long, broader than sepals; lip obovate, apiculate, 5–6 mm

long, 3 mm wide, spur straight, slender, 3.5–7 mm long; column short and stout, 1 mm long.

Epiphyte on twigs and small branches of trees in coastal forest, near the sea in Kilifi district and on the Shimba hills; 250–500 m; flowering season variable, usually January or June.

Aerangis hologlottis   BOB CAMPBELL

Also recorded from coastal forests in Tanzania and Mozambique, and from the Royal Botanic Gardens, Peradeniya, Sri Lanka, where it is apparently indigenous.

Aerangis kirkii (Reichenbach f.) Schlechter

Stem woody, covered in closely overlapping leaf bases, up to 6 cm long. Leaves 2–7, very close together, oblanceolate or linear-lanceolate, the apex widely dilated, bilobed and usually curled downwards, dark green or greyish green with ridged venation, up to 15 cm long, 3 cm wide, but usually much smaller. Inflorescences one to several, arising below the leaves with 2–6 white flowers all facing one way. Flowers flat, up to 4 cm in diameter, the apical one largest and opening first; dorsal sepal erect, ovate-lanceolate, acuminate, 18–25 mm long; lateral sepals longer and narrower, spreading, 22–28 mm long; petals spreading, smaller than the sepals, 16–20 mm long; lip oblong in the lower half, acuminate or apiculate, 16–20 mm long, spur often curving forward, inflated in the lower half, 6–7.5 cm long; column short, 4 mm long.

In coastal bush and in riverine forest at low altitudes inland, on small trees, lianes and bushes, usually in rather dense shade; sea level to 450 m; flowering between April and June.

Also known from similar habitats in Tanzania and Mozambique.

Aerangis kirkii   BOB CAMPBELL

Aerangis kotschyana (Reichenbach f.) Schlechter

Stem usually short and woody, bearing a fan of leaves in the upper part. Leaves 3–20, obovate-oblong, apex unequally bilobed, the shorter lobe often absent, 6–20 cm long, 2–8 cm wide. Inflorescences one or several, axillary racemes, usually

Aerangis kotschyana   BOB CAMPBELL

arching or pendent with 10–20 conspicuous flowers. Flowers white, sometimes tinged with pink or green when young, up to 5 cm in diameter; dorsal sepal erect, or arching forward over the column, elliptic-lanceolate, apiculate; lateral sepals spreading, lanceolate, apiculate; petals strongly reflexed, oblanceolate, apiculate; lip deflexed, subpandurate, apiculate, the margins often reflexed in the lower half, two prominent crests on the upper surface in front of the spur opening, spur curved and twisted in the lower third, 13–25 cm long; column short and wide, 3–6 mm long.

In light shade, high in the tree canopy but usually on the larger branches and tree trunks, also in old bushes and smaller trees, around Lake Victoria and in the Shimba hills; sea level to 1500 m; flowers June to July and December to January.

Widespread in warm, humid savannah regions and in forests of tropical Africa from Guinea to Kenya and south to Mozambique.

Aerangis luteo-alba (Kraenzlin) Schlechter var. *rhodosticta* (Kraenzlin) J. Stewart

Syn. *Aerangis rhodosticta* (Kraenzlin) Schlechter
Stem short and inconspicuous, 1–3 cm long except in very old plants. Leaves 2–8, usually lying in one plane, linear, ligulate or linear-lanceolate, sometimes falcate, unequally bilobed at the apex, dark green, up to 15 cm long, 6–15 mm wide. Inflorescences arising from the stem below the leaves, arching or pendent racemes bearing 5–25 flowers in the upper part. Flowers white or cream with a

Aerangis luteo-alba   BOB CAMPBELL
var. *rhodosticta*

red column, arranged in two rows, all in the same plane, 2–4 cm in diameter; sepals oblanceolate, acute, 10–15 mm long; petals obovate, equalling or a little longer than the sepals; lip obovate or rhomboid, widest above the middle, acute, 15–20 mm long, 7–15 mm wide, spur slender, incurved, 2.3–4 cm long; column short and thick, 2–3 mm long.

On small twigs and branches of bushes and trees, rarely on trunks, often near rivers; recorded from Mt Kenya, Kakamega, Kericho and Narok district; 1250–2200 m; usually flowers in May (west of the Rift Valley) or September (eastern highlands).

Widespread in a belt across equatorial Africa from the highlands of Ethiopia and Kenya to Mt Cameroon, and southwards as far as southwest Tanzania and Angola.

The variety *luteo-alba*, which has creamy-yellow tepals and column, is recorded only from Zaïre and western Uganda; flowers with an orange-yellow column have also been reported from western Uganda.

Aerangis somalensis (Schlechter) Schlechter

Stem short and upright. Leaves 2–6, oblong-ligulate, leathery, greyish green with a darker reticulate venation, unequally or subequally bilobed at the

Aerangis somalensis   BOB CAMPBELL

apex, margins thickened, 2–11 cm long, 13–34 mm wide. Inflorescences one or several, arising below the leaves, 10–20 cm long and bearing 4–17 flowers. Flowers white, sometimes tinged with pink or green, 1–2 cm apart, up to 2.5 cm in diameter; dorsal sepal ovate, apiculate, arching forward over

Aerangis luteo-alba var. *rhodosticta*   BOB CAMPBELL

the column, 8–10 mm long; lateral sepals oblique or reflexed, 9–14 mm long; petals spreading, oblong apiculate, 8–11 mm long; lip oblong-ligulate, with margins reflexed in the lower half, apiculate, 9–13 mm long, spur straight or slightly curved, 10–15 cm long; column thick, up to 4 mm long.

On trees and at the base of branching shrubs in relict patches of woodland, along streams and near

Aerangis thomsonii

rock outcrops on prominent hills in the dry, eastern parts of the country; 1000–1500 m; flowers March to April and October to November.

This species appears to be widely scattered throughout eastern Africa. To date it has been recorded in Ethiopia, southern Tanzania, Malawi, Zimbabwe and the Transvaal Province of South Africa, as well as Kenya.

At one time this species was confused with *Aerangis verdickii*, which has larger plants with plain, greyish-green leaves and larger flowers with longer spurs. It is widespread in the southern and eastern parts of Africa but has not yet been recorded in Kenya.

Aerangis thomsonii (Rolfe) Schlechter
Syn. *Aerangis friesiorum* Schlechter

Stems woody and elongated, 10–100 cm long, often several in close proximity. Leaves 8–20, alternate, 1–3 cm apart, ligulate, bilobed at the apex, margins entire, dark green, 8–28 cm long. Inflorescences borne at the nodes, arching racemes bearing 4–10 white flowers. Flowers held erect in two rows, 1.5–3.5 cm apart; dorsal sepal erect, lanceolate-elliptic, cuspidate, curving forward at the apex, 22–33 mm long; lateral sepals strongly reflexed, lanceolate-elliptic, acuminate, winged on the back, 25–32 mm long; petals reflexed, oblique, lanceolate-elliptic, acute, 20–25 mm long; lip reflexed, elliptic-lanceolate, acuminate, margins recurved below, inrolled above, 20–25 mm long, spur pendulous, flexuous, cylindrical but widened and flattened in its terminal half, 10–15 cm long; column erect, widened towards the apex, 6–8 mm long.

In shady places, usually rather low down on trunks and branches in highland forests, often overhanging streams; recorded from all the highland districts and many isolated hills; 1600–3000 m; flowers in March and April and again in October and November.

Restricted to the mountains of Kenya and northern Tanzania and once recorded from the Uganda side of Mt Elgon.

Aerangis ugandensis Summerhayes
Stem woody, pendent or erect, up to 20 cm long but usually much shorter except on old plants. Leaves 4–12, distichous, oblanceolate, often falcate, unequally bilobed at the apex, dark green with black dots, 5–15 cm long, 1–2 cm wide. Inflorescences 1–5, arising from the axils of the lower leaves, always pendent, 7–12 flowered. Flowers white or greenish, 5–12 mm apart, up to 2 cm in diameter; dorsal sepal erect, oblong-lanceolate, apiculate, 6–12 mm long, lateral sepals similar but often slightly reflexed; petals reflexed, oblong-lanceolate, acute, 6–10 mm long; lip oblong, cuspidate, 6–10 mm long, spur straight and narrow, 1–2.5 cm long; column terete below, up to 2 mm long.

In moist forests, usually in dense shade, rather

Aerangis ugandensis   BOB CAMPBELL

low down on large tree trunks and often with the roots in a deep growth of moss; frequent near rivers west of the Rift Valley; 1500-2200 m; flowers between May and July.

Quite common in very shady places in the cooler rain forests of Uganda and eastern Zaïre.

Angraecopsis Kraenzlin

About a dozen orchid species from Africa and Madagascar are now recognised as members of this genus, three of which have been recorded in Kenya. At first sight *Angraecopsis gracillima*, which with its white flowers is the largest of the Kenya species, looks rather different from the other two species that have many small pale green flowers. Summerhayes classified the two groups in separate sections but kept them together in one genus because they all have a three lobed lip. The suffix *-opsis* means 'having the appearance of', so the name of this genus refers to the fact that it looks similar to *Angraecum*.

CULTIVATION

All the species can be maintained in cultivation. The smaller ones are much easier if they are mounted on a piece of hardwood or bark and all can be grown in this way. *Angraecopsis gracillima* also grows well in a free-draining compost in a pot. The smaller species come from higher altitudes and therefore need cooler conditions at night and benefit from drying out periodically.

Key to the species of *Angraecopsis*
1   Flowers white, with spur more than
        2.5 cm long . . . . *A. gracillima*
    Flowers pale green or yellowish green,
        spurs less than 2 cm long   2

2   Spurs slender throughout their length,
        7–13 mm long . . . . *A. amaniensis*
    Spurs enlarged and bulbous at the apex . . . . .
    . . . . *A. breviloba*

Angraecopsis amaniensis Summerhayes
Stem very short, upright or pendent, less than 5 mm long, bearing a few leaves in the upper part, sometimes leafless, and with many long, flattened roots below which are much more conspicuous than the leaves. Leaves 1–3 per stem, linear, greyish green, 1–3 cm long, 3–5 mm wide.

Inflorescences slender, pendent, several, 3–20 cm long with 10–20 flowers arranged along their length. Flowers pale green, star-shaped, 7–10 mm in diameter; dorsal sepal elliptic, 4 mm long, up to 2 mm wide; lateral sepals linear 7–9 mm long, 1 mm wide; petals lanceolate, acute, 3–4 mm long, 1.5 mm wide; lip 3-lobed, side lobes very small, midlobe linear, up to 4 mm long, spur cylindrical, straight or curved, 7–13 mm long; column minute.

On *Podocarpus* and other trees in highland forests, where it often occurs in large clumps on the trunks and main branches, also recorded from conifer plantations; 1500–2100 m; flowering in April and May.

First described from the Usambara Mountains in Tanzania and now known also from Mozambique, Malawi, Zambia and Zimbabwe at lower altitudes than in Kenya.

This species is extremely similar to the following one but easily distinguished from it when in flower by the longer inflorescences and longer, narrow spur. Though they are such small plants they can be quite spectacular when bearing many inflorescences.

Angraecopsis amaniensis   BOB CAMPBELL

Angraecopsis breviloba Summerhayes

Stem very short, upright or pendent, less than 5 mm long, bearing a few leaves in the upper part, sometimes leafless, and with many long, flattened roots below which are much more conspicuous than the leaves. Leaves 1–3 per stem, linear-elliptic or oblanceolate, greyish green, 1–4 cm long, 3–5 mm wide. Inflorescences slender, pendent, usually several, 3–10 cm long with 10–15 flowers densely arranged along their length. Flowers pale green or yellowish green, star-shaped, 7–10 mm in diameter; dorsal sepal elliptic, 3–5 mm long, up to 1.5 mm wide; lateral sepals similar; petals lanceolate, obtuse, 3–4 mm long, 1–1.5 mm wide; lip obscurely 3-lobed, side lobes very small, midlobe lanceolate, up to 4 mm long, spur bulbous at the apex, slender below, 4–5 mm long; column minute.

Angraecopsis breviloba   BOB CAMPBELL

On small trees and bushes, often near streams but also along ridges in montane forests; recorded from Ngong hills, Kikuyu forests and in Londiani district; 1500–2400 m; flowering in May to July and also November to January.

Also known from Tanzania where it has been recorded in citrus plantations as well as in the wild.

This species is extremely similar to the preceding one but easily distinguished from it when in flower by the shorter inflorescences and short, bulbous spur. Though they are such small plants they can be quite spectacular when bearing many inflorescences.

Angraecopsis gracillima (Rolfe) Summerhayes

Stem short, upright or pendent, 1–7 cm long bearing two rows of leaves in the upper part and shortly hairy roots below. Leaves 2–10 per stem, linear, often falcate, obtusely bilobed at the blunt apex, 6–15 cm long, 8–15 mm wide. Inflorescences slender, usually erect, 5–20 cm long with 4–20 flowers close together in the apical quarter. Flowers white, usually with the lateral sepals and petals reflexed so they look very narrow; dorsal sepal ovate, up to 3 mm long; lateral sepals dependent on either side of the lip, spathulate, 7–9 mm long; petals ovate or triangular, adnate to the lateral sepals for two thirds of their length, 2–5 mm long and wide; lip 3-lobed, side lobes linear and shorter than the wider midlobe, up to 5 mm long, spur slender and usually curved, 3–4 cm long; column short.

Angraecopsis gracillima   BOB CAMPBELL

On branches and trunks of small trees and in the canopy of evergreen forest, usually with the roots shrouded in a thin layer of moss, recorded in the warmer forests to the west of the Rift Valley, in Kericho, Kakamega and Kavirondo districts; 1500–1850 m; flowering between May and August.

Also recorded from Uganda and Zambia.

Angraecum Bory

The name *Angraecum* has, in the past, been given to a very wide range of African orchids with a monopodial habit of growth, but its use is now restricted to those species in which the flowers have a concave lip enveloping the column at its base. Furthermore, the column has a very short, emarginate rostellum at its apex. But these characteristics are shared by a great variety of species, both large and small, with a variety of shapes and colours of leaves and with white, green or ochre coloured flowers. More than 200 have been described, mostly from Madagascar and the adjacent islands. Twelve have been described from Kenya.

The name *Angraecum* is derived from a Malay word *angurek*, which is also used for other epiphytic orchids in the *Vanda* alliance. It was first used by the French explorer Bory, in his Voyages (1804), for a plant collected in the island of Réunion, *Angraecum eburneum*. This is a large species that grows on coral and volcanic rocks and also as an epiphyte. Rather similar plants with larger flowers occur in Madagascar and the Comoro Islands, while others with smaller flowers occur in Zanzibar, Pemba and near the coast of Tanzania and Kenya. Originally described as separate species, these plants are all now considered to be subspecies of the widespread and variable *A. eburneum*.

CULTIVATION

All the species of *Angraecum* are easy to grow in cultivation. However, it is important to know the original source of each species because individual requirements vary, in particular the day and night temperatures that are maintained are very important for healthy growth. *Angraecum dives, A. eburneum,* and *A. teres* grow near the coast and require warm night temperatures, high humidity and thrive with bright light. The montane species, *Angraecum chamaeanthus, A. conchiferum, A. decipiens, A. humile* and *A. sacciferum,* require much cooler conditions at night with warm temperatures and considerable shade during the day. They can tolerate drier conditions for part of the year but need high humidity during the growing period. The widespread *Angraecum erectum* grows in a wide variety of conditions without difficulty. All species grow well in pots or baskets with a bark-based compost mix. Some of the smaller ones also grow well mounted on slabs of bark or cork oak.

Key to the species of *Angraecum*

1   Leaves flat, at least in the upper half   3
     Leaves terete or bilaterally flattened   2

2 Leaves terete, more than 5 cm long. . . . . . .
. . . . *A. teres*
Leaves flattened, clasping the stem on each
side, less than 1 cm long . . . . . . *A. humile*

3 Lip white, orbicular or funnel shaped,
the largest part of the flower. 4
Lip white, green or yellow, similar to the
seals and petals in colour and shape,
small 6

4 Leaves thick and fleshy, more than 20 cm
long; inflorescences with 5–30 flowers . . . .
. . . . *A. eburneum* ssp. *giryamae*
Leaves not thick, less than 15 cm long;
inflorescences with 1–2 flowers 5

5 Flowers with lip on upper side; spur
3–6 cm long . . . . *A. conchiferum*
Flowers with lip on lower side; spur
12–16 cm long . . . . *A. infundibulare*

6 Stems short, less than 5 cm long; leaves
arising close together; flowers less
than 7 mm in diameter 7
Stems elongated; leaves widely spaced;
flowers at least 1 cm in diameter 9

7 Flowers white . . . . *A. chamaeanthus*
Flowers green 8

8 Flowers with pedicel and ovary twisted
through 360° . . . . *A. sacciferum*
Flowers with straight pedicel and ovary . . . .
. . . . *A. decipiens*

9 Flowers 1–2 per inflorescence 10
Flowers 3 or more per inflorescence 12

10 Flowers white or pink; spur slender . . . .
. . . . *A. erectum*
Flowers green or pinkish bronze; spur
inflated at the tip 11

11 Spur less than 3 mm long . . . . *A. viride*
Spur 10–25 mm long . . . . . . *A. cultriforme*

12 Leaves narrow, erect; usually many
inflorescences at each flowering . . . .
. . . . *A. dives*
Leaves wide, horizontal or pendent;
inflorescences few at each flowering . . . . .
. . . . *A. firthii*

Angraecum chamaeanthus Schlechter

Plants are diminutive epiphytes, only a few cm high. Stems erect, short, 1–5 mm high. Leaves 2–4, arranged in a small fan, linear or ligulate, 1–2 cm long, 1.5–2.5 mm wide, slightly bluish green. Inflorescences simple, erect or curved, bearing 4–10 tiny flowers. Flowers white or pale green, only 2–3 mm in diameter; sepals oblong or elliptic, rounded at the apex; petals oblong or obovate; lip broadly ovate, obscurely 3-lobed, with a short conical spur at its base; column fleshy, minute.

Usually growing as a twig epiphyte in small trees and bushes in montane forests and easily over-looked; recorded only once in Kenya in the forest along the Kikuyu escarpment; *c.* 2400 m; flowering in June.

Also found in suitable habitats in southern Tanzania, Zambia and Malawi.

Angraecum chamaeanthus   BOB CAMPBELL

Angraecum conchiferum Lindley

Plants are straggling epiphytes, easily recognised by the flattened roots which have a rough, warty surface, and branching stems. Stems often some-what flattened, 3–5 mm wide and up to 30 cm long but usually shorter, surrounded by the overlap-ping, black-dotted leaf sheaths. Leaves in two rows near the apex of stems, linear, unequally bilobed at the apex, often twisted at the base so that they lie in one plane, 3–7 cm long, 5–7 mm wide. Inflor-escences slender, with 1 or 2 flowers, arising oppo-site a leaf. Flowers large, 4–6 cm in diameter, with a white lip and pale yellowish-green sepals and petals; dorsal sepal longer and lateral sepals wider and longer than petals, all linear-lanceolate, up to 3 cm long; lip large, orbicular with a central keel and an elongated apex, up to 12 mm wide, usually held on the upper side of the flower, spur curved, 3–5 cm long; column conspicuous, with the rostellum lobes framing the keel on the lip.

Angraecum conchiferum   BOB CAMPBELL

Forests on isolated hills, rather rarely collected in Kenya and so far known only from the forests along the slopes of the Aberdare Mts, the southern forests on Mt Kenya, Ol Doinyo Sapuk in Machakos district and Ol Doinyo Orok in the Namanga hills; 1800–2400 m; cultivated specimens flower from September to November.

Widespread on hills and mountains along the eastern side of Africa but nowhere common; also recorded from Tanzania, Malawi, Mozambique, Zimbabwe and South Africa (E. Cape).

Angraecum cultriforme Summerhayes
Plants untidy and often pendent with numerous elongated roots among the leaves. Stems straight or curved, somewhat two-edged, up to 15 cm long. Leaves in two rows, ligulate, falcate, very unequally bilobed at the apex, 2–6 cm long, 5–8 mm wide, usually yellowish green or pinkish green, sometimes with darker dots. Inflorescences arising below the roots, opposite to a leaf, bearing a single flower but occasionally up to 4 flowers, often arising from the same point in subsequent years. Flowers pink, greenish brown or apple green; sepals linear-lanceolate, acuminate, up to 18 mm long; petals linear-lanceolate, acuminate, to 14 mm long; lip ovate-lanceolate, acuminate, 8–12 mm long, 4–6 mm wide, spur straight or slightly curved, 10–25 mm long, swollen at the tip; column *c*. 2 mm long.

Rarely collected in Kenya, in the forests on the southeastern slopes of the Aberdares and as an epiphyte in coastal bush near the Tanzanian border and near Lungulunga in Kwale district; near sea level and at 2200 m; flowering in March and in July (in cultivation).

Widespread along the warmer coastal areas of eastern Africa from Tanzania, through Zambia, Malawi, Zimbabwe, Mozambique and South Africa (Natal) and on some of the forested mountains in southern Tanzania.

It seems strange that a single species of epiphyte should be found in such very different habitats as the coastal forests and the forests on the slopes of the Aberdare Mts. However, the plants that I have studied, alive and in herbaria, have very similar flowers and I have found it difficult to separate them. The only apparent difference is that the plants near the coast tend to be more pinkish bronze in coloration. The plant shown in the photograph came from the Aberdares. More field studies are clearly desirable.

Angraecum cultriforme   BOB CAMPBELL

Angraecum decipiens Summerhayes
Plants are dwarf epiphytes, only a few cm high. Stems erect, short, 1–5 mm high. Leaves 2–4, arranged in a small fan, linear or ligulate, falcate, 15–35 mm long, 2.5–3.5 mm wide, rather fleshy. Inflorescences simple, curved, bearing 5–15 tiny flowers. Flowers pale green or yellowish green, only 2–4 mm in diameter; dorsal sepal elliptic or obovate, subacute to obtuse, 1.7–2.3 mm long, *c*. 1 mm wide; lateral sepals obliquely elliptic-obovate, acute or subacute, *c*. 2 mm long; petals elliptic, subacute to obtuse, 1.6–2 mm long; lip

Angraecum decipiens   BOB CAMPBELL

entire, concave, ovate, obtuse, 1.5–2.1 mm long, with a short straight, clavate spur *c.* 1.5 mm long; column fleshy, minute.

Usually growing as a twig epiphyte in small trees and bushes in very shady habitats and easily overlooked; recorded in Kenya in the Langata forest and from the western slopes of Mt Kenya; 1600–2200 m; flowering in April.

Also found along the rim of Ngurdoto Crater, near Arusha, Tanzania.

Angraecum dives Rolfe

Plants erect, epiphytic or lithophytic. Stems 1–5 cm long, rooting near the base. Leaves 2–10, erect, linear, with rounded lobes at the apex, 5–20 cm long, 5–15 mm wide. Inflorescences usually many, erect or arching, with 8–25 flowers on slender peduncles. Flowers green or yellowish green; sepals elliptic-lanceolate, acute, 5 mm long, 1.3–1.5 mm wide; petals lanceolate, acute or acuminate, recurved, 5 mm long, 1.2 mm wide; lip concave, ovate, acuminate, 4 mm long, 2.5 mm wide, spur subclavate, upcurved beside the ovary, 2–3 mm long; column very short.

On coral and other rocks near the coast and in coastal woodlands, usually in bright light; often found on baobab trees and also on much smaller trees and shrubs, often rather near the ground; from sea level to 80 m inland; recorded in flower from September to November.

Also recorded in similar habitats in Tanzania, and on the islands of Zanzibar, Pemba and Socotra.

Angraecum dives   BOB CAMPBELL

Angraecum eburneum Bory ssp. *giryamae* (Rendle) Senghas & Cribb
Syn. *Angraecum giryamae* Rendle

Plants large, robust, erect, with many fleshy roots of great length. Stems thick, 15–100 cm long, 2–3 cm in diameter. Leaves 6–10 succulent or leathery, usually light yellowish green, erect, ligulate, with unequal rounded lobes at the apex, 15–50 cm long, 3–7 cm wide. Inflorescences erect or ascending, bearing 8–20 large flowers and conspicuous blackish bracts. Flowers green with a white lip on the upper side, scented in the evening; sepals reflexed, linear-lanceolate, 3–4.5 cm long, 5–7 mm wide; petals reflexed, similar to sepals; lip

Angraecum eburneum ssp. *giryamae*
with *Polystachya tessellata* at Kilifi   K.O.S.

transversely oblong to broadly ovate, almost 3-lobed with a central apiculus between the rounded side lobes, 2–3 cm long, 2.8–4 cm wide, spur pointed behind the dorsal sepal, 4–6 cm long; column fleshy, green, 5 mm long with paler rostellum lobes.

Widespread at the coast both near the sea on coral cliffs as an epiphyte, and on isolated hills further inland as an epiphyte and on rocks; sea level to 350 m; flowering from July to September.

Also known from similar habitats in northern Tanzania, and on the islands of Pemba and Zanzibar.

Angraecum eburneum ssp. *giryamae*   BOB CAMPBELL

Angraecum eburneum was described originally from Réunion and is now known to be variable and widespread among the islands of the western Indian Ocean. The differences in the size of the flowers and the length of the spur in the various localities are now used to recognise four subspecies rather than separate species as in the past.

Angraecum erectum Summerhayes
Plants erect and scrambling with numerous white roots along the stem. Stems often greatly elongated, 20–40 cm high, distinctly two-edged and covered in rather glaucous green overlapping leaf sheaths. Leaves stiff and leathery in two rows, linear lanceolate, very unequally bilobed at the apex, 3–6 cm long, 5–12 mm wide. Inflorescences arising opposite a leaf, usually immediately below a root, bearing 1–2 flowers. Flowers white, pale yellowish green or pale salmon pink, scented in the evening; sepals and petals often somewhat reflexed, lanceolate, acuminate, 10–14 mm long, 2–

4 mm wide, sepals wider than petals; lip lanceolate, acuminate, similar to sepals, with a linear callus in the basal half, spur straight or curved, slender, 15–30 mm long; column short and stout.

Widespread in north and central Kenya and in Masai district in forests and scrub where it is seasonally dry; often to be found in patches of forest along rivers and dry gulleys, usually in the shade, and growing vertically among small trunks and branches; 1700–2350 m; recorded in flower from March to October.

Also recorded in similar habitats in northern Uganda, western Tanzania and Zambia.

Angraecum erectum   BOB CAMPBELL

Angraecum firthii Summerhayes
Plants epiphytic with an elongate stem bearing leaves and roots along its length. Stems upright, somewhat compressed so that they appear flattened, 10–30 cm long. Leaves dark green, rather thin, oblanceolate or oblong, unequally rounded at the apex, 8–12 cm long, 1.5–2.5 cm wide. Inflorescences short, slender, bearing 3–5 flowers. Flowers yellowish green; dorsal sepal lanceolate, long acuminate, 12–20 mm long, 3.5–3.8 mm wide; lateral sepals similar; petals similar but smaller; lip somewhat 3-lobed, 12–13 mm long, 4–6 mm wide, the side lobes wide, erect, the midlobe recurved, linear, spur S-shaped, 15 mm long; column 2 mm long.

Epiphytic in the warmer forests inland; rather rarely collected near Fort Ternan and Kakamega; 1450–1600 m; flowering in June.

Also recorded in Uganda and Cameroon.

Angraecum humile Summerhayes

Plants epiphytic, very small. Stems elongate, usually 1–4 cm long, straight or curved, bearing leaves in two rows and fine roots from the base. Leaves equitant, very small, elliptic or oblanceolate in side view, 5–7 mm long, 2–3 mm wide. Inflorescences very short, in the axils of the leaves, bearing 2–4 flowers. Flowers white or pale green, 2–4 mm in diameter; sepals elliptic oblong; petals similar; lip concave, ovate, acute, 1.6 mm long, spur clavate from a broad mouth, as long as the lip; column very short, anther cap pointed.

An epiphyte on mossy twigs of trees and branches, usually in the canopy of dwarf montane and riverine forest in central and western Kenya; very small and easily overlooked; 1650–2500 m; flowering from August to October.

Elsewhere recorded only from Tanzania, in Lushoto district.

Angraecum infundibulare Lindley

Plants epiphytic with long branching stems growing in clumps and bearing roots among the leaves. Stems bilaterally compressed, straight or

Angraecum infundibulare   BOB CAMPBELL

branching, usually pendent with the apical part upturned, to 100 cm long but often shorter. Leaves in two rows, narrowly elliptic or oblanceolate, unequally bilobed at the apex, the lobes rounded, 10–22 cm long, 1.5–3 cm wide. Inflorescences protruding through the sheath above the leaf axil, bearing a single flower. Flower pale green with a large white lip; sepals linear lanceolate, acuminate, margins recurved, 6–8.5 cm long, less than 1 cm wide; petals linear, slightly shorter than sepals; lip concave, ovate to oblong-ovate, 6–8 cm long, 5–5.5 cm wide, with a long apicule to 12 mm long, spur funnel shaped at the base, curved, S-shaped and finally pendent, 16–20 cm long; column fleshy, 5 mm long.

In warm forests where humidity is high, only recorded along the Yala river in west Kenya; 1300 m; flowering in June or July.

Well known in Uganda and also recorded from Nigeria, Cameroon and Principe.

Angraecum sacciferum Lindley
Plants epiphytic or lithophytic, very small. Stems short, almost absent or up to 5 cm long. Leaves in a short fan or in two rows on either side of stem,

Angraecum sacciferum   BOB CAMPBELL

linear to narrowly elliptic, unequally bilobed at the apex, 1–6 cm long, 3–5 mm wide, usually twisted at the base to lie in one plane. Inflorescences 1–several, often arising from the same point in successive years, bearing 2–5 flowers. Flowers green, pedicel and ovary strongly twisted so that the lip is uppermost; sepals elliptic-oblong, 2–4 mm long, 1.5–

2 mm wide; petals lanceolate, acute, 2.4–3 mm long; lip deeply concave, broadly ovate, 2.7–3.5 mm long, 3.5 mm wide, spur shortly cylindrical, truncate, to 2 mm long; column very short.

Widespread in upland forests where humidity is high, growing as an epiphyte and on rocks by streams; recorded from Mt Elgon, Kakamega, Yala river, Ngong hills and some of the hills in Teita district; 1600–2400 m; flowering from March to June.

Also known from Tanzania and Uganda, westwards to Cameroon and southwards through Zaïre to Malawi, Mozambique, Zimbabwe and South Africa (Transvaal, Natal and Cape Province).

Angraecum teres Summerhayes
Plants rather small with a short pendent stem less than 2 cm long. Leaves narrow, terete, always pendent but sometimes arranged in a small fan, 4–15 cm long, apiculate. Inflorescences arching or pendent, up to 15 cm long, slender, 2–10 flowered.

Angraecum teres   BOB CAMPBELL

Flowers small, greenish ochre; dorsal sepal ovate-lanceolate, acuminate, 7–8 mm long, 3–4 mm wide; lateral sepals lanceolate, similar to dorsal sepal but narrower; petals lanceolate, acuminate, slightly longer than sepals; lip ovate or obscurely 3-lobed, 5 mm long, spur ascending above the ovary, to 2 cm long; column very short.

Epiphytic on the boles of small trees and on large branches; rather rarely collected from only a few localities near the coast; sea level to 200 m; flowering in March.

Also known from northern Tanzania, in similar habitats near the sea.

Angraecum viride Kraenzlin

Plants pendent with numerous slender, elongated roots among the leaves. Stems straight or curved, somewhat two-edged, up to 45 cm long. Leaves in two rows, linear-elliptic, unequally acutely bilobed at the apex, 2–5 cm long, 4–6 mm wide, pale green. Inflorescences arising below the roots, opposite to a leaf, bearing 1–2 flowers, often arising from the same point in subsequent years. Flowers green; sepals lanceolate, acuminate, 3–5 mm long; petals lanceolate, acuminate, to 4 mm long; lip concave, ovate, acuminate, 3–4 mm long, 2.5–3 mm wide, spur straight or slightly curved, clavate, 1.8–2.5 mm long; column less than 1 mm long.

Epiphyte in warm forest near the coast; only recorded from the Shimba hills; 300 m; flowering in May.

Also recorded from northern Tanzania, in Lushoto district.

Ansellia Lindley

Leopard orchid

Only one species of *Ansellia* is currently recognised in Africa although at least six names have been published for plants from different areas. The flowers are extremely variable, in size, shape, basic colouring, and the colour and size of their characteristic spots. Attempts have been made in the past to relate these differences to the size of the plants, their distribution and ecology, e.g by Piers (1968) and Summerhayes (1937, 1968). But there are often intermediates that do not satisfactorily fit in the various categories proposed. In the recently published account of the *Flora of Tropical East Africa*, Orchidaceae, Part 2 (Cribb, 1984), only one name is recognised, *Ansellia africana*, although the great variability within this species is described.

The genus is named in honour of the gardener John Ansell, who first collected specimens on the island of Fernando Po (Bioko) in West Africa. It is immediately recognisable by its large, cane-like pseudobulbs that arise close together from a basal rhizome, often surrounded by a nest of narrow and pointed, upright roots and attached to the host tree or to rocks by many thick white roots. The spotted flowers are borne in a branching inflorescence at the apex of each pseudobulb, and, after the first flowering, they also arise from other nodes that have lost their leaves. Plants have been collected in South Africa (Natal) that are pure lemon yellow, lacking spots of any kind.

CULTIVATION

This species is very easy to maintain in cultivation in brightly lit, warm conditions. The plants grow well in pots or baskets and form an extensive root system in well-drained compost. Although wild plants are often found in places that are seasonally quite dry, plants grow best in cultivation if they are well supplied with water and dilute fertiliser while new pseudobulbs are developing and then kept rather dry to encourage flowering. The flowers are sweetly scented in sunshine and very attractive to bees who pollinate them.

Ansellia africana Lindley

Plants large, erect, epiphytic or lithophytic. Pseudobulbs long and cane-like, yellow, ridged on the surface, bearing leaves in the upper part, 50–120 cm tall, plants near the coast usually shorter. Leaves 8–10, ligulate or narrowly lanceolate, acute, 15–40 cm long, 1.5–5 cm wide. Inflorescences simple or branched, bearing 10–100 flowers, closely or laxly arranged. Flowers yellow or greenish yellow, lightly or heavily spotted with reddish brown, the lip yellow; dorsal sepal elliptic, obtuse, 1.5–3 cm long, 0.5–1 cm wide; lateral sepals similar but longer; petals elliptic, rounded at the apex, slightly shorter and wider than the sepals; lip 3-lobed, the side lobes erect on either side of the column, the mid-lobe bearing 2–3 longitudinal keels on its upper surface; column stout, up to 1 cm long, bearing 4 pollinia in 2 pairs at its apex.

Formerly conspicuous on *Hyphaene* palms at the coast, this large orchid can still be found in parts of the country that are hot and dry by day except in the rainy season; plants on the Yatta Plateau and in the Rift Valley are mostly much larger than those from other areas and the spots on the flowers are less distinctly outlined, while those from the coast have fewer but larger flowers with clear spots; flowers heavily marked with dark spots have been found on plants on Mt Elgon; sea level to 2200 m; flowering in January and February and also in September.

Widespread throughout tropical Africa and south as far as South Africa (Natal).

Bolusiella Schlechter

The fan shaped plants of the dwarf epiphytes in this genus make them instantly recognisable. They also have rather easily recognised small white flowers that often do not open fully, each supported by a conspicuous black bract.

There are five or six species in tropical and southern Africa. They are found on the twigs and branches of bushes and small trees, often in rather exposed situations. The genus was named in honour of Harry Bolus, a Cape Town stockbroker and amateur botanist. His illustrated works on the orchids of South Africa (1888–1911) were a major contribution to African orchidology at the turn of the century.

CULTIVATION

Plants are easily maintained if collected on the

Ansellia africana

BOB CAMPBELL

Ansellia africana   BOB CAMPBELL

small branches and twigs to which they are usually attached in the wild. They can be difficult to establish on a fresh mount in a greenhouse and need a rather fine medium, such as that usually used for seedlings, if grown in a pot. In Kenya they occur at medium or high altitudes and do best in a cool greenhouse where there is a drop in temperature at night.

Key to the species of *Bolusiella*
Leaves with a groove along the upper surface . . . . **B. iridifolia**
Leaves without a groove along the upper surface . . . . **B. maudiae**

Bolusiella iridifolia (Rolfe) Schlechter
Erect dwarf epiphyte with short stem and very slender roots in a tuft at the base of the plant. Leaves 4–6, arranged in a fan, tapering from base to apex with a groove along the upper surface, rigid and rather fleshy, glabrous, 2–5 cm long, 1.5–5 mm broad. Inflorescences longer than the leaves, slender racemes bearing many flowers in the axils of conspicuous small bracts, 2–6 cm long. Flowers white; tepals free, subequal, 1–3 mm long, 0.7–1.4 mm broad; lip oblong-ligulate, obtuse, 1–5 mm long, 0.7–1.1 mm broad, spur short cylindrical or conical.

Two subspecies have been recognised in Kenya:

ssp. *iridifolia* has been found in many areas at high altitude, where it grows on the twigs and branches of forest trees and scrub; 2300–2600 m; flowering from April to July. Elsewhere this species has been recorded from Tanzania, Uganda and many parts of West Africa, and from the island of Grande Comore.

This subspecies has larger flowers with a longer and narrower spur than ssp. *picea*.

ssp. *picea* Cribb has been found in the Chyulu hills, where ssp. *iridifolia* has also been collected. The flowers are smaller with a shorter, more conical spur. Here it grows on bushes and small trees near the top of the hills, often with its tuft of slender roots anchored amongst lichens; 1500 m; flowering in May. This subspecies has also been recognised in other parts of Africa, notably in Tanzania, Malawi, Zambia and Zimbabwe.

Bolusiella maudiae (Bolus) Schlechter

Syn. *Bolusiella imbricata* (Rolfe) Schlechter
Erect dwarf epiphyte with short stem and very slender roots in a tuft at the base of the plant. Leaves 4–8, arranged in a fan, rigid and rather fleshy, straight or curved, glabrous, 1–3.5 cm long, 0.3–1 mm broad. Inflorescences longer than the leaves, slender racemes bearing many flowers in the axils of conspicuous small bracts, 2–6 cm long. Flowers white; tepals free, subequal, 3–4 mm long, 1–1.5 mm broad; lip obscurely 3-lobed, side lobes rounded, midlobe oblong-ligulate, 2–3 mm long, 0.7–1 mm broad, spur cylindrical, slightly incurved, 1.5–2 mm long.

Bolusiella maudiae   BOB CAMPBELL

Grows on twigs and branches of small trees and bushes in the warmer forests of western Kenya; 1200–1900 m; flowers from June to September.

This species was described first from Natal in South Africa, and is now known to be widespread in Africa, from Kenya to Ghana and the Ivory Coast and in Uganda, Tanzania, Malawi and Zambia.

Bulbophyllum Thouars

This genus is easily recognisable because the plants have a creeping rhizome that forms a mat over the tree or rock on which they grow. At intervals along this rhizome are spaced green or yellow pseudobulbs, each bearing one or two leaves. Many fibrous roots arise from the base of each pseudobulb and also from the rhizome. The leaves are often thick and fleshy and last for many years. The inflorescences always arise from the base of the pseudobulb and, in the African species, bear many small flowers, sometimes over a long season. In one section the flowers are borne on a flattened, fleshy rachis, rather in the shape of a knife blade. Four Kenya species have this kind of inflorescence: *B. falcatum*, *B. maximum*, *B. sandersonii* and *B. scaberulum*. These were originally described by Lindley in a separate genus, *Megaclinium*, but this genus has long been reduced to a section of *Bulbophyllum*. The flowers are green, reddish, purplish or brownish, often not opening fully, and have a characteristic mobile lip which assists the pollinator to carry away the pollinia.

Bulbophyllum is a very large genus with more than 1000 species in the tropical parts of the world. It is particularly abundant in New Guinea where more than 600 species have been recorded. It was first described in 1822 by the French botanist, Aubert A. Du Petit Thouars, when he used the name for a species from Réunion, *Bulbophyllum nutans*. The generic name refers to the vegetative plant with its conspicuous bulb and leaf (Greek, *phyllon*) or leaves. Approximately 90 species have been recorded from Africa so far, 12 of these from Kenya. It seems strange that the species with the largest flowers, *Bulbophyllum longiflorum* (syn. *Cirrhopetalum umbellatum*, *C. africanum*), has not yet been discovered in Kenya though it is known in both Uganda and Tanzania as well as elsewhere in Africa.

The names used in the following account do not always follow the treatment of the genus made by

Vermeulen (1987) in his monograph of the African species of *Bulbophyllum*. Notes are provided at the end of the species accounts where differences are explained.

CULTIVATION

Bulbophyllum plants are difficult to establish from small pieces of rhizome; plants with several pseudobulbs, always more than three, are much more likely to succeed than smaller ones. Seedlings are also not difficult. Once established, they grow very well in shallow pots, on rafts, shallow baskets, or mounted on pieces of wood or cork oak bark. The compost needs to be capable of holding moisture but free-draining. Most species come from the more humid and warm parts of Africa so they grow well under intermediate to warm conditions. Only those from higher altitudes will flourish in a cool house.

Key to the species of *Bulbophyllum*

1 Pseudobulbs bearing a single leaf at the apex. 2
    Pseudobulbs bearing two leaves at the apex. 5

2 Plants very small, pseudobulbs less than 1 cm high; inflorescence slender with tiny flowers 2–5 mm apart . . . . ***B. intertextum***
    Plants larger, pseudobulbs more than 1 cm high, inflorescence swollen with flowers close together 3

3 Pseudobulbs 1.5–8 cm apart on the rhizome; inflorescence upright, more than 20 cm long, ... 4
    Pseudobulbs clustered, never more than 1 cm apart; inflorescence usually pendent with conspicuous straw coloured bracts . . . . ***B. josephi***

4 Lip purple, covered with conspicuous hairs . . . . ***B. distans***
    Lip reddish, fleshy and rugose but not hairy . . . . ***B. encephalodes***

5 Rachis flattened, with flowers along or near the midline on each side 6
    Rachis terete, may be swollen but not flattened, flowers arranged around the circumference but sometimes all twisted to face the same way 9

6 Inflorescence at least 25 cm high; rachis more than 2 cm wide; . . . . ***B. maximum***
    Inflorescence less than 20 cm long; rachis up to 1 cm wide 7

7 Dorsal sepal fleshy, elongated from a narrow base, rounded at the apex, often yellow or orange . . . . . ***B. falcatum***
    Dorsal sepal tapering from a wide base, pointed 8

8 Inflorescence bearing 6–16 flowers, dull violet or light green overlaid with purplish dots . . . . ***B. sandersonii***
    Inflorescence bearing 24–40 flowers, dull purplish violet, inner surface of lateral sepals striped white and purple . . . . ***B. scaberulum***

9 Lip with long slender hairs at the apex or along all the margins 10
    Lip without hairs or with a few only at the base 11

10 Lip with long slender hairs surrounding its entire margin . . . . ***B. cochleatum***
    Lip with few long slender hairs surrounding the apex, sometimes with shorter hairs on the margins near the base . . . . ***B. vulcanicum***

11 Flowers in two rows, all facing to one side; bracts 6–7 mm long, black or reddish; flowers reddish brown or deep red . . . . ***B. bequaertii***
    Flowers in two rows on opposite sides of axis; bracts 9–12 mm long, straw coloured; flowers whitish or rose pink . . . . ***B. bidenticulatum*** ssp. ***joyceae***

Bulbophyllum bequaertii De Wildeman
Plants epiphytic with a creeping rhizome, bearing pseudobulbs 1–4 cm apart. Pseudobulbs narrowly cylindrical, tapering slightly from the base, 4.5–11 cm long, with 2 apical leaves. Leaves thin, sub-erect, linear, rounded, 12–20 cm long, up to 8–16 mm wide. Inflorescences 12–50 cm long, many flowered, with bracts in two rows. Flowers almost hidden by bracts, all facing one way, pink or deep reddish purple; dorsal sepal fleshy, ovate, obtuse, 4–5 mm long, 2–2.5 mm wide; lateral sepals fleshy, oblong-ovate, obtuse, 3.5–5 mm long, *c.* 1.5 mm wide; petals oblong, subacute, *c.* 1.2 mm long; lip deflexed, oblong or oblanceolate, fleshy, glabrous

or with very short cilia along the margins, up to 3 mm long; column 1.5 mm long, with acute stelidia.

Bulbophyllum bequaertii   HERMANN MEYER

Epiphyte in warm and humid forests; widespread in western Kenya from the Kaimosi area to Kakamega, Sotik, SW Mau and Kericho districts; 1200–2600 m; flowering starting in May and June, but continuing almost throughout the year as the inflorescences grow gradually longer.

Widespread in tropical Africa; recorded in Cameroon, Fernando Po, Zaire, Uganda and Tanzania.

Vermeulen (1987) treats this variable species as part of *Bulbophyllum cochleatum*, recognising two varieties, var. *tenuicaule* and var. *bequaertii*. It seems to me that in Kenya *B. cochleatum* and *B. bequaertii* are best accepted as two distinct and separate species. *Bulbophyllum bequaertii* usually has much longer inflorescences with reddish flowers, whereas *B. cochleatum* is easily recognised by its yellowish flowers that have a differently shaped, dark purple lip.

Bulbophyllum bidenticulatum J.J. Vermeulen ssp. *joyceae* J.J. Vermeulen

Plants epiphytic with a creeping rhizome, bearing pseudobulbs 1–3 cm apart. Pseudobulbs ovoid or narrowly conical, 5–6 angled, 1.5–4 cm long, with 2 apical leaves. Leaves leathery, suberect, linear-elliptic, rounded, 4–10 cm long, up to 1 cm wide. Inflorescences erect, up to 16 cm long, many flowered, with conspicuous whitish, papery, boat shaped bracts that are much larger than the flowers. Flowers rose pink with a yellow lip; dorsal sepal ovate, acute or shortly acuminate, *c.* 6 mm long, 3.4–4.5 mm wide; lateral sepals oblique, ovate, acuminate, 6–7 mm long, 2.3–3 mm wide; petals orbicular, shortly clawed, 1.7–2.8 mm long; lip very fleshy, obscurely 3-lobed in the basal half, side lobes suberect, rounded, midlobe oblong, obtuse; column 1.7–2 mm long, with rounded ventral wings and short stelidia near the apex.

Epiphytic in the tree canopy along the Kiptiget river, Kericho district; not known elsewhere as yet; *c.* 2100 m; flowering in May.

This subspecies was named after the author who discovered it in 1970 while rescuing her dachshund from a mossy branch of a tree growing out over the river. It has larger flowers than ssp. *bidenticulatum* which Vermeulen described in 1987 from Guinea, Liberia and the Ivory Coast. In West Africa the plants occur at lower altitudes and have also been collected growing on rocks. It is close to

Bulbophyllum bidenticulatum   BOB CAMPBELL
ssp. *joyceae*

Bulbophyllum bifarium, under which name it was placed at one time, including in the *Flora of Tropical East Africa,* Orchidaceae, Part 2 (Cribb, 1984).

Bulbophyllum cochleatum Lindley

Plants epiphytic with a creeping rhizome, bearing pseudobulbs 2.5–3.5 cm apart. Pseudobulbs cylindrical, tapering slightly from the base, 3–6 cm long, purple spotted, with 2 apical leaves. Leaves leathery, suberect, linear, rounded, 8–12 cm long, up to 8 mm wide. Inflorescences up to 20 cm long, many flowered, with bracts in two rows. Flowers all facing one way, yellow green or orange with a dark purple lip; dorsal sepal lanceolate, acute, up to 7 mm long, 2.8 mm wide; lateral sepals lanceolate, acute, 6–7 mm long, 2.2 mm wide; petals linear, subacute, 2.2 mm long; lip linear, fleshy, with long cilia on all the margins, up to 5 mm long; column 1.5 mm long, with acute stelidia pointing forwards.

Epiphytic in warm forests; recorded near Lake Victoria, on the lower slopes of Mt Elgon, near Kakamega, Sotik and Kericho; 1800–2200 m; flowering from May to December.

Widespread in tropical Africa; also recorded from Uganda, Tanzania, Zaïre to Guinea, Sudan, Malawi and Zambia.

Bulbophyllum distans Lindley

Plants epiphytic with a stout creeping rhizome and yellow pseudobulbs 3.5–6 cm apart. Pseudobulbs 4-angled, conical or narrowly conical, 2.5–5 cm

Bulbophyllum cochleatum   BOB CAMPBELL

long, bearing a single leaf. Leaf fleshy, suberect, elliptic-oblong, rounded, 9–12 cm long, 2.3–4 cm wide. Inflorescences erect, to 60 cm long but flowers opening successively, usually only one at a time. Flowers with green or purple sepals and petals and a dark maroon or purple lip; dorsal sepal lanceolate, acute, 7–8 mm long; lateral sepals lanceolate, acute, 8 mm long; petals linear-lanceolate, falcate, acuminate, 2.5–3 mm long, 0.3 mm wide; lip highly mobile, swollen and with two glabrous ridges at the base, covered with purple hairs that are short near the base and long above, 6 mm long; column short with slender, curved stelidia *c.* 5 mm long.

Epiphytic in forest near Kakamega.; only known from one collection so far; 1400 m; flowering over a long period.

Widespread in tropical Africa; also recorded from Uganda and from Zaïre to Liberia, and Angola.

Bulbophyllum encephalodes Summerhayes

Plants epiphytic with a stout creeping rhizome and yellowish pseudobulbs 2–8 cm apart. Pseudobulbs 4-angled, ellipsoid, 2–2.8 cm long, bearing a single leaf. Leaf fleshy, suberect, elliptic-oblong, rounded, 7–12 cm long. Inflorescences 12–30 cm long, bearing many small flowers in the apical third. Flowers fleshy, green with maroon margins and lip or entirely maroon; dorsal sepal ovate, acute, 4–5 mm long; lateral sepals ovate, acuminate, 4.5–5.5 mm long; petals obong, subacute, 2.5–3 mm long; lip very fleshy and sculptured so that it resembles the surface of a brain, 2.5 mm long; column short with very short stelidia.

Epiphytic in the forests near Kakamega, Kaimosi and Kericho; 1500–1800 m; flowering in November and December.

Widespread in tropical Africa; recorded from Uganda and Tanzania, westwards through Zaïre, Burundi and Cameroon, south to Malawi, Zambia and Zimbabwe.

Bulbophyllum falcatum (Lindley)
                              Reichenbach f.

Plants epiphytic with a creeping rhizome, bearing pseudobulbs 2.5–5 cm apart. Pseudobulbs ovoid or ovoid-conical to subcylindric, angled, 2–5 cm long, with 2 apical leaves. Leaves leathery, suberect, elliptic-oblanceolate, or oblanceolate, rounded, 6–12 cm long, 1–2.5 cm wide. Inflorescences up to 20 cm long, rarely longer; rachis flattened bilaterally, up to 14 cm long, 0.8 cm wide, often bent at an angle to the peduncle. Flowers facing into the rachis, reddish purple with orange or yellow margins on the dorsal sepal; dorsal sepal oblong-spathulate, 4–6 mm long, 2.2–2.6 mm wide; lateral sepals reflexed in the apical half, ovate-triangular, subacute, 3.5–4 mm long, 2.8–3.5 mm wide; petals falcate, linear, 2–2.8 mm long; lip recurved, ovate, rounded, *c.* 2 mm long; column short with rounded ventral wings.

Epiphytic in warm and humid forests, collected recently near the Yala river in west Kenya; 1500 m; flowering in October.

Widespread in equatorial Africa; recorded from Uganda westwards to Zaïre, Guinea and Sierra Leone.

Bulbophyllum falcatum   BOB CAMPBELL

borne close together. Pseudobulbs ovoid, 3–10 mm long, bearing a single leaf. Leaf thin, erect, linear-oblong, obtuse or rounded, 1–5 cm long, 3–7 mm wide. Inflorescences erect, 5–10 cm long, slender, with 2–12 rather small flowers. Flowers greenish or reddish; dorsal sepal ovate, acute, 3.5 mm long; lateral sepals ovate, acute or acuminate, 4 mm long; petals oblong-elliptic, rounded, 2 mm long; lip fleshy, recurved, obscurely 3-lobed in the basal half; column short, with upright, blunt stelidia.

Epiphytic in the crown of trees and amongst mosses on branches and trunks in the warm forests; recorded from Kakamega district, Teita hills and near the coast; 100–1800 m; flowering from August to October.

Widespread in tropical Africa; also recorded from Tanzania and westwards to Zaïre, Cameroon, Nigeria, Ivory Coast, Guinea, Sierra Leone, Liberia, Ivory Coast, Equatorial Guinea, and Gabon, and from Ethiopia, south to Zambia, Malawi, Zimbabwe and Angola; also recorded from the Seychelles Islands.

Bulbophyllum josephi (Kuntze) Summerhayes
Syn. *Bulbophyllum mahonii* Rolfe
Bulbophyllum schlechteri De Wildeman

Plants epiphytic with a stout creeping rhizome bearing reddish or yellowish wrinkled pseudobulbs close together or up to 3 cm apart. Pseudobulbs conical-ovoid, often somewhat flattened, 1.5–3.5 cm long, bearing a single leaf. Leaf leathery, erect, narrowly oblong or oblanceolate, obtuse, shortly petiolate, 8–16 cm long, 1–2.4 cm wide. Inflorescences arching or pendulous, 8–25 cm long, peduncle slender and bearing many flowers close together. Flowers white, greenish white or yellow, often tinged reddish; dorsal sepal narrowly lanceolate, acuminate, *c.* 7 mm long, 1 mm wide;

Bulbophyllum encephalodes   BOB CAMPBELL

Bulbophyllum intertextum Lindley
Plants epiphytic, very small, up to 5 cm high, with a slender rhizome and yellowish pseudobulbs

lateral sepals linear-lanceolate, long acuminate, 7–8 mm long; petals obovate-elliptic, rounded, 3 mm long; lip recurved, ovate, obtuse, *c.* 2 mm long, with 2 longitudinal central ridges, margins papillose; column short, stelidia short, less than 1 mm long.

Epiphytic in warm forests, recorded from Kakamega, Kaimosi, Kericho and the Teita hills; 850–2100 m; flowering in most months from May through to February.

Widespread in tropical Africa; also recorded from Tanzania, Uganda, westwards through Zaïre, Rwanda, Burundi, to Cameroon and from Ethiopia south to Malawi, Zimbabwe and Mozambique.

Bulbophyllum maximum (Lindley) Reichenbach f.

Syn. *Bulbophyllum oxypterum* (Lindley) Reichenbach f.

Plants epiphytic with a stout creeping rhizome, bearing pseudobulbs 2–10 cm apart. Pseudobulbs ovoid or ellipsoid, slightly flattened, 3–5-angled, sometimes with large swellings on the edges, bearing 2, rarely 3, apical leaves. Leaves narrow, elliptic

Bulbophyllum josephi   BOB CAMPBELL

Bulbophyllum maximum   BOB CAMPBELL

or oblong-elliptic, rounded, 3–15 cm long, 1–3 cm wide. Inflorescences erect, 18–50 cm long, rarely longer; rachis flattened bilaterally, with undulate margins, up to 40 cm long, 1.2 cm wide, often bent at an angle to the peduncle, green or purplish brown, often spotted. Flowers aligned nearer one side of rachis than the other, yellow or green, heavily spotted with purple; dorsal sepal lanceolate, acute, 5–7 mm long, 1.3–1.5 mm wide; lateral sepals recurved, falcate, ovate, acuminate, 4–5.5 mm long, 3–3.5 mm wide; petals falcate, oblong, acute or obtuse, 2.5–3 mm long; lip fleshy, recurved, narrowly oblong, rounded, dentate in the basal half, 2.5–3 mm long; column 1 mm long, with rounded ventral wings.

Epiphytic in open woodland, coastal and riverine forests; found in Kenya in all the coastal districts, Maungu hill and near Thika; sea level to 1500 m; flowering for a long period from January to July.

Widespread in tropical Africa in open forests and woodland in the warmer areas; also recorded from Ethiopia and from Zaïre westwards to Guinea and Sierra Leone, south to Mozambique, Zimbabwe and Angola.

In the past B. oxypterum and B. maximum have often been treated as separate species with the latter name being given to larger specimens. However, they have very similar flowers and it seems likely that only one variable species should be recognised. Bulbophyllum maximum is the earlier name. A larger species that is also related and has been collected in Uganda and Tanzania is Bulbophyllum platyrhachis. This occurs in more humid forests and may be only a more luxuriant form of B. maximum that has grown larger in the different ecological conditions. Vermeulen (1987) does not recognise B. platyrachis as distinct from B. maximum.

Bulbophyllum sandersonii (Hooker f.) Reichenbach f.

Syn. Bulbophyllum tentaculigerum Reichenbach f.
Plants epiphytic with a stout creeping rhizome, bearing pseudobulbs 3–6 cm apart. Pseudobulbs ovoid to narrowly conical, 4–5-angled, 3–5 cm long, with 2 apical leaves. Leaves narrow, elliptic or oblong-elliptic, rounded, 4–12 cm long, 1–2 cm wide. Inflorescences erect, 8–20 cm long, rarely longer; rachis swollen and flattened bilaterally, with undulate margins, up to 15 cm long, 1.2 cm wide, often spotted with purple or papillose. Flowers aligned nearer one side of rachis than the other, whitish or purple, heavily spotted and striped with purple; dorsal sepal erect, linear-lanceolate,

rounded, 7–10 mm long, 2 mm wide; lateral sepals recurved, wide at the base, acuminate, 3.5–5 mm long; petals curved, linear, clavate and swollen at the apex, 5–6.5 mm long, curving forwards on either side of lateral sepals; lip fleshy, recurved, ovate, rounded, 2 mm long and wide; column 3 mm long, stelidia very short and rounded.

Bulbophyllum sandersonii   BOB CAMPBELL

Epiphytic in highland woodland and forests; found on the eastern slopes of the Aberdare Mts; 1900–2300 m; flowering in November.

Widespread in the cooler forests of Africa; also recorded from Uganda and Zaïre to West Africa, and south to Angola and South Africa (Transkei).

This species and the following one are very hard to distinguish except when they are in flower. Then the shorter inflorescences with fewer flowers that have wider lateral sepals, narrow, club shaped petals and a more prominent column make B. sandersonii easy to identify.

Bulbophyllum scaberulum (Rolfe) Bolus

Syn. Bulbophyllum congolanum Schlechter
Plants epiphytic with a stout creeping rhizome, bearing pseudobulbs 2–10 cm apart. Pseudobulbs ovoid, narrowly ovoid or ellipsoid, 4–5-angled, 2–5.5 cm long, with 2 apical leaves. Leaves suberect, leathery, narrowly elliptic, rounded, 4–12 cm long, 1–2 cm wide. Inflorescences erect, 18–30 cm long, rarely longer; rachis flattened bilaterally, up to 20 cm long, 18 mm wide, green or purplish brown, often spotted or striped, with smooth margins. Flowers aligned nearer one side of rachis than the other, purple or green, heavily spotted with purple, not opening fully; dorsal sepal linear-lanceolate, acute, 6–7 mm long, 1.3–1.5 mm wide; lateral

sepals recurved, falcate, ovate, acuminate, 4–5.5 mm long, 2–3 mm wide; petals falcate, linear, acute, 3–4 mm long; lip fleshy, deflexed, ovate, rounded, 2–2.5 mm long; column 1.5 mm long, with short 2-lobed stelidia.

Epiphyte in riverine and coastal forest, in the crown of trees and on their trunks; recorded near Malindi and in the Sokoke forest, in the Shimba hills, and at Mrima hill; sea level to 100 m; flowering January to July.

Widespread in tropical and southern Africa; recorded from Guinea to Ethiopia and south to Angola and South Africa (E. Cape).

Not difficult to distinguish from the preceding species when in flower by its slender petals that are shorter than the lateral sepals and usually longer inflorescences. In Kenya the habitats of these two species are also very different.

Bulbophyllum vulcanicum Kraenzlin

Plants epiphytic with a creeping rhizome, bearing pseudobulbs 4.5–6 cm apart. Pseudobulbs narrowly cylindric-conical, tapering slightly from the base, 5–11 cm long, with 2 apical leaves. Leaves leathery, suberect, linear-oblong or narrowly oblong-elliptic, rounded, 12–15 cm long, up to 10–18 mm wide. Inflorescences erect, up to 30 cm long, many flowered, with bracts in two rows. Flowers all facing one way, greenish yellow suffused with purple or deep purple; dorsal sepal lanceolate, acute, up to 7 mm long, 1.5–2.8 mm wide; lateral sepals reflexed, lanceolate, acute, 5–7 mm long, 1.6–2.2 mm wide; petals linear-lanceolate, acute, up to 2.2 mm long; lip linear, fleshy, with long cilia at the apical margins and none or shorter cilia below, up to 5 mm long; column 1.5 mm long, with long stelidia.

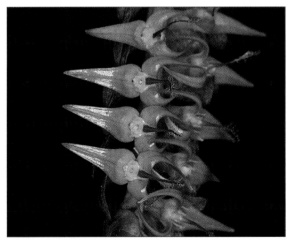

Bulbophyllum vulcanicum   HERMANN MEYER

Epiphytic in montane forests; so far only collected near Kericho; 1900–2300 m; flowering from July through to March.

Also occuring in adjacent countries; recorded from Zaïre, Uganda, Rwanda and Burundi.

Calyptrochilum Kraenzlin

Only two species have been described in this genus, which was established by the German botanist Fritz Kraenzlin in 1895. The name is derived from two Greek words *kalyptro* (a veil or covering) and *cheilos* (lip), presumably a reference to the way the lip sometimes appears to conceal the rest of the flower. Both species are epiphytes that form large clumps on forest trees and are sometimes conspicuous on isolated trees in grasslands. They are both widespread in the warmer parts of Africa, and *Calyptrochilum christyanum*, which is recorded from Kenya, is one of the most widespread of all African epiphytic orchids. It has smaller leaves and fewer flowers than *Calyptrochilum emarginatum*, which is restricted to the western side of the continent from Guinea south to Angola.

CULTIVATION

These species grow well in cultivation provided the plants are kept in suitably warm and humid conditions. They can succeed in a pot but do better when mounted so that the stems can assume their normally pendent position. It is better to start with seedlings or small plants as large ones can be very difficult to get established. Whether large or small, the plants should be tied very firmly to a supporting log or piece of bark so that the new roots can gradually become attached without being damaged.

Calyptrochilum christyanum (Reichenbach f.) Summerhayes

Plants epiphytic forming large clumps with long woody stems bearing many roots. Stems simple, rarely branched, 12–50 cm long. Leaves in two rows, ligulate, fleshy with a distinctive slightly rugose surface, 6–10 cm long, 1–2 cm wide. Inflorescences borne opposite the leaves, very short and crowded with flowers. Flowers white, tinged with pink or apricot, spur usually greenish; dorsal sepal ovate to ovate-elliptic, 5–10 mm long, 2–4 mm wide; lateral sepals similar but slightly oblique, apiculate; petals oblong-elliptic, obtuse to apiculate,

5–8 mm long, 2–3 mm wide; lip 3-lobed, appearing 4-lobed because the midlobe is emarginate, 7–12 mm long, 7–10 mm wide, spur wide at the mouth, strongly bent and constricted in the middle, the apex inflated, 9–11 mm long; column short and fleshy.

Epiphytes forming large clumps like mistletoe in tall forest trees or trees that have become isolated in areas formerly forested; only known at present from coastal areas and on some of the isolated hills inland; sea level to 1000 m; flowering in June.

Widespread throughout Africa from Sudan and Ethiopia westwards to Gambia and south to Mozambique and Angola.

Calyptrochilum christyanum   BOB CAMPBELL

Chamaeangis Schlechter

Several species of *Chamaeangis* were mentioned by the German botanist Rudolf Schlechter when he established this genus in 1918. He derived the name from the Greek words *chamai* (lowly) and *angos* (vessel), a reference to the small flowers many of which have a swollen spur. Although the flowers are very small, they are colourful, green, yellow or an apricot orange. There are usually several inflorescences on each flowering plant. Normally they are longer than the leaves, and the small flowers are borne close together, sometimes in whorls.

Altogether about 15 species have been described in this genus, seven from Africa and three occurring in Kenya. Most of the Madagascar and Comoro Islands species have now been transferred to the genus *Microterangis* on account of their different column structure, but not all botanists accept this distinction.

CULTIVATION

These species are amongst the easiest of epiphytic orchids to grow, either mounted on a piece of bark or in a pot. They need to be kept very well drained but respond well to frequent watering and feeding during the growing season. They flower regularly every year, sometimes more than once.

Key to the species of *Chamaeangis*
1 Inflorescences erect, flowers with spurs
        uppermost . . . . *C. sarcophylla*
   Inflorescences arching or pendent, flowers
        with spurs on lower side 2

2 Leaves fleshy, swollen; flowers with swollen
        spur . . . . *C. vesicata*
   Leaves flat, not swollen; flowers with
        slender spur . . . . *C. odoratissima*

Chamaeangis odoratissima (Reichenbach f.)
                                Schlechter
   Syn. *Chamaeangis urostachya* (Kraenzlin)
                                Schlechter

Plants epiphytic, often pendent with the apical part of the stem upturned, rooting near the base. Stems thickened, often greatly elongated, 20–45 cm long, 4–6 mm in diameter. Leaves in two rows fleshy but not swollen, flat, oblanceolate, slightly falcate and drooping, unequally bilobed at the apex, 10–24 cm long, 2–3 cm wide. Inflorescences longer than the leaves, with many small flowers in whorls of 2–6. Flowers yellow or yellow-green, 3–4 mm in diameter; sepals elliptic, obtuse, 1–2 mm long; petals round or elliptic, 1.5 mm long; lip concave, ovate, obtuse, 2 mm long, spur straight or incurved, cylindric, 5–9 mm long; column 0.5 mm long.

On large trees in the warmer parts of the country, near the coast, Teita hills, and also in western Kenya from Kakamega to Mt Elgon; sea level to 2300 m; flowering in April and June to December.

Widespread throughout tropical Africa; also recorded from Uganda and Tanzania, westwards to Sierra Leone, and south to Malawi and Angola.

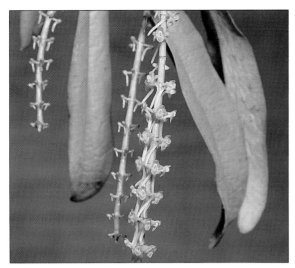

Chamaeangis odoratissima   BOB CAMPBELL

Chamaeangis sarcophylla   BOB CAMPBELL

Chamaeangis sarcophylla Schlechter

Syn. *Chamaeangis orientalis* Summerhayes
Plants upright or pendent with short stems rooting from the base. Stems covered in overlapping leaf bases, 2–15 cm long. Leaves fleshy and swollen or rather shrunken in dry seasons, dark bluish grey in colour, linear, falcate, unequally bilobed at the apex, 6–30 cm long, 5–25 mm wide. Inflorescences usually several, arching or upright, somewhat swollen and bearing many flowers in whorls of 2–4. Flowers pale apricot, orange, or salmon red, 3–5 mm in diameter; sepals ovate to oblong-elliptic, laterals recurved, 2–3.5 mm long; petals recurved, ovate or lanceolate, obtuse, 2–3.6 mm long; lip ovate-oblong, obtuse or obscurely 3-lobed at the apex, 2–3.5 mm long, spur cylindric, 9–19 mm long, arranged parallel to the rachis; column 0.5–1 mm long.

Widespread in highland forests, usually rather high up in the tree canopy; from the Chyulu hills and Mt Kenya to Loita hills, forests around Kericho, and Mt Elgon; 1500–2400 m; flowering from March to July and sometimes in December.

Recorded from similar habitats in Uganda and Tanzania, and in Zaïre, Rwanda, and Malawi.

Chamaeangis vesicata (Lindley) Schlechter

Plants epiphytic with pendent leaves, rooting from the base of a short stem. Stems usually less than 10 cm long, arching or pendent. Leaves fleshy or coriaceous, linear, falcate, pointed at the obliquely bilobed apex, dull bluish green in colour, 20–40 cm long, less than 1.5 cm wide. Inflorescences pendent, usually longer than the leaves, bearing many flowers in pairs. Flowers pale green or yellow with

paler spurs, 3–6 mm in diameter; sepals ovate, acute, 2–3 mm long; petals lanceolate, acute, 2.5–3 mm long; lip ovate, subacute, 2.5–3 mm long, spur incurved, greatly swollen at the apex 7–12 mm long; column 1–1.5 mm long.

Widespread in the highland forests of Kenya including around the north and west sides of Nairobi, in many of the same places as *Chamaeangis sarcophylla* but usually in more shady situations; 1100–1800 m; flowering in March to May and also September to October.

Chamaeangis vesicata   BOB CAMPBELL

Recorded from similar habitats in Uganda and Tanzania and over a wide area of tropical Africa, westwards to Rwanda, Zaïre, Guinea and Sierra Leone.

Chaseella Summerhayes

This strange orchid was first described in 1961 in honour of Norman Chase, who made many interesting discoveries in Zimbabwe after he retired. It is clearly close to *Bulbophyllum* and *Genyorchis* but distinguished from both those genera by the tuft of linear leaves that surmounts each tiny pseudobulb. The specific epithet *pseudohydra* describes this morphology extremely well.

I collected this species from a tree overhanging the Kiptiget river in Kericho district in May 1970. Whilst fishing for trout from a branch of a fallen tree, I very nearly fell into the river. In saving myself, and my fishing rod, I grabbed a handful of moss and other vegetation from a branch above my head. Among the plants I found this orchid, which was quite unlike any that I had ever seen. Each tiny pseudobulb with its topknot of leaves reminded me of the short shoots of a larch putting forth new needles in early spring. I sent material to Kew where Peter Hunt identified it as *Chaseella*, perhaps the same species as the one that had been described from Zimbabwe, but possibly different. Unfortunately the plant I kept never flowered and in due course it was added to the collections in the East African herbarium. Visitors to the Kericho area should look out for more material of this tiny plant.

The description given below is based on specimens from Zimbabwe (see illustration in Ball, 1978).

Chaseella pseudohydra Summerhayes
Tiny epiphytic plants with a long slender rhizome bearing pseudobulbs at intervals of 2–2.5 cm. Pseudobulbs yellowish green, oblong-ovoid, 6–8 mm high and *c.* 5 mm in diameter, bearing 6–11 leaves at the apex. Leaves in a whorl, linear, stiff, *c.* 8–12 mm long, needle-like. Inflorescence arising from the base of the pseudobulb, 1–2 flowered. Flowers small, dark red; sepals narrowly ovate, to 4 mm long; petals elliptic, rounded at the apex, less than 2 mm long; lip mobile, somewhat recurved, ovate, *c.* 2 mm long and wide.

Known only from Kericho district from the canopy of a single tree along the Kiptiget river; *c.* 2000 m; flowering unknown.

Possibly the same species as originally described from Honde gorge, Umtali district, Zimbabwe.

Cribbia Senghas

The genus *Cribbia* was established in 1986 in honour of Phillip Cribb, the distinguished orchid botanist at the Royal Botanic Gardens, Kew. So far only one species has been described, but at least two more have been collected recently in West Africa. *Cribbia* species are rather similar in some respects to species of *Diaphananthe* and to *Mystacidium* and not all that different from some species of *Angraecopsis*. However, the species known do not fit easily into any of these genera as they are currently circumscribed and are thus kept separate in this new genus.

Cribbia brachyceras was originally described in 1934 as a species of *Aerangis*, but only two years later Summerhayes transferred it to the genus *Rangaeris*. It is very different from the two white flowered members of this genus that occur in Kenya. The typical members of all these genera are very easily recognised and separated, but there are some species that do not seem to fit easily within the established genera. Further work on generic limits in the *Aerangidinae* is long overdue.

CULTIVATION

This species is easily maintained as a mounted plant or in a pot and because it is very floriferous it is a welcome addition to a collection of African orchids. It is a plant from the African highlands, so requires cool nights with higher temperatures by day and high humidity during the growing season. If it is grown in a pot, the compost should drain freely but be moisture-retentive.

Cribbia brachyceras (Summerhayes) Senghas
Syn. *Rangaeris brachyceras* (Summerhayes)
Summerhayes
Plants small epiphytic, rarely lithophytic, rooting at the base of the short stems. Stems upright or arching, up to 20 cm long. Leaves suberect or spreading, in two rows, linear-oblong, unequally rounded at the apex, 8–13 cm long, 7–15 mm wide. Inflorescences usually several, suberect, with 7–15 well-spaced flowers, 4–18 cm long. Flowers pale green or pale yellowish brown, almost translucent; dorsal sepal oblong-lanceolate, acute, 5–7 mm long, 1–2 mm wide; lateral sepals deflexed, linear or linear-oblanceolate, acute, 6–7.5 mm long, 1–1.5 mm

Cribbia brachyceras BOB CAMPBELL

wide; petals oblong or elliptic-oblong, obtuse or
rounded, 5 mm long, 1.4–2 mm wide; lip entire,
recurved at tip, lanceolate, acute, 5 mm long, 3 mm
wide, spur decurved, cylindric, slightly inflated towards the apex, 5–6 mm long; column 2 mm long.

Usually found amongst mosses on trunks and
the larger branches of trees in forests; also recorded
from mossy rocks; restricted to the western parts of
Kenya near Kericho, Kaimosi and Kakamega;
1500–2000 m; flowering in June.

Recorded from Uganda but apparently absent
from Tanzania; widespread in similar habitats
from Zaïre to Liberia and south to Zambia.

Cyrtorchis Schlechter

Species of *Cyrtorchis* are amongst the easiest of
African epiphytic orchids to place in a genus but
some of the most difficult to identify individually.
They all have star-shaped flowers in which the
sepals, petals and lip are remarkably similar and
often recurved. The spur at the base of the lip is
often curved, and it is presumably these features of
the flower that gave rise to the generic name, from
the Greek words *kyrtos* (a swelling or curve) and
orchis (orchid). The rather stiff, upright plants with
leaves in two rows on either side of the stem are

also characteristic of most species. Another feature is the large pale bracts that turn black or dark brown by the time the flowers have opened. All the flowers are sweetly scented, particularly in the evening.

About 15 species of *Cyrtorchis* are now known throughout the continent, but many of them are extremely variable. The variation may be related to habitat and to changes in the habitat, which occur during the life of these long-lived plants. Four species are recorded from Kenya, and they can be distinguished more or less by their size.

CULTIVATION

These epiphytes with a vandaceous habit of growth are easily maintained in cultivation. They grow well in a pot or basket of free draining compost such as bark. Most of them produce small branches (keikeis) from the lower part of the stem after some of the leaves have fallen, so that specimen plants are produced in a relatively short time. Attention must be paid to growing and resting seasons, since the plants do not need much water or food when they are not in active growth. Smaller plants of all the species are also established easily on pieces of bark and grow well when mounted in this way.

Key to the species of *Cyrtorchis*

1   Flowers close together, bracts less than
        5 mm apart   2
     Flowers well spaced, bracts at least 5 mm
        apart   3

2   Leaves less than 10 mm wide, V-shaped in
        cross-section . . . .   **C. praetermissa**
     Leaves 10 mm wide or more, flat in cross
        section . . . .   **C. brownii**

3   Leaves suberect, bracts 5–11 mm long . . . . . .
        . . . .   **C. neglecta**
     Leaves spreading, bracts more than
        15 mm long . . . .   **C. arcuata**

Cyrtorchis arcuata (Lindley) Schlechter
Plants upright, epiphytic or lithophytic, often forming large clumps in old plants. Stems up to 30 cm long bearing leaves in two rows and thick roots with brownish tips from the basal part. Leaves linear-ligulate or narrowly oblong, un-equally bilobed at the tip, the lobes rounded, 12–22 cm long, 1.5–3.5 cm wide. Inflorescences axillary or below the leaves, 6–20 cm long bearing 5–14 flowers, bracts ovate 15–33 mm long. Flowers

white, tinged with green or salmon pink, fading to orange; sepals lanceolate, acuminate, recurved, 18–50 mm long, 5–7 mm wide; petals similar but shorter, 12–25 mm long; lip similar to the petals, up to 36 mm long, spur curved or S-shaped, 3–8 cm long; column 2–2.5 mm long.

One of the most widespread orchids in Kenya and can be found on trees and rocks almost any-where in the country where the natural vegetation is undisturbed, usually where the plants receive bright sunlight; sea level to 3000 m; flowering in March and April and again in September and October.

Also recorded from Uganda and Tanzania and widespread throughout the rest of Africa.

This species is very variable and several different subspecies have been recognised in different parts of its range. The Kenya plants are very similar to those from eastern South Africa, where the type specimen was collected, but mostly they are a little larger in all respects. Summerhayes (1960) gave the name ssp. *variabilis* to all the plants from east-ern Africa, but I have not followed this treatment here.

Cyrtorchis brownii (Rolfe) Schlechter
Plants upright, epiphytic, usually rather small. Stems usually single, up to 20 cm long bearing leaves in two rows and thick roots with brownish tips. Leaves linear, leathery, unequally bilobed at the tip, the lobes rounded, 6–12 cm long, 7–15 mm wide. Inflorescences axillary or below the leaves, 3–9 cm long bearing 5–12 flowers, bracts ovate, 6–8 mm long and only 3–4 mm apart. Flowers white, tinged with green, fading to orange; sepals lan-ceolate, acuminate, recurved, 10–13 mm long, 2–3 mm wide; petals similar but shorter, 8–9 mm long; lip similar to the petals, up to 10 mm long, spur straight, 2–4 cm long; column 1–1.5 mm long.

Only known from riverside forests on Mt Kasigau in the Teita hills and in Kakamega district; 1000–1530 m; flowering in October.

Also recorded from Uganda and Tanzania; widespread from Sierra Leone to Zaïre.

Cyrtorchis neglecta Summerhayes
Plants upright, epiphytic or lithophytic, often forming clumps in old plants. Stems 20–40 cm long bearing leaves in two rows and thick roots with brownish tips from the basal part. Leaves suberect, linear, leathery, unequally bilobed at the tip, the lobes rounded, 8–24 cm long, 1–3 cm wide. Inflorescences axillary or below the leaves, 3–9 cm long bearing 4–10 flowers, bracts ovate, 5–11 mm

long and 5–10 mm apart. Flowers white, tinged with salmon pink, fading to orange; sepals lanceolate, acuminate, recurved, 12–20 mm long, 4–7 mm wide; petals similar but shorter, 10–16 mm long; lip similar to the petals, up to 16 mm long, spur straight, 3–5 cm long; column 2–2.5 mm long.

Only recorded from isolated hills near the coast; sea level to 1000 m; flowering in March.

Also known from northeastern Tanzania and from Burundi.

This species is very similar to *Cyrtorchis arcuata* but is in all respects smaller and the flowers are borne closer together than in that species.

Cyrtorchis praetermissa Summerhayes

Plants upright, epiphytic or lithophytic. Stems up to 20 cm long bearing leaves in two rows and thick roots with brownish tips from the basal part. Leaves linear, stiff, spreading, conspicuously V-shaped in cross section, unequally bilobed at the tip, the lobes rounded, 5–10 cm long, 8–12 mm wide. Inflorescences axillary or below the leaves, 6–10 cm long bearing 3–11 flowers, bracts ovate, 4–5 mm long and 3–5 mm apart. Flowers white, tinged with green, fading to orange; sepals lanceolate, acuminate, recurved, 8–11 mm long, 2.5–5 mm wide; petals similar but shorter, 8 mm long;

Cyrtorchis arcuata

Cyrtorchis praetermissa

lip similar to the petals, up to 9 mm long, spur incurved, 2–3 cm long; column 1 mm long.

On forest trees and shrubs in woodland, also on rocks, formerly known from Thika district and also in the area near the Mara river, widespread in west Kenya; 1500–2300 m; flowering in May and June.

Also recorded from Uganda and Tanzania, and elsewhere in Africa from Zaïre and Rwanda, through Zambia, Malawi and Zimbabwe to South Africa (Transvaal).

Diaphananthe Schlechter

Syn *Rhipidoglossum* Schlechter
Sarcorhynchus Schlechter

The pale green or yellowish flowers of most of the species of *Diaphananthe* are not always transparent, but it was this feature which gave the German botanist Rudolf Schlechter the idea for the generic name, from the Greek words *diaphanes* (transparent) and *anthos* (flower). Many of the plants make rather untidy specimens in the wild, with straggling, branching stems that produce

roots in many directions. The roots are often the first part to catch your eye, and, when wet, they exhibit characteristic white streaks along their length. The flowers are mostly small, on short inflorescences, but some are longer and they are often produced in great numbers. Viewed close-up they are very attractive and relatively easy to distinguish by the shape of the lip and spur.

Two genera, *Rhipidoglossum* and *Sarcorhynchus*, have been recognised as distinct from *Diaphananthe* in the past and some botanists still treat them separately. I have followed the practice adopted in *Flora of Tropical East Africa*, Orchidaceae, Part 3 (Cribb, 1989) and kept all the species in *Diaphananthe*. Only one Kenya species was formerly in *Sarcorhynchus*, *Diaphananthe bilobata*. It has wider leaves than most other species of *Diaphananthe* and a distinctively bilobed lip, but these characters do not seem to be sufficient for separation into a different genus. *Rhipidoglossum* formerly included all those species of *Diaphananthe* in which each of the two pollinia is attached by a short stalk to its own viscidium, whereas in *Diaphananthe* there is a shared viscidium. Also there is often a tooth or crest in the mouth of the spur in *Diaphananthe*, which is absent from or rather obscure in species allocated to *Rhipidoglossum*. But, apart from these minute details, the overall appearance of all the plants and flowers is remarkably similar.

Altogether some 45 species of *Diaphananthe* have now been described from Africa, 12 of which have been found in Kenya.

CULTIVATION

All these species can be grown in cultivation without difficulty though most of them grow better when mounted on a piece of bark than planted in a pot. Due regard should be paid to the altitudinal range of each species in the wild, as some will require much cooler night temperatures than others.

Key to the species of *Diaphananthe*

1 Leaves curved and thickened, leathery or fleshy, more than 15 cm long, hanging down on either side of the horizontal or pendulous stem   2
  Leaves thin and straight, if thickened then under 12 cm long, variously arranged on a long or short stem   3

2 Flowers borne singly along the racemes . . . . ***D. lorifolia***
  Flowers in clusters of 2–4 along the racemes . . . . ***D. fragrantissima***

3 Leaves few, narrow, 2–5 mm wide   4
  Leaves conspicuous, more than 5 mm wide   5

4 Dorsal sepal *c.* 2 mm long, spur swollen, 2 mm long . . . . ***D. adoxa***
  Dorsal sepal 3–4 mm long, spur swollen, 4 mm long . . . . ***D. tanneri***

5 Flowers white . . . . ***D. tenuicalcar***
  Flowers pale yellow, green, or greenish red, not white   6

6 Lip ovate, as long or longer than wide and widest towards the base   7
  Lip flabellate, broader than long and widest near the apex which may be lobed   8

7 Spur 10–12 mm long, slightly swollen towards the tip . . . . ***D. rohrii***
  Spur 5–6 mm long, cylindric, slender . . . . ***D. montana***

8 Lip with a prominent tooth or crest in the mouth of the spur   9
  Lip lacking a tooth in the mouth of the spur . . . . ***D. xanthopollinia***

9 Spur more than 8 mm long   10
  Spur less than 7 mm long   11

10 Leaves ovate-elliptic; lip deeply bilobed at the apex . . . . ***D. bilobata***
   Leaves linear or oblanceolate; lip rectangular . . . . ***D. pulchella***

11 Leaves tinged with reddish purple, at least on the lower surface, flowers often reddish . . . . ***D. rutila***
   Leaves entirely green or yellowish green, flowers pale, yellow or green . . . . ***D. subsimplex***

Diaphananthe adoxa Rasmussen
  Syn. *Rhipidoglossum adoxum* (Rasmussen) Senghas

Plants epiphytic with long straggling stems bearing leaves in the upper part and many greyish roots which are more noticeable than the leaves. Stems 5–25 cm long. Leaves rather insignificant, 5–12, linear, falcate, yellowish green often flecked with dark green markings, 3.5–10 cm long, 1.5–5 mm wide. Inflorescences few and small, 2–4 cm long, bearing 3–8 flowers. Flowers very small, green or yellowish green; dorsal sepal lanceolate, acute, up to 2 mm long, 1 mm wide; lateral sepals longer, to 3 mm long, 1 mm wide; petals ovate, obtuse or rounded, 2 mm long, 1.2 mm wide; lip entire, ovate, obtuse, smooth, 2 mm long and wide, spur club shaped up to 2 mm long; column less than 1 mm long.

Upland evergreen forest, known from near Nairobi and from the hills west of Namanga; 1500–2000 m; flowering in May.

Originally described from Ethiopia, this rather insignificant species has now also been recognised in Uganda.

Diaphananthe bilobata (Summerhayes) Rasmussen
  Syn. *Sarcorhynchus bilobatus* Summerhayes

Plants epiphytic with elongated stems and many roots in the lower part. Stems usually pendent or upturned at the apex only, elongated, up to 50 cm long. Leaves up to 20 along the upper part of the stem, twisted at the base to lie in one plane, elliptic or oblong-elliptic, unequally roundly bilobed at the apex, 3–10 cm long, 1.5–5 cm wide. Inflorescences usually several, often 2–3 from the same node in the upper part of the stem, bearing 15–30 flowers rather close together, usually longer than the leaves. Flowers fresh green or whitish; dorsal sepal oblong, obtuse, 4–7 mm long, lateral sepals oblong, obtuse, 5–7 mm long; petals obovate, elliptic, obtuse, 4–5 mm long; lip elongated, obscurely 3-lobed, with a bilobed tooth in the mouth of the spur, 5–7 mm long, the side lobes rounded recurved, the midlobe deeply bilobed at its apex, spur slightly incurved, 9 mm long; column 2 mm long.

Diaphananthe bilobata   BOB CAMPBELL

In humid forests and thickets; collected fairly recently in thickets west of the Isuria escarpment in west Kenya; *c.* 1800 m; flowering in April.

Originally described from Uganda, now known also from Zaïre, Burundi and Rwanda.

Diaphananthe fragrantissima (Reichenbach f.) Schlechter

Plants usually epiphytic with horizontal or pendent stems firmly attached to the host tree by slender roots at the base. Stems 5–50 cm long, up to 10 mm thick, covered in old leaf bases. Leaves fleshy, pendent, linear, falcate, pointed, 15–40 cm long, 1–4 cm wide. Inflorescences pendulous, usually

several bearing 50–100 flowers, 15–35 cm long. Flowers pale green, pale yellow or white, usually borne in whorls of four; dorsal sepal linear-triangular, acute, 8–22 mm long, 2–4 mm wide; lateral sepals slightly falcate, linear, acute, 9–11 mm long, 2–3 mm wide; petals linear to obovate, acuminate, 8–15 mm long; lip rectangular, 10–15 mm long, 6–10 mm wide, with a tooth in the mouth of the spur, 3-lobed at the apex, the midlobe elongated and acuminate, side lobes rounded with fimbriate margins, spur bent near the base, 6–12 mm long; column 2 mm long.

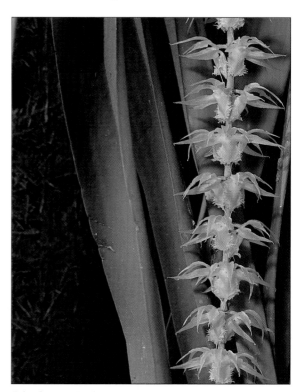

Diaphananthe fragrantissima   BOB CAMPBELL

In the warmer forests and undisturbed bushland, on isolated hills near the coast, in Teita district, and in western Kenya; 1000–1500 m; flowering from February to May.

Also recorded in Uganda and Tanzania; widespread in tropical Africa from Sudan and Ethiopia westwards to Cameroon and south to Mozambique, Zimbabwe, Angola and South Africa (Natal).

Diaphananthe lorifolia Summerhayes

Plants epiphytic with long hanging stems, leafy in the upper part. Stems 8–40 cm long. Leaves in 2 rows, falcate, linear, unequally obtusely bilobed at the apex, 14–25 cm long, 1–2 cm wide, twisted at the base to lie in one plane. Inflorescences pendent, shorter than the leaves, 7–15 cm long, with 5–25 flowers. Flowers pale yellow, white or pinkish; dorsal sepal lanceolate to narrowly elliptic, acute, 5–8 mm long, 2–3 mm wide; lateral sepals oblong-ovate, acute, 6–9 mm long, 2–3 mm wide; petals lanceolate to oblong, acute, 5–6.5 mm long, c. 2 mm wide; lip entire, round to ovate, shortly apiculate, sometimes with a slightly fimbriate margin, with a small tooth in the mouth of the spur, 5–8 mm long and wide, spur slender, 5–9 mm long; column 2.5–3 mm long.

On trunks and the large lower branches of trees with a light canopy, in montane and riverine forest, in Teita hills, west of Mt Kenya, Rift Valley, SW Mau, Kericho and Yala river; 1000–2200 m; flowering throughout the year.

First described from the forests of southwest Mau; now also known from Uganda (Mt Elgon), Tanzania, Sudan and Ethiopia.

Diaphananthe montana (Piers)
Cribb & J. Stewart

Syn. *Angraecum montanum* Piers
Rhipidoglossum montanum (Piers) Senghas
Plants epiphytic with rather short stems that are usually obscured by a mass of thick grey roots. Stems 5–10 cm long, held away from the host by the prominent roots. Leaves 2–6, greyish green, linear or narrowly lanceolate, unequally bilobed at

Diaphananthe montana   BOB CAMPBELL

the apex, 1.5–6 cm long, 2–6 mm wide. Inflorescences usually several, arising below the leaves, 2–4 cm long bearing 4–9 flowers. Flowers green, yellowish green or orange, 6–9 mm in diameter; dorsal sepal ovate, obtuse, 3.5–4 mm long; lateral sepals elliptic or ovate, obtuse, 4–5 mm long; petals round or ovate, obtuse, 3 mm long; lip concave, ovate, 3 mm long, 2.5–3 mm wide, with an obscure callus at the base, spur cylindric, slightly curved, 5 mm long; column 1 mm long.

First described from the Ngong hills and now known from several similar habitats in the Kenya highlands including Cherangani hills, several sites on Mt Kenya, and Ol Doinyo Orok near Namanga; epiphytic on twigs and branches of bushes and trees usually amongst mosses and lichens; 2300–2750 m; recorded in flower at various times during the year.

Not yet recorded from outside Kenya.

Diaphananthe pulchella Summerhayes
Plants epiphytic with rather short or slightly elongated stems bearing many thick grey roots. Stems 5–15 cm long with leaves towards the apex.

Diaphananthe pulchella   BOB CAMPBELL

Leaves 2–6, greyish green, leathery, oblanceolate, falcate, unequally bilobed at the apex, 3–10 cm long, 4–10 mm wide. Inflorescences usually several, pendulous, arising below the leaves, to 15 cm long, bearing up to 12 flowers. Flowers pale green, cream or pale yellowish green, 1.5–2 cm in diameter; dorsal sepal ovate, obtuse or acuminate, 4–8 mm long; lateral sepals oblique, elliptic or ovate, obtuse, 5–9 mm long; petals ovate to elliptic, acute or obtuse, 4–8 mm long; lip flabellate or rectangular, obscurely 2–4-lobed, 6–9 mm long, 6–9 mm wide, notched at the apex, with a tooth in the mouth of the spur, spur cylindric, slightly curved, 8–14 mm long; column 2–3 mm long.

Epiphytic and occasionally lithophytic on the drier slopes of montane forests, riverine bush and woodland; collected from Mt Elgon, Nyeri, Ngong hills, and other hills in Kajiado district, Karen, and Mua hills near Machakos; 1500–2500 m; usually flowering in May and June, also recorded in November.

First described from the Usambara Mts in Tanzania, now also known from Uganda, Zaïre, Zambia and Malawi.

Diaphananthe rohrii (Reichenbach f.) Summerhayes
Syn. *Diaphananthe quintasii* Rolfe

Plants epiphytic with rather short stems and grey roots. Stems 2–5 cm long, held away from the host by the prominent roots. Leaves 2–7, dark greyish green, linear or narrowly lanceolate, falcate, unequally bilobed at the apex, 5–15 cm long, 6–22 mm wide. Inflorescences usually several, arising below the leaves, 5–17 cm long bearing 4–9 flowers. Flowers dark green or yellowish green, not transparent, 6–9 mm in diameter; dorsal sepal oblanceolate, acute, 3.5–4 mm long; lateral sepals linear to obovate, obtuse, 3–4 mm long; petals linear, obtuse, 3–4 mm long; lip ovate, acute, 3–4 mm long, 1.7–2.3 mm wide, with an obscure tooth in the mouth of the spur, spur incurved, club shaped or cylindric, 10–12 mm long; column 2.4 mm long.

Epiphytic in highland forests but frequently overlooked; recorded from Mt Elgon, Mau Summit, Mt Nyiru and the Kinangop; 2100–2800 m; flowering from March to July.

First recorded from Ethiopia, now also known from high altitude forests in Uganda and northern Tanzania and from many parts of equatorial Africa as far west as the Ivory Coast.

Diaphananthe rutila (Reichenbach f.) Summerhayes
Syn. *Rhipidoglossum rutilum* (Reichenbach f.) Schlechter

Plants epiphytic, pendent, often in large untidy masses. Stems 5–40 cm, long, sometimes branched, often flushed reddish purple. Leaves along upper part of stem in two rows, narrowly elliptic or oblanceolate, unequally bilobed at the apex, 8–15 cm long, 1–3 cm wide, dull bluish green usually flushed red or purple on the lower surface.

Diaphananthe rutila   BOB CAMPBELL

Inflorescences often arising from the same point more than once, below the leaves, 5–20 cm long bearing 10–40 flowers. Flowers greenish pink or deep red, 4–8 mm in diameter; dorsal sepal elliptic or obovate, obtuse, 3–5 mm long; lateral sepals slightly shorter and narrower; petals broadly ovate or round, obtuse, 2–4 mm long and wide; lip wider than long, retuse at apex, spur incurved, 5–10 mm long; column 1 mm long.

Widespread in riverine forest and more open forest and bush, also in old coffee plantations; one of the commonest epiphytic orchids in Kenya, found in all districts from the Shimba hills to west Kenya; 100–2200 m; flowering in May and November.

Also recorded from Uganda and Tanzania and widespread westwards to Sierra Leone and south to Zimbabwe.

Diaphananthe subsimplex Summerhayes
Plants epiphytic, pendent, often in large, untidy tangled masses. Stems 10–40 cm, long, often branched. Leaves along upper part of stem in two rows, linear, unequally bilobed at the apex, 2–5 cm long, 5–10 mm wide, yellowish green. Inflorescences below or among the leaves, 2–8 cm long bearing 5–12 flowers. Flowers greenish or pale

yellow, 4–7 mm diameter; dorsal sepal elliptic or oblong, obtuse, 2.7–4 mm long; lateral sepals oblong to oblong-elliptic, 3.3–4.5 mm long; petals ovate, obtuse or acute, 2.5–3.6 mm long and wide; lip as wide as long, retuse at apex, 2.5–3.6 long, with an obscure tooth in the mouth of the spur, spur slightly incurved, cylindrical, 4–7 mm long; column 1.5 mm long.

Diaphananthe subsimplex   BOB CAMPBELL

Widespread in montane forests and on forest margins, usually on the lower branches of trees; around Mt Kenya, in the highlands of west Kenya, in the Chyulu hills and Ol Doinyo Orok; 1800–2600 m; flowering in May and June.

Also recorded in northern Uganda and in Tanzania, Malawi and Zimbabwe.

Diaphananthe tanneri Cribb
Syn. *Rhipidoglossum tanneri* (Cribb) Senghas
Plants epiphytic with long straggling stems bearing leaves in the upper part and many greyish roots that are more noticeable than the leaves. Stems 5–25 cm long. Leaves insignificant, 5–12, linear, falcate, 3–4.5 cm long, 1.5 mm wide. Inflorescences few and small, 2–3 cm long, bearing 4–7 flowers. Flowers very small, bright green; dorsal sepal lanceolate, rounded to subacute, to 3.5 mm long, 1.5 mm wide; lateral sepals spreading, elliptic, rounded, 3–3.7 mm long, 1.5 mm wide; petals elliptic-ovate, acute, 3 mm long, 1.2–1.7 mm wide; lip entire, recurved, ovate, acute, smooth, 2–2.5 mm long, 1.5 mm wide, with an obscure bilobed callus at the base, spur swollen towards apex, 4 mm long; column less than 1 mm long.

Originally described from northern Tanzania, now also known from isolated hills near the coast in Kenya; 800 m; flowering in April.

Also recorded from Tanzania.

Diaphananthe tenuicalcar Summerhayes
Plants epiphytic, pendent, often in large untidy masses. Stems 10–30 cm long, often branched. Leaves usually only 2–8 along upper part of stem in two rows, linear-lanceolate, falcate, unequally

Diaphananthe tenuicalcar   BOB CAMPBELL

bilobed at the apex, 1–6 cm long, 5–13 mm wide, yellowish green. Inflorescences below the leaves, 1–3 cm long bearing up to 7 flowers. Flowers white, sweetly scented, 7–12 mm in diameter; dorsal sepal elliptic or oblong, obtuse, 4 mm long; lateral sepals oblong to oblong-elliptic, 4–5 mm long; petals ovate, obtuse or acute, 4 mm long; lip wider than long, retuse at apex, 4.5–6.5 mm long, with a tooth in the mouth of the spur, spur slender, cylindric, 15–25 mm long; column 2 mm long.

Only recorded from a few localities at the edge of highland forests in Londiani district; 2100–2400 m; flowering in June.

Rather rare; also known from northern Uganda and Ethiopia.

Diaphananthe xanthopollinia (Reichenbach f.) Summerhayes

Syn. *Rhipidoglossum xanthopollinium* (Reichenbach f.) Schlechter

Plants epiphytic, pendent, often in large masses. Stems 6–45 cm long, sometimes branched. Leaves along upper part of stem in two rows, linear to oblanceolate, unequally bilobed at the apex, 3–15 cm long, 5–15 mm wide, yellowish green. Inflor-

Diaphananthe xanthopollinia   BOB CAMPBELL

escences below or among the leaves, 8–15 cm long bearing 5–25 flowers. Flowers pale yellow, 5–9 mm in diameter; dorsal sepal oblong-elliptic to ovate, obtuse, 3–5 mm long; lateral sepals oblong to oblong-elliptic, 3.3–5 mm long; petals round to broadly ovate, obtuse, 2.5–4 mm long and wide; lip wider than long, retuse or 2–4-lobed at apex, 3–4.5 mm long, with a low transverse callus in the mouth of the spur, spur slightly incurved, cylindrical, 5–7 mm long; column 1.5–2 mm long.

Widespread in warm humid forests, usually at lower altitudes than *Diaphananthe subsimplex*; recorded around Lake Victoria, Kakamega, from Maungu hill in Teita district and on isolated hills in the coastal districts; 600–1800 m; flowering in May and September.

Jumellea Schlechter

Named in honour of a French botanist from Marseilles, Professor Henri Jumelle, this genus of about 45 species is almost confined to Madagascar, the Comores and the Mascarene islands of the western Indian Ocean. Only two species are known from various parts of eastern Africa, one of them quite widespread.

All the species have a vandaceous habit of growth though the stems may be long or short. They are easily recognised by their single-flowered inflorescences, though there is often more than one inflorescence at each flowering, and by the characteristic arrangement of the parts of the flower. The dorsal sepal is upright and a wide space separates it from the lateral sepals and petals that are arranged on either side of the lip, thus giving the flower an almost bilabiate appearance. Unlike *Angraecum*, where the broad base of the lip enfolds the column, the lip in *Jumellea* flowers is narrow at the base and inserted below the column without any overlapping.

The two African species have both been recorded in Kenya but are rather rare. The most recently described is *Jumellea usambarensis* that has larger stems with wider leaves, and smaller flowers with much longer spurs.

CULTIVATION

Many species of *Jumellea* are easily maintained in cultivation in a well-drained compost in a pot or basket. They need environmental conditions that are sometimes difficult to supply in combination:

strong light, good drainage, high humidity and good air movement. Good drainage after watering, and a prolonged dry period when the plants are not in active growth, are very important if the plants are to survive and flower well. *Jumellea filicornoides* has been maintained by many growers who have grown attractive specimen plants, but the few who have tried *J. usambarensis* do not report success. Probably it would be easier to start with nursery-raised seedlings rather than collecting mature plants from the wild.

Key to the species of *Jumellea*

Stems up to 30 cm long, often branched, leaves
   1–1.3 cm wide; flowers with spur 2–3 cm long
. . . . *J. filicornoides*
Stems up to 80 cm long, unbranched, leaves
   1.5–2 cm wide; flowers with spur 8–9 cm long
. . . . *J. usambarensis*

Jumellea filicornoides (De Wildeman) Schlechter

Plants epiphytic or lithophytic with long woody stems, leafy in the upper part. Stems simple or branched, 15–40 cm long, becoming pendent when long. Leaves 6–14 in two rows, ligulate, unequally bilobed at the apex, fleshy or leathery, 4–13 cm long, 1–1.3 cm wide. Inflorescences with a single flower on short peduncles sheathed with bracts which turn black. Flower white, scented in the evening; dorsal sepal narrowly elliptic or ligulate, obtuse, margins undulate or crisped at the base, 13–20 mm long, 3–4 mm wide; lateral sepals similar, falcate, reflexed and decurved; petals narrowly elliptic or ligulate, obtuse, reflexed, slightly smaller than sepals; lip rhombic, narrow at the base, with a shallow central keel, 16–20 mm long, 5–6 mm wide, spur parallel to the ovary then bent, cylindric, 2–3 cm long; column 2 mm long.

Grows on large trees in riverine forests and occasionally on rocks; uncommon on several isolated hills near the coast and in Teita district, also recorded from Ol Doinyo Orok near Namanga; 700–1800 m; flowering in February to April.

First described from Mozambique, this species is now known from coastal areas of Tanzania, and also from Malawi, Zimbabwe and South Africa (Natal and Transvaal).

Jumellea usambarensis J.J. Wood

Plants epiphytic with long woody stems bearing many roots, leafy in the upper part. Stems simple,

Jumellea filicornoides   JOYCE STEWART

usually growing in clusters of several stems together, 30–80 cm long. Leaves 6–10 in two rows, oblong-ligulate, equally or almost equally bilobed at the apex, leathery, 10–13 cm long, 1.5–2 cm wide. Inflorescences with a single flower on short peduncles sheathed with bracts which turn black. Flower white with green spur, scented in the evening; dorsal sepal ovate-elliptic, obtuse, margins undulate or crisped at the base, 13–16 mm long, 6 mm wide; lateral sepals oblong-ligulate, obtuse, 17 mm long, 4 mm wide; petals linear-ligulate, obtuse, reflexed, slightly smaller than sepals; lip rhombic, narrow at the base, with a shallow central keel, acute, 16–17 mm long, 6 mm wide, spur parallel to the ovary then bent, cylindric, sometimes coiled, 8–9 cm long; column 2 mm long.

Maparashu hill in Kajiado district is the only site known in Kenya to date; *c.* 1600 m; flowering in December.

First described from the Usambara Mts in Tanzania and also now known from Malawi.

Liparis L.C. Richard

This genus of about 250 species of terrestrial or epiphytic herbs has an almost cosmopolitan distribution, mainly in the tropics. They have short stems that are often swollen to form a pseudobulb at the base. There are one or more leaves that often have a limp, slightly greasy feel while others are shiny. The Greek word *liparos* (greasy or shiny) was used to provide the generic name. Most of the species have small flowers in shades of green, brown or dark red, with characteristically very narrow petals and a broad lip.

Twelve species have been described from East Africa of which only two are recorded from Kenya.

CULTIVATION

The plants are easily maintained in cultivation, either in shallow pots or pans of well-drained epiphyte compost or when well established on pieces of tree fern fibre. They grow best in cool conditions where the temperature drops to 10°C at night or even less. They need to be kept moist in the period of active growth. After flowering the plants should be allowed to dry off while the leaves become thin, turn brown and eventually shrivel or fall. After a further rest a new shoot appears at the base of the old pseudobulb, and watering and feeding should begin again.

Key to the species of *Liparis*

Lateral sepals free to the base; lip at least 8 mm wide, margins smooth . . . . *L. bowkeri*
Lateral sepals united for half their length or more; lip less than 6 mm wide, margin toothed . . . . *L. deistelii*

Liparis bowkeri Harvey
Syn. *Liparis neglecta* Schlechter

Epiphytic or terrestrial herb with shoots up to 25 cm high, arising close to the pseudobulb of the previous season but usually at an angle to it. Pseudobulbs swollen, conical to cylindric, up to 7 cm high with 2–5 leaves. Leaves light green, thin, lanceolate to ovate or broadly ovate, up to 12 cm long, with a short petiole. Inflorescence terminal, up to 15 cm long, with 2–25 light green or yellowish flowers that turn orange with age. Flowers 12–15 mm in diameter; dorsal sepal oblong-lanceolate or linear, 8–11 mm long, 1–2 mm wide; lateral sepals free, falcate, narrowly elliptic, 5–9 mm long, 2–4 mm wide; petals spreading, linear, 5–11 mm long; lip deflexed, auriculate at the base, orbicular to transversely elliptic, obtuse or rounded at the apex, 5–7 mm long, 6–8 mm wide, callus near the base of the lip small, somewhat bifid; column slender, incurved at a right angle in the middle, 3–3.5 mm long.

On mossy rocks and banks on the forest floor, and amongst mosses on tree trunks and branches throughout the highland forests and including the Chyulu hills; 1350–2700 m; flowering in April and September.

Widespread in the highland forests along the

Liparis bowkeri   BOB CAMPBELL

eastern side of Africa from Ethiopia to South Africa (Natal) and rather variable in size throughout this wide range.

Liparis deistelii Schlechter

Epiphytic or terrestrial herb with shoots up to 15 cm high arising 4–12 cm apart above a slender creeping rhizome. Pseudobulbs fleshy, up to 4 cm high with 2–3 small sheathing leaves at the base and 3 larger leaves above. Leaves light green, thin, ovate to oblong-lanceolate, 5–8 cm long, acute at the apex, gradually tapering to the sheathing base. Inflorescence terminal, with 2–12 yellow, green or purplish flowers. Flowers 10–15 mm in diameter; dorsal sepal up to 10 mm long, 3 mm wide at the base; lateral sepals joined almost to the apex, orbicular, slightly auricled at the base, curved up beneath the lip; petals linear, up to 11 mm long; lip narrow at the auricled base with a bilobed callus, then widening to become flabellate, emarginate, up to 7 mm long and wide, margins dentate; column slender, curved, up to 5 mm long.

Liparis deistelii   BOB CAMPBELL

On mossy banks and amongst moss on the trunks of tree ferns and other forest trees, also on rocks and fallen trees in shade, often near rivers, throughout the highland forests; 1700–2750 m; flowering in May and June and also in November.

Widespread in highland areas across tropical Africa from Ethiopia to Cameroon and south to Malawi.

Margelliantha Cribb

This genus of pretty little orchids was described in 1979 by the Kew botanist Phillip Cribb. Four species are known to date, all immediately recognisable by the white or pale yellow flowers which are unusual amongst African orchids, many of which have reflexed parts, in remaining partly closed, or almost bell shaped. The name is derived from the Greek words *margelis* (pearl) and *anthos* (flower). In *Margelliantha leedalii*, the type of the genus and the only species that has been recorded from Kenya, the resemblance to a pearl is most marked because all the tepals are a glistening white. The whiteness is accentuated by the bright green anther cap at the apex of the column.

All the species grow in montane forests, often on isolated hills, where they are often enveloped in mist or low cloud while the surrounding country may be hot and dry. The plants have their roots embedded in moss and lichens on the branches of trees and shrubs thus occupying a special micro-habitat in places where orchids are rather unexpected.

CULTIVATION

The few people who have tried to grow *Margelliantha* species have found them not difficult in conditions similar to those that succeed with some of the smaller *Diaphananthe* species.

Margelliantha leedalii Cribb

Plants epiphytic, small, with thin roots at the base of short stems. Stems upright or pendent, 1.5–4 cm long, with few leaves at the apex. Leaves 3–6, ligulate, unequally bilobed at the apex, 4–8 cm long, 6–8 mm wide. Inflorescences usually several arising below the leaves, up to 7 cm long, and bearing 3–8 flowers. Flowers glistening white with green anther cap, only partially open; dorsal sepal ovate, obtuse, 4–5 mm long, 3 mm wide; lateral sepals falcate, obtuse, 4–5 mm long, 3 mm wide; petals obovate to almost round, obtuse, 3–4 mm long, 3 mm wide; lip flabellate, emarginate, 5–6 mm long, 6–8 mm wide, spur slightly incurved, clavate, 6–7 mm long; column 2–3 mm long.

On the mossy branches of trees and shrubs; only recorded in Kenya from Kasigau hill to date; *c.* 1500 m; flowering in June.

Margelliantha leedalii   BOB CAMPBELL

Originally recorded from the Uluguru Mts in Tanzania and also from Iringa district. Not known elsewhere.

Microcoelia Lindley

This well-known genus of African and Madagascan orchids is always easily recognised. The plants consist of a mass of grey roots arising from short stems which bear only a few brownish scale leaves. Green leaves are absent. During the flowering season each plant is transformed by the appearance of many tiny white flowers on long racemes. At the base of the lip each has a tiny spur. The generic name is derived from the Greek words *mikros* (small) and *koilia* (abdomen) and alludes to the spur, which in the type species, *Microcoelia exilis*, is small and round.

Some 27 species of *Microcoelia* have been described to date, 10 of which have been recorded in Kenya. They all have a rather distinct and localised distribution, and it is easier to identify them if one knows which species to expect in each area. In the coastal forests four species may be encountered, including *M. exilis*. The others are the tiny *M. smithii* and the much larger flowered species *M. physophora* and *M. obovata*, both quite distinct. *Microcoelia obovata* and *M. exilis* also grow in the hotter areas inland as far up as Machakos. Recently two species, which were previously only known in Malawi and Tanzania, have been found on some of the isolated hills not far from the coast: *M. corallina*, with its lovely red column, and the much larger *M. megalorrhiza* that has conspicuous verrucose roots. In the forests around Nairobi there is the very floriferous *M. stolzii* and the tiny *M. moreauae*. West of the Rift Valley, in the warmer bush and forested areas, *M. globulosa* and the more attractive *M. koehleri* can still be found.

CULTIVATION

All the species of *Microcoelia* survive well in cultivation provided they are not overwatered and provided they have plenty of light. The plants need to be allowed to dry out well between waterings. When the weather is cooler, water should be withheld completely. In a humid glasshouse the plants can absorb sufficient moisture from the atmosphere for their limited needs.

Microcoelia corallina

BOB CAMPBELL

Key to the species of *Microcoelia*

1　Spur globose, 1 mm in diameter . . . *M. exilis*
　　Spur conical, cylindric or inflated, not
　　　globose 2

2　Roots markedly verrucose
　　. *M. megalorrhiza*
　　Roots smooth 3

3　Column bright salmon red . . . . *M. corallina*
　　Column white or pale brown 4

4　Spur bulbous or swollen at or near the
　　　apex 5
　　Spur not inflated at the apex 6

5　Spur straight or recurved, swollen at the
　　　apex only; lip less than 3 mm long . . . .
　　. . . . . *M. physophora*
　　Spur incurved, conically inflated near the
　　　apex; lip obovate, more than 6 mm long . . .
　　. . . . . *M. koehleri*

6　Lowermost floral bracts sheathing the
　　　rachis and pedicel 7
　　Lowermost floral bracts inserted below the
　　　pedicel and not sheathing the rachis . . . 9

7　Lip narrowly ovate, acute . . . . . . *M. smithii*
　　Lip oblong or pandurate 8

8　Sepals less than 3.5 mm long; lip
　　　2.2–3.3 mm long . . . . *M. globulosa*
　　Sepals 3.7–7 mm long; lip 5–7.5 mm long . . . .
　　. . . . . *M. obovata*

9　Inflorescences densely flowered, up to
　　　40 flowers . . . . *M. stolzii*
　　Inflorescences laxly flowered, up to
　　　8 flowers . . . . *M. moreauae*

Microcoelia corallina Summerhayes

Small epiphytic plant with a mass of silvery-grey roots radiating from the short stem to form a mound. Inflorescences 2–5 cm long, usually several, each bearing up to 15 flowers, the upper flowers with much shorter pedicels than the lower ones. Flowers white with salmon red midline on sepals and petals, red basal patch on lip, and column also salmon red; dorsal sepal ovate, acute, 5 mm long, 2 mm wide; lateral sepals similar but oblique, with a rounded lobe on outer edge at the base; petals elliptic to oblong, obtuse, apiculate, 4 mm long, 2 mm wide; lip almost round, 5 mm long, 4 mm wide, spur slender at the base, tapering to an inflated apex, 6 mm long.

Dry hot woodland, usually growing on smooth barked trees, on isolated hills at low altitudes; 200–500 m; flowering in October.

Also known from southern Tanzania and Malawi.

Microcoelia exilis Lindley

Small epiphytic plant with a mass of silvery-grey, branching roots radiating from the short stem to form a tangled, ball shaped mass. Inflorescences arching or pendent, up to 25 cm long, usually several, all densely flowered with 50–80 tiny flowers. Flowers white with yellowish or brownish-green spur, *c.* 2 mm in diameter; dorsal sepal obovate, acute, 1 mm long; lateral sepals obliquely ovate, subacute, 1 mm long; petals ovate, obtuse, apiculate, 0.5–1 mm long; lip concave, ovate to almost round, 0.5–1 mm long, spur globose, less than 1 mm long and wide; column minute.

Microcoelia exilis　　　　　　　　　BOB CAMPBELL

Usually a twig epiphyte in warmer bush, thicket and open woodland habitats; recorded from all the coastal districts and inland as far as Teita, Machakos and Tana river districts; sea level to 1500 m; recorded in flower throughout the year, but mostly November to April.

Also recorded from Uganda and Tanzania, westwards to Zaïre and southwards in Malawi, Zambia, Mozambique, Zimbabwe and South Africa (Natal). Also recorded in Madagascar.

Microcoelia globulosa (Hochstetter) L. Jonsson
Syn. *Microcoelia guyoniana* (Reichenbach f.) Summerhayes

Small epiphytic plant with long silvery-grey roots radiating from the short stem, often loosely attached to the host. Inflorescences 2–9 cm long, usually rather sparse but 5–10 may appear, bearing up to 15 flowers each, the basal bracts sheathing and with 2 hook-shaped processes opposite the flowers. Flowers white, base of tepals and ovary yellowish green, spur orange brown at tip; dorsal sepal ovate, acute, apiculate, 2–3 mm long, 1–1.5 mm wide; lateral sepals similar or slightly narrower; petals obovate to elliptic or oblong, apiculate, 2–3 mm long, 0.8–1.2 mm wide; lip pandurate, thickened on each side of the mouth of the spur, 2–3 mm long, 1.2–1.8 mm wide, spur slender, conical, bent at right angles from the base of the lip, 2–3 mm long; column minute.

An epiphyte of twigs or small branches at the edge of thicket, patches of bush and riverine woodland; only recorded from the Rift Valley and further west in Kenya, including Baringo, Ravine and Nakuru districts, Mara river area, and Kakamega; 1600–1950 m; flowering January to April.

Also recorded from Uganda and Tanzania; first described from Ethiopia and now known to be widely distributed westwards to Nigeria and south to Malawi, Zimbabwe, Zambia and Angola.

Microcoelia koehleri (Schlechter) Summerhayes
Syn. *Microcoelia pachystemma* Summerhayes

Small epiphytic plant, sometimes pendent, with green roots flecked with white, flattened and radiating from the short stem, often forming a small mound at right angles to the host. Inflorescences 2–7 cm long, usually up to 7 simultaneously, each bearing up to 20 flowers, the basal bracts sheathing. Flowers whitish, spur orange brown or salmon pink at tip; dorsal sepal narrowly oblong, acuminate, apiculate, 5–7 mm long, 1.5–2.2 mm wide; lateral sepals slightly asymmetric, narrowly oblong, acuminate, 6–8 mm long; petals ovate to narrowly ovate, apiculate, 5–6 mm long, 1.6–2 mm wide; lip large, broadly ovate, with upturned erose margins, 6–7 mm long, 4–5 mm wide, spur curved, slender, tapering, with a slight inflation near the apex, 6–7 mm long; column 2 mm long, anther cap orange.

Epiphyte on twigs and branches and also occasionally on rocks in undisturbed habitats; known only from the Kisumu and Kakamega areas in west Kenya; 1500–1600 m; flowering in March.

Also recorded in Uganda and Tanzania, westwards as far as Nigeria and south to Malawi and Zambia.

Microcoelia koehleri   BOB CAMPBELL

Microcoelia megalorrhiza (Schlechter) Summerhayes

Small epiphytic plant with long, distinctly verrucose, grey roots up to 70 cm long radiating from the short stem, often loosely attached. Inflorescences 2–10 cm long, usually up to 7 simultaneously, each bearing up to 20 flowers, bracts sheathing. Flowers glistening white, spur tinged orange brown at tip; dorsal sepal narrowly elliptic, acuminate, apiculate, 7 mm long, 2 mm wide, forming a hood with the petals; lateral sepals similar or slightly narrower, 6–9 mm long, 1.6–2 mm wide; petals similar to dorsal sepal, acuminate, 5–7 mm long, 1.8–2.4 mm wide; lip large, subspathulate, 3-lobed, side lobes thickened and upright, midlobe ovate, deflexed, 7–8 mm long, 2–3 mm wide, spur slender, curved, tapering to an acute apex, 8 mm long; column 2 mm long.

Epiphytic in dry woodland, usually in the canopy of large bushes and trees; recently collected on isolated hills near the coast; sea level to 500 m; flowering in December and January.

Also recorded in Tanzania and Malawi.

Microcoelia megalorrhiza   BOB CAMPBELL

Microcoelia moreauae L. Jonsson
Very small epiphytic plant with silvery-grey roots up to 5 cm long, radiating from the short stem, adhering closely to the bark. Inflorescences 2–3 cm long, up to 4 simultaneously, bearing up to 8 flowers each, basal bracts not sheathing. Flowers white, spur green at tip; dorsal sepal oblong, obtuse, 2 mm long; lateral sepals similar, oblique, slightly longer; petals oblong, obtuse, 1.4–2 mm long; lip concave, oblong, obtuse, 1–2 mm long, spur slender, conical, bent at right angles from the base of the lip, 1.5–2 mm long; column minute.

Epiphytic on twigs of trees and large bushes in seasonally dry montane forest; around Nairobi, Ngong and also in Meru district; 1500–1800 m; flowering from August to October.

Also recorded from Tanzania, Malawi and Zimbabwe.

Microcoelia obovata Summerhayes
Small epiphytic plant, sometimes pendent, with stiff straight roots radiating from the short stem. Inflorescences erect or pendent, 2–9 cm long, usually up to 10 simultaneously, all bearing up to 20 flowers, the basal bracts sheathing. Flowers whitish, brownish at the base of tepals and spur; dorsal sepal obovate to oblong, obtuse, apiculate, 4–6 mm long, 1.2–2 mm wide; lateral sepals slightly asymmetric, oblong, acute, apiculate, apically reflexed, 5–7 mm long; petals asymmetric, oblong

Microcoelia moreauae   BOB CAMPBELL

Microcoelia obovata   BOB CAMPBELL

to obovate, apiculate, apically reflexed, 4–6 mm long, 1.3–1.8 mm wide; lip broadly obovate, folded, with a thickening on each side of the spur mouth, 5–7.5 mm long, 3–5 mm wide, spur incurved, slender, semicircular in cross section, 3–5.5 mm long; column 1–1.6 mm long.

Epiphytic in the warm and dry woodlands and bush and on scattered trees in grassland, often growing in rather exposed places; near Tana river, Teita and Machakos districts and near Kwale; sea level to 1100 m; flowering December to February.

Also recorded from Tanzania and Mozambique.

Microcoelia physophora (Reichenbach f.) Summerhayes

Small epiphytic plant, sometimes pendent, with long roots triangular in cross section radiating from the short stem. Inflorescences erect, 2–9 cm long, usually up to 6 simultaneously, each bearing up to 15 flowers, the basal bracts sheathing. Flowers white and green; dorsal sepal hooded, ovate, acute, 1.5–2.5 mm long, 1–1.5 mm wide; lateral sepals slightly asymmetric, ovate, acute, apiculate, connate below the ovary, 2–3 mm long; petals ovate, obtuse, 1.5–2.5 mm long, 0.7–1 mm wide; lip 3-lobed, midlobe short, obtuse, side lobes indistinct, rounded, concealing mouth of spur, 1–3 mm long, 0.5–1 mm wide, spur at right angles to ovary, tapering into a distinctly swollen egg-shaped apex, 7–10 mm long; column 1 mm long.

Epiphyte of twigs in coastal forest; only known from one collection near Gazi, Kwale district; flowering in March.

Also known from Tanzania and Zanzibar, and from Madagascar.

Microcoelia smithii (Rolfe) Summerhayes

Very small epiphytic plant with silvery-grey roots up to 12 cm long, radiating from the short stem and forming a mound that supports it away from the host. Inflorescences 2–5 cm long, up to 12 simultaneously, each bearing 5–10 flowers, basal bracts sheathing. Flowers white, spur green at tip; dorsal sepal ovate, acute, 2–3 mm long; lateral sepals similar but oblique, slightly longer; petals oblong, obtuse, 1.4–2 mm long; lip concave, ovate, obtuse, 2–3 mm long, spur slender, conical, bent at right angles from the base of the lip, 1.5–2 mm long; column minute, anther cap yellow.

Microcoelia smithii   BOB CAMPBELL

Epiphytic in dry evergreen forest and thicket near the coast; in Kwale district and near Kilifi; sea level to 500 m; flowering in August and September.

Also known from coastal parts of Tanzania.

Microcoelia stolzii (Schlechter) Summerhayes
Syn. *Microcoelia ericosma* Summerhayes

Small epiphytic plant with many long silvery-grey roots radiating from the short stem, forming a ball shaped mass. Inflorescences erect or pendent, 5–12 cm long, 5 or more simultaneously, each bearing up to 40 flowers, the basal bracts not sheathing the rachis. Flowers white, spur green at tip; dorsal sepal obovate to ovate, obtuse, apiculate, 2.5–3.5 mm long, 1–1.5 mm wide; lateral sepals similar or slightly narrower, oblique; petals obovate to elliptic or oblong, apiculate, 2–3 mm long, 0.8–1.2 mm wide; lip pandurate, narrowly obovate to ovate, obtuse, 3–3.5 mm long, 1.5–2 mm wide, spur tapering from the mouth then narrowed to a conical apex, 1.5–2.5 mm long; column minute.

Epiphytic on twigs and branches in forest or woodland; formerly common around Nairobi and in forest on isolated hills including Kasigau and the Nguruman escarpment; 1500–2000 m; flowering in December.

First described from Tanzania, now also known from Malawi, Zambia, Mozambique and Zimbabwe.

This species has been confused with *Microcoelia globulosa* (syn. *M. guyoniana*) in several previous publications on Kenya orchids. It can be dis-

tinguished from that species by its non-sheathing bracts and much more densely flowered inflorescences. The plants are noticeably more compact and are usually found in areas of rather cooler temperatures than *M. globulosa*.

Nephrangis Summerhayes

This monotypic genus was established by the Kew botanist Victor Summerhayes in 1948 to accommodate a species that was different from all other species of *Tridactyle* with which it had previously been placed. Although the growth habit is similar,

Microcoelia stolzii

BOB CAMPBELL

the translucent flowers are different, particularly the lip that has two rounded lobes above a narrow base from which the spur descends. The narrow, almost needle-like leaves are also quite distinctive when the plants are not in flower.

This orchid is quite widely distributed in tropical Africa but rarely collected. It was first described from Zaïre. The name is derived from two Greek words *nephros* (kidney) and *angos* (vessel), referring to the distinctive shape of the lip lobes.

CULTIVATION

This orchid has not been grown in cultivation so far as I know. I would expect growers to be successful with it as a mounted plant given the same treatment as the warmer growing species of *Tridactyle*.

Nephrangis filiformis (Kraenzlin)
Summerhayes
Syn. *Tridactyle filiformis* (Kraenzlin) Schlechter
Plants epiphytic usually pendulous. Stems slender, elongated, sometimes branching, leafy in the apical part, rooting at the base only. Leaves widely spaced, terete but somewhat flattened, often curved, pointed, 2–9 cm long, 1–2 mm in diameter. Inflorescences short, arising opposite the leaves, *c.* 1 cm long and bearing 1–4 flowers. Flowers translucent, pale brown or brownish green with a white lip; dorsal sepal ovate to almost round, obtuse, 1.5–2.5 mm long, 1.5–2 mm wide; lateral sepals similar but oblique, connate at the base; petals narrowly elliptic to linear, acute, 1.7–2.5 mm long, 0.5 mm wide; lip narrow and concave at base, abruptly spreading into 2 reniform or round lobes, total length 4–5 mm, spur narrowly conical, obtuse, 4–9 mm long; column 1 mm long.

Epiphytic on branches of the canopy of woodland trees; recorded from Kakamega forest; 1500 m.

Also recorded from Tanzania and Uganda, Zaïre, Liberia and Zambia.

Oberonia Lindley

This genus was named in honour of Oberon, king of the fairies, a whimsical allusion to the beautiful tiny flowers of all the species. More than 100 species have been described from tropical Asia and there are also representatives in Australia and the Pacific islands. One species is known from tropical Africa, Madagascar and the Comoro Islands.

The most distinctive character of this genus is that the plants always look flattened, as if they have been in a press. The plants are sometimes upright, but are often found growing horizontally or pendent from the underside of branches. The stems grow in small tufts with many fibrous roots at the base. The leaves are fleshy, alternating along the stem and laterally compressed. The inflorescence is a terminal raceme of many minute flowers, usually arranged in a dense spiral or in whorls. They need to be studied with a hand lens to appreciate that they are non-resupinate, and the lip is delicately fringed.

CULTIVATION

The African *Oberonia* is easily maintained in small pots of well-drained composts provided great care is exercised with watering: the roots are very fine and easily become saturated. Plants can also be grown as mounted specimens provided they are kept in a humid but buoyant environment. They do best in shaded conditions; night-time temperature needs to be around 15 °C and day-time temperatures considerably warmer.

Oberonia disticha (Lamarck) Schlechter
A small epiphytic herb with few to many leafy stems, 2–15 cm long. Leaves distichous, fleshy, bilaterally compressed, lanceolate, acute in side

Oberonia disticha   ERIC LA CROIX

view, 2–5 cm long, decreasing in size towards the tip of the shoot. Inflorescence terminal, 4–10 cm long, a densely many flowered raceme. Flowers minute, yellow to orange, up to 2 mm in diameter; sepals ovate; petals elliptic-oblong; lip oblong-pandurate, apparently 2- or 4-lobed, margins erose; column very tiny; pollinia 4, waxy.

Epiphyte of shady humid forests; only known from Kakamega and the Teita hills; 470–1250 m; flowering in September.

Widespread in humid forests, westwards to Cameroon and southwards to northern South Africa (Transvaal), but apparently nowhere common.

Polystachya Hooker

This genus is easily recognised amongst all the other pseudobulbous epiphytes by the way the flowers are borne. The ovary is not twisted, or resupinated, so that the lip is at the top of the flower protruding between the paired lateral sepals. These sepals cohere together at the base and, with the extended foot of the column, form a small, chin-shaped hood, or *mentum*, which may be long or short and is a characteristic feature of the flower.

Plants are easily recognised when they are not in flower by the pseudobulbs bearing one or more leaves and the old stems of terminal inflorescences. Thus they are easily distinguished from bulbophyllums in which the inflorescence arises from the base of the pseudobulb. The name of the genus is derived from the Greek words *poly* (many) and *stachys* (spike or ear of grain), presumably referring to the many spikes of small flowers. In the type species from the American tropics, *Polystachya luteola*, the inflorescence does somewhat resemble an ear of wheat, especially before the small flowers open. The flowers are minutely hairy in many of the species and some are delightfully fragrant. Many are very pretty, although small, and have contrasting colours on the lip or anther cap.

About 200 species of *Polystachya* have been described, mostly from Africa. A small number occur in other parts of the tropics, in Central and South America, Australia, New Guinea, Indonesia, Philippines and Madagascar. Species of *Polystachya* can be found in most parts of the African continent south of the Sahara, but many have extremely limited distributions. The beautiful *Polystachya bella*, for example, is currently known only from the forests around Kericho in western Kenya. In this account 31 species are recorded from Kenya and it is likely that more of these attractive little orchids will be discovered.

CULTIVATION

These small plants are easily maintained in a compost suitable for epiphytes in a clay or plastic pot, or in a basket. Some species also do well mounted on a piece of wood or bark. In a relatively short time a small group of pseudobulbs will become an attractive plant bearing many flowering stems. For success in cultivation it is most important to pay attention to the stage of growth of each plant and treat it correctly at each season. Many polystachyas flower on the new growths and after flowering the plants need to be maintained with frequent watering and regular feeding so that the pseudobulbs and leaves develop fully. After a few months of this regime the plants rest and may lose their leaves, though some are more or less evergreen. Dormant buds for the new season's growth are often visible for several months before they start into growth. For the continued success of the plant, it is best to allow this to happen naturally rather than hastening new growths by premature watering. Most *Polystachya* species require good light to promote flowering in the following season, but may need shade from direct sun in the hottest part of the day.

Key to the species of *Polystachya*

1 Pseudobulbs or stems narrowly cylindric or (rarely) swollen at the middle, each one arising about half way along the length of the preceding one. 2
   Pseudobulbs or stems close together on a basal rhizome, often in dense tufts, sometimes swollen at the base or narrowly cylindric 6

2 Leaves under 6 mm wide 3
   Leaves over 10 mm wide 4

3 Ovary and outer surface of sepals hairy . . . .
   . . . . **P. lindblomii**
   Ovary and outer surface of sepals without hairs . . . . **P. spatella**

4 Flowers small; sepals up to 3 mm long . . . . .
   . . . . **P. fusiformis**
   Flowers larger; sepals over 5 mm long . . . 5

5 Sepals yellow or brown, acuminate . . . .
. . . . *P. simplex*
Sepals lime green, rounded and apiculate . . .
. . . . *P. eurygnatha*

6 Plants with one leaf on each pseudobulb,
at least when flowering 7
Plants without leaves or with more than
one leaf on each pseudobulb at
flowering 11

7 Leaves under 10 mm wide 8
Leaves over 10 mm wide 9

8 Flowers white with mauve anther cap . . . . . .
. . . . *P. caespitifica* ssp. *latilabris*
Flowers greenish yellow with mauve
anther cap . . . . *P. tenuissima*

9 Inflorescence axis hairy . . . . *P. pachychila*
Inflorescence axis smooth, without
hairs 10

10 Flowers pink, more than 10 mm in
diameter . . . . *P. bicarinata*
Flowers white, pink or yellow, less than
8 mm in diameter . . . . . . *P. cultriformis*

11 Stems elongated, gradually tapering from
base to apex or narrowly cylindric
throughout, not thickened to form a
pseudobulb 12
Stems short and thickened into a more
or less rounded pseudobulb, or, if
elongated, with a rounded pseudobulb
at the base only 19

12 Flowers small, 3–5 mm from tip of
mentum to apex of lip 13
Flowers larger, 8–12 mm from tip of
mentum to apex of lip 17

13 Inflorescence simple, flowers in a
cylindrical spike, bracts sharply
pointed 14
Inflorescence branched, flowers in
several short lax or dense groups,
bracts not conspicuous 15

14 Flowers white; midlobe of lip ovate to
oblong-elliptic . . . . *P. polychaete*
Flowers pale green, lip edged purple;
midlobe of lip narrowly linear-
lanceolate, much narrower than side
lobes . . . . *P. adansoniae*

15 Leaves fleshy, 5–15 mm wide, V-shaped
in cross section . . . . *P. golungensis*
Leaves thin, more than 10 mm wide,
flat 16

16 Lip with a fleshy callus, ridged, along the
centre towards the base . . . . *P. tessellata*
Lip lacking a central callus . . . . *P. modesta*

17 Flowers hairy on outer surface; basal
sheaths of stem green . . . *P. bennettiana*
Flowers hairless; basal sheaths of stem
brown or black 18

18 Leaves rounded at the tip; flowers 1–8 . . . . .
. . . . *P. transvaalensis*
Leaves pointed; flowers usually more
than 10, but opening few at a time . . . . . .
. . . . *P. albescens* ssp. *kraenzlinii*

19 Stems leafy at flowering time, usually
flowering early on new growth 20
Stems almost without leaves at flowering
time, flowering on mature growths . . . 29

20 Pseudobulbs oval, laterally compressed;
flowers bright yellow-orange . . . . *P. bella*
Pseudobulbs rounded or conical; flowers
not bright yellow-orange 21

21 Flowering stems 10–30 cm tall . *P. vaginata*
Flowering stems under 10 cm tall 22

22 Column with numerous hairs just below
the stigma . . . . *P. disiformis*
Column without hairs 23

23 Plant over 10 cm tall; flowers white with
purple flushed lip . . . . *P. piersii*
Plant less than 6 cm tall; flowers yellow-
green, brownish, purplish or reddish
but not white 24

24 Lip thin, flat or curved, easily flattened . . . .
. . . . *P. heckmanniana*
Lip fleshy, recurved, difficult to flatten
out 25

25 Flowers pink, lip orange on the inner
surface . . . . *P. confusa*
Flowers not pink and orange 26

26 Sepals purplish red or yellow flushed
purple 27
Sepals yellow, greenish yellow, or
greenish brown 28

27   Bracts more than 10 mm long; sepals
        purplish red . . . . *P. holstii*
     Bracts less than 6 mm long; sepals
        yellow flushed purple . . . . *P. fischeri*

28   Bracts acuminate or mucronate, more
        than 5 mm long; lateral sepals more
        than 8 mm long . . . . . *P. campyloglossa*
     Bracts ovate, less than 3 mm long;
        lateral sepals less than 6 mm long . . . .
        . . . . *P. teitensis*

29   Flowers greenish yellow . . . . . *P. steudneri*
     Flowers white, pink or lilac 30

30   Flowers flat and open, more than 8 mm
        in diameter . . . . *P. dendrobiiflora*
     Flowers partly closed, under 6 mm in
        diameter . . . . *P. eurychila*

Polystachya adansoniae Reichenbach f.

Plants small, epiphytic or lithophytic, erect, 10–20 cm high. Pseudobulbs cylindric or narrowly conical, 3–9 cm high, up to 1 cm wide. Leaves 2–3, suberect, linear or ligulate, slightly bilobed at the apex, 8–20 cm long, 6–16 mm wide. Inflorescence erect to 12 cm long, cylindric, densely many flowered, arising from within a compressed sheath, bracts narrow and pointed, bristle-like, 4–8 mm long. Flowers very small, pale green or greenish

Polystachya adansoniae   BOB CAMPBELL

yellow, lip edged or completely coloured purple, anther cap purple; dorsal sepal ovate, acuminate, 3.5 mm long, 1.5 mm wide; lateral sepals obliquely ovate, acuminate, 4–5.5 mm long, 2–3 mm wide, mentum short, conical, 3 mm high; petals linear, acute or acuminate, 3 mm long; lip 3-lobed in the apical half, much recurved in the middle, up to 4 mm long, 3 mm wide, side lobes erect, rounded, midlobe lanceolate, acuminate, callus fleshy with long hairs, between the side lobes; column 1.5 mm long.

Found in the woodlands and forests of the Rift Valley, and throughout western Kenya; 1450–2000 m; flowering April to June.

Also recorded in Uganda and Tanzania; widespread in tropical Africa, westwards to Guinea and southwards to Malawi and Zimbabwe.

Polystachya albescens Ridley ssp. *kraenzlinii* (Rolfe) Summerhayes

Plants epiphytic or lithophytic, glabrous, 20–50 cm tall. Pseudobulbs clustered, slender, covered with loose tubular sheaths and leaf bases that become brown or black with age, to 30 cm long, 4–7 mm in diameter. Leaves 2–5, widely spaced, spreading,

Polystachya albescens   JOYCE STEWART
ssp. *kraenzlinii*

Polystachya bella

BOB CAMPBELL

ligulate or narrowly elliptic, acute, 9–12 cm long, 1–2 cm wide. Inflorescence erect or recurved in the apical half, simple or branched, usually shorter than the leaves, 5–20 cm long. Flowers glabrous, pale greenish yellow or cream tinged with purple; dorsal sepal lanceolate, acute, 6–8 mm long, 3–4 mm wide; lateral sepals obliquely triangular-ovate, acute, 7–11 mm long, 5–8 mm wide, mentum conical to 5–9 mm high; petals oblanceolate, subacute or obtuse, 5–7 mm long, 1–2 mm wide; lip obscurely 3-lobed above the middle, 6–9 mm long, 5–7 mm wide, side lobes erect obliquely triangular, midlobe ovate to rounded, recurved, callus a fleshy ridge along the basal third of lip; column 1 mm long.

On rocks or trees in warm forests, mostly on hilltops; only recorded on Mt Marsabit, in the Chyulu hills and on some of the hills in Teita district; 900–1650 m; flowering in August.

Also recorded in Tanzania, in Lushoto district; not known elsewhere.

This species has sometimes been misidentified as *Polystachya transvaalensis*, but is usually a much larger plant, with longer leaves that are pointed at the apex, not rounded.

Polystachya bella Summerhayes

Plants epiphytic, erect, dark green, to 20 cm high. Pseudobulbs upright, oval, laterally compressed, with 2 sheaths with leaf-like blades enveloping the base, and 2 leaves at the apex. Leaves 2, elliptic or oblong-ligulate, rounded and somewhat unequally bilobed at the apex, leathery, dark green, 5–16 cm long, 2–4 cm wide. Inflorescence erect, flowering on the new growth, simple or branched, pubescent, up to 25 cm high. Flowers yellow or orange with a darker stripe along the centre of the lip; dorsal sepal lanceolate, acute, 12–15 mm long, 3 mm wide; lateral sepals obliquely triangular-lanceolate, acute, 15–18 mm long, 5 mm wide, mentum broadly conical; petals linear-oblanceolate, acute, 8–11 mm long, 1.5 mm wide; lip lanceolate, indistinctly 3-lobed, strongly recurved, 9–12 mm long, 5 mm wide, callus low and linear, near the base; column incurved, 3 mm long.

Only known on shady, mossy branches of tall trees in the forests near Kericho; doubtfully recorded from Mt Elgon and the Cherangani hills; 1800–2350 m; flowering in December and January.

Not known elsewhere; *Polystachya laurentii* is very similar but creamy white in colour and occurs in Uganda, Rwanda and Zaïre. Quite different from the West African *Polystachya obanensis* with which it has sometimes been misidentified.

Polystachya bennettiana Reichenbach f.
Syn. *P. stricta* Rolfe

Plants epiphytic, glabrous except for the inflorescence, 20–40 cm tall. Pseudobulbs clustered, slender, covered with loose tubular sheaths and leaf bases that become straw coloured with age, to 25 cm long, 2–5 mm in diameter. Leaves 4–6, widely spaced, spreading, ligulate or narrowly elliptic, acute, 10–20 cm long, 1–2 cm wide. Inflorescence erect or recurved in the apical half, many branched, 8–30 cm long. Flowers hairy on outer surface, pale greenish yellow or cream with reddish markings on lip, ovary densely hairy; dorsal sepal concave, oblong-lanceolate, 7–10 mm long, 2–4 mm wide; lateral sepals obliquely triangular or lanceolate, acute, 9–11 mm long, 5–7 mm wide, mentum broadly conical to 6 mm long; petals oblanceolate, subacute, 6–8 mm long, 1–2 mm wide; lip 3-lobed at or above the middle, hairy all over the upper surface, 7–10 mm long, 6–7 mm wide, side lobes obliquely triangular, midlobe ovate to rounded, recurved, callus a fleshy keel along the basal third of lip; column 2 mm long.

On large trees in open woodland and riverine forest; on hills in the northern half of the country and also in the drier forests west of the Rift Valley; 900–1900 m; flowering January to May.

Also recorded from Uganda, Ethiopia, westwards as far as Nigeria, and Zambia.

This species is sometimes confused with *Polystachya transvaalensis* when not in flower, but is easily recognised by its usually larger inflorescences with hairy stems, hairy ovaries and the outer surface of the sepals densely hairy.

Polystachya bicarinata Rendle

Plants epiphytic, glabrous. Pseudobulbs clustered, narrowly conical, dark green, 6–30 cm long, *c.* 10 mm in diameter. Leaf single, ovate to obovate, obtuse, auriculate at the base, rather thin, 6–26 cm long, 1.5–3 cm wide. Inflorescence terminal, branched, shorter than the leaf, bearing 5–30 flowers not all open at once, bracts conspicuous, ovate-triangular, up to 10 mm long. Flowers white or pale pink; dorsal sepal ovate-triangular, apiculate, 8–12 mm long, 3–4 mm wide; lateral sepals oblique, triangular, apiculate, 9–11 mm long, 8–9 mm wide, keeled on the outer surface, mentum up to 9 mm high; petals spathulate or linear, acute to obtuse, 7–9 mm long, 2–3 mm wide; lip strongly recurved, 3-lobed in the lower third, 8–10 mm long, 5–7 mm wide, side lobes rounded, erect, midlobe rounded or quadrate, apiculate, callus central between the side lobes; column *c.* 2 mm long.

Epiphytic in highland forests, usually in areas of high humidity; recorded in the Aberdare Mts, Mt Elgon, Cherangani hills and in all the highland forests west of the Rift Valley; 1800–2600 m; flowering January to March.

Also recorded from Uganda, Rwanda and Zaïre.

Polystachya bicarinata   BOB CAMPBELL

Polystachya campyloglossa Rolfe

Plants epiphytic or lithophytic, glabrous. Pseudobulbs clustered, ovoid to ovoid-conical, 1–12 cm long, 8–12 mm in diameter. Leaves 2–3, ligulate to oblong-ligulate or oblong-lanceolate, rounded and

Polystachya campyloglossa   BOB CAMPBELL

unequally bilobed at the apex, 5–10 cm long, 7–20 mm wide. Inflorescence terminal, erect, longer than the leaves, bearing 2–8 flowers, bracts ovate, mucronate, densely pubescent. Flowers variable in colour and size, shortly hairy on the outer surface, sepals olive or yellow-green, petals white, lip white with red or purplish veins on the side lobes; dorsal sepal ovate, acute, 8–13 mm long, 4–7 mm wide; lateral sepals obliquely ovate-triangular, acute, 8–14 mm long, 7–10 mm wide, mentum broadly conical 6–9 mm high; petals oblanceolate, obtuse or spathulate, 7–9 mm long, 2–3 mm wide; lip with a short broad claw at the base, 3-lobed, strongly recurved, 8–11 mm long, 6–9 mm wide, side lobes erect, rounded, densely pubescent, midlobe oblong or ovate, fleshy, oblong, acute, glabrous, except in the centre and with a conical callus at the base between the side lobes; column, short and stout, 3 mm long.

Epiphyte on small trees and bushes, occasionally on rocks; in forest on hills that are regularly cloud covered; 1100–2700 m; flowering from March to July.

Also known from Uganda, northern Tanzania and Malawi. This species seems very similar to *Polystachya sandersonii*, a common epiphyte in eastern South Africa and Swaziland that has reddish spots on the lip and lacks the purple veins on the side lobes.

Polystachya caespitifica Kraenzlin ssp.
latilabris (Summerhayes) Cribb & Podzorski
Syn. *Polystachya latilabris* Summerhayes

Plants small, epiphytic, glabrous. Pseudobulbs clustered, narrowly cylindric, dark green, 1–5 cm long, up to 2 mm in diameter. Leaf single, linear, cuneate at the base, retuse, 6–10 cm long, 5–9 mm wide. Inflorescence terminal, branched, shorter than the leaf, bearing up to 6 flowers, bracts inconspicuous. Flowers white or cream with mauve anther cap and mauve on the lip with yellow callus; dorsal sepal ovate-elliptic, apiculate, 4–8 mm long, 3–4 mm wide; lateral sepals oblique, triangular, apiculate, 4–8 mm long, 3–6 mm wide, mentum ovoid-conical, 5–6 mm high; petals oblanceolate, subacute to obtuse, 4–7 mm long, 2–3 mm wide; lip weakly recurved, 3-lobed towards the apex, broadly elliptic in outline, 4–7 mm long, 7–11 mm wide, side lobes ovate, falcate, midlobe subquadrate, apiculate, disc glandular-pubescent; column 1–2 mm long.

Epiphytic in highland forests where humidity is high; recorded from Ngong hills, Mt Kenya, Aberdare Mts, Cherangani hills and several other forests west of the Rift Valley; 1800–2700 m; flowering in January, April and July.

Elsewhere known only from Mt Meru in northern Tanzania.

Polystachya caespitifica
ssp. *latilabris*   BOB CAMPBELL

Polystachya confusa Rolfe

Plants epiphytic or lithophytic, glabrous. Pseudobulbs clustered, very small, conical, 1.3 cm long, 6–8 mm in diameter. Leaves 2–3, ligulate to oblong-ligulate, rounded and unequally bilobed at the apex, to 4 cm long, 7 mm wide. Inflorescence terminal, erect, bearing 2–6 flowers, bracts ovate. Flowers pink or rose red with a striking yellow or orange stripe on the centre of the lip and dark

Polystachya confusa   BOB CAMPBELL

purple column, somewhat hairy on the outer surface; dorsal sepal ovate, acuminate, 4–6 mm long, 2–3 mm wide; lateral sepals obliquely ovate-triangular, 7–9 mm long, 6–7 mm wide; petals oblong-ligulate, acute, 4–5 mm long, 1.2 mm wide; lip with a long narrow claw at the base, 3-lobed in the middle, 7–9 mm long, 3–3.6 mm wide, side lobes erect, narrow, triangular, midlobe fleshy, oblong, acute; column 1–1.3 cm long.

An epiphyte at high altitudes in the north and west of Kenya; recorded from Mt Kulal and in the Cherangani hills; 2700–3000 m; flowering November through to March.

Also known from northern Tanzania where it has been recorded from Mt Kilimanjaro and Mt Meru.

Polystachya cultriformis (Thouars) Sprengel
Syn. *Polystachya kirkii* Rolfe

Plants epiphytic or lithophytic, glabrous. Pseudobulbs clustered, narrowly cylindric to conical, 2–18 cm long, 2–15 mm in diameter. Leaf single, ovate, obovate to elliptic, acute to obtuse, auriculate at the base, rather thin, 3–36 cm long, 1.5–5 cm wide. Inflorescence terminal, branched, usually longer than the leaf, bearing up to 50 flowers not all open at once, bracts ovate-triangular, up to 4 mm long. Flowers white, yellow, green or pale pink, rather variable in size; dorsal sepal ovate triangular, apiculate, 4–8 mm long, 3–4 mm wide; lateral sepals oblique, triangular, apiculate, 5–8 mm long, 3–6 mm wide, keeled on the outer surface, mentum conical up to 7 mm high; petals spathulate or linear,

Polystachya cultriformis   BOB CAMPBELL

acute to obtuse, 3–7 mm long, 1–2 mm wide; lip strongly recurved, 3-lobed in the apical half, 4–8 mm long, 3–6 mm wide, side lobes rounded, midlobe rounded or quadrate, apiculate, callus fleshy, central; column 0.5–3 mm long.

A very common epiphyte in all forests, often near rivers; can be found throughout the country except at sea level; 330–2700 m; flowering January to July and irregularly throughout the year.

Also recorded from Tanzania and Uganda, and in many other parts of Africa, westwards to Cameroon and Gabon and south to South Africa (Natal). Also recorded from Madagascar, the Mascarene islands and the Seychelles.

Polystachya dendrobiiflora Reichenbach f.
Syn. *Polystachya tayloriana* Rendle
Plants epiphytic, lithophytic or terrestrial, 40–90 cm high. Stems clustered together, pseudobulbous at the base only, 1–5 cm long, the pseudobulbs often forming ascending chains. Leaves 5–10, linear, folded, light green, deciduous, 8–25 cm long, 5–15 mm wide. Inflorescence erect, branched, usually developing after the leaves have fallen, covered with straw-coloured sheaths, producing flowers over a long period on slender stalks in small groups along the main axis. Flowers showy, pale pink with darker pink or purple markings on the lip, usually resupinate; dorsal sepal oblong-lanceolate to ovate-lanceolate, subacute to obtuse, 6–12 mm long, 3–4 mm wide; lateral sepals obliquely oblong-lanceolate, subacute to obtuse, 7–8 mm long, 3–5 mm wide, mentum on the lower side of the flower conical, 3–4 mm high; petals oblong-elliptic to obovate, rounded, 6–11 mm long, 2–4 mm wide; lip shortly clawed, entire, recurved, ovate-oblong, margin wavy, 7–11 mm long, 4–5 mm wide, callus a hairy cushion in the lower third; column winged, 2.5–4 mm long.

Polystachya dendrobiiflora   BOB CAMPBELL

Often epiphytic on the stems of *Xerophyta* plants and adjacent to them in soil; also occurring on rocks in the drier and warmer parts of southeastern Kenya including Chyulu hills, Teita hills and hills near Kibwezi; 650–1700 m; flowering in November and December, also in June.

Also recorded from Tanzania, Burundi, Zaïre and southwards through Malawi to Zimbabwe and Angola.

This *Polystachya* is unique in the genus in having the lip on the lower side of the flower, which thus resembles a small *Dendrobium* flower.

Polystachya disiformis Cribb
Plants epiphytic, glabrous. Pseudobulbs clustered, very small, ovoid, 1 cm long, 8–10 mm in diameter. Leaves 2–3, narrowly elliptic-lanceolate, obtuse or rounded at the apex, to 4 cm long, 8 mm wide. Inflorescence terminal, erect, bearing 3–9 flowers, bracts ovate. Flowers yellow or dull green, sepals lined with red, lip magenta with a greenish-yellow callus, somewhat hairy on the outer surface; dorsal

Polystachya disiformis   BOB CAMPBELL

sepal ovate, acute, 4–6 mm long, 3 mm wide; lateral sepals obliquely ovate-triangular, acute, 7–9 mm long, 6–7 mm wide, mentum to 6 mm high; petals narrowly linear-lanceolate, subacute, 5 mm long, 1 mm wide; lip with a long narrow claw for nearly half its length, 3-lobed in the middle, 9–12 mm long, 5 mm wide, side lobes erect, rounded, 2.5 mm long and wide, midlobe fleshy, oblong-lanceolate, acute, callus fleshy, glabrous, disc pubescent at the base; column short, stout, 1 mm long with a cluster of long bristles below the stigma.

Only known from montane forest on the Teita hills; 1200–1500 m; flowering in September.

Also recorded from forests on hills in Lushoto district of northern Tanzania where it flowers in April.

Polystachya eurychila Summerhayes

Plants epiphytic or lithophytic, 25–40 cm high. Stems erect, close together, fleshy, scarcely pseudobulbous but narrowly conical to 20 cm high, 8 mm in diameter at the base. Leaves 3–5, erect or curved, soon deciduous, narrowly linear-lanceolate, grass-like, acute, to 30 cm long, 6–8 mm wide. Inflorescence developing after the leaves have fallen, not or scarcely branched, covered with straw coloured sheaths. Flowers white or pale lilac rose edged with purple or magenta, anther cap purple, lip yellow edged with magenta; dorsal sepal oblong-elliptic, rounded, 3–4 mm long, 2 mm wide; lateral sepals round-triangular, obtuse, with a short apiculus on the back below the apex, 4–5 mm long and wide, mentum conical, subacute, 3 mm long; petals ligulate or spathulate, 3 mm long, 1 mm wide; lip with a short claw, very broadly 3-lobed in the apical half, 4 mm long, 6–7 mm wide, whole surface minutely mealy or hairy, side lobes spreading, longer and wider than midlobe; column 2 mm long.

Polystachya eurychila   BOB CAMPBELL

On *Acacia* trees especially near rivers and on undisturbed rocks that are seasonally wet; recorded near Kitale and in few other places west of Rift Valley; 1800–2300 m; flowering in March and April, August and September.
Also known in Uganda and Ethiopia.

Polystachya eurygnatha Summerhayes

Plants epiphytic, erect or pendulous, eventually forming a large branching mass. Stems slender, cylindric or fusiform, each new growth 4–12 cm long, arising from the centre of the previous growth, leafy in the apical part. Leaves broadly lanceolate, acute, 2–8 cm long, 5–15 mm wide. Inflorescence terminal on each growth, shorter than the leaves, branched, with many flowers. Flowers yellowish green with lime-green lip, anther cap brown or purplish; dorsal sepal, elliptic-oblong, obtuse, 4–5 mm long, 2.5 mm wide; lateral sepals obliquely ovate, apiculate, 6 mm long, 4–5 mm wide, forming a broad mentum 3.5 mm high, 3 mm wide, shortly bilobed at the apex; petals spathulate-oblong, rounded at the apex, 3.5 mm long, 1 mm wide; lip 3-lobed, 6 mm long, 4 mm wide, side lobes rounded, midlobe broadly quadrate-ovate, truncate, fleshy; column 2 mm long.

Only known from humid forests in Kericho district; 2000–2350 m; flowering in March and April.
Also recorded from Uganda.

Polystachya eurygnatha   BOB CAMPBELL

Polystachya fischeri Kraenzlin
Syn. *Polystachya kilimanjari* Kraenzlin
Plants epiphytic, glabrous. Pseudobulbs clustered, ovoid to narrowly conical, up to 3 cm long, 1 cm in diameter. Leaves 2–3, linear to narrowly oblanceolate, obtuse or rounded at the apex, to 11 cm long, 8–12 mm wide. Inflorescence terminal, erect, bearing few to many flowers, densely hairy, bracts ovate or cordate, mucronate. Flowers yellow flushed with red, hairy on the outer surface, lip with a yellow callus, anther cap crimson; dorsal

sepal ovate-lanceolate or lanceolate, acute, 6–8 mm long, 3 mm wide; lateral sepals obliquely triangular-lanceolate, acuminate, 7–9 mm long, 5 mm wide, mentum to 4 mm high; petals oblanceolate, rounded, 6 mm long, *c.* 2 mm wide; lip 3-lobed, strongly recurved in the basal half, side lobes erect, rounded, *c.* 6 mm long, 5 mm wide, midlobe ovate, similar to side lobes in size, fleshy, disc sparsely pubescent at the base; column short, stout, less than 1 mm long.

Only known from forest on the Rabai hills in Kilifi district; 500 m; flowering in February and March.

Also recorded from dry evergreen forests on hills in northern Tanzania.

Polystachya fusiformis (Thouars) Lindley

Plants epiphytic, erect or pendulous, eventually forming a large branching mass. Stems slender, cylindric or fusiform, each new growth 8–23 cm long, arising from the centre of the previous growth, leafy in the apical part. Leaves lanceolate or elliptic, acute, 5–15 cm long, 2–3 cm wide, larger leaves at the apex, often with wavy margins. Inflorescence at the tip of the young growth, shorter than the leaves, branched, with many flowers close together. Flowers with pale purplish-brown sepals and white lip, small, often setting seed without opening; dorsal sepal, elliptic-oblong, subacute, 2 mm long, 1.3 mm wide; lateral sepals obliquely ovate, subacute, 3 mm long, 2 mm wide, forming a

Polystachya fusiformis   BOB CAMPBELL

mentum 2 mm high; petals oblong-obovate, obtuse, 2 mm long, 1 mm wide; lip 3-lobed in the middle, 2.5 mm long and wide, side lobes oblong, small, midlobe quadrate-ovate, obtuse, fleshy; column 1.5 mm long.

Forming large clumps in the warmer forests around Lake Victoria and in Kakamega; 1700–2350 m; flowering in June.

Also recorded in Tanzania and Uganda; widespread in tropical Africa westwards to Ghana and south to South Africa (Natal and Transvaal). Also recorded in Madagascar and Mauritius.

Polystachya golungensis Reichenbach f.

Syn. *Polystachya coriacea* Rolfe

Plants epiphytic or lithophytic, 10–45 cm high. Pseudobulbs slender, conical-cylindric, 2–6 cm high, growing close together on a basal rhizome. Leaves 2–4, suberect, ligulate, fleshy, folded and V-shaped in cross section, unequally bilobed at the apex, lobes round, 5–18 cm long, 5–20 mm wide.

Polystachya golungensis   BOB CAMPBELL

Inflorescence much longer than the leaves, branched, to 40 cm long, with many flowers borne in short dense clusters on the sheath-covered branches. Flowers small, bright yellow-green; dorsal sepal ovate, apiculate, 2–3 mm long, 1 mm wide; lateral sepals obliquely ovate-triangular, 2–4 mm long, 1–2 mm wide, mentum rounded, to 2 mm high; petals oblanceolate, acute, 1–3 mm long, 0.5 mm wide; lip 3-lobed in the middle, 2–3 mm long, 1–2 mm wide, side lobes narrowly elliptic, rounded, shorter than midlobe, callus a cushion of mealy hairs near the base; column minute.

On small and large trees or on rocks in seasonally dry forest; recorded in Kakamega and other parts of west Kenya, also on Maungu hill in Teita district; 1000–1350 m; flowering in November and in March.

Also recorded in Tanzania and Uganda; widespread in tropical Africa westwards to Mali and Nigeria, and south to Mozambique and Zimbabwe.

Polystachya heckmanniana Kraenzlin

Plants epiphytic or lithophytic, glabrous, very short. Pseudobulbs clustered, ovoid to conical, 0.8–3 cm long, 7–11 mm in diameter. Leaves 2–3, narrowly oblong-elliptic to elliptic, rounded at the apex, purple below, to 4 cm long, 7–14 mm wide. Inflorescence terminal, erect, bearing 1–3 flowers, bracts lanceolate, acuminate. Flowers often solitary, large for the size of the plant, outer surface glabrous, sepals cream, yellow or yellow-green, lip white or pale brown, side lobes veined purple, callus yellow, column white with purple spotting; dorsal sepal ovate, acuminate, 11–13 mm long, 5–7 mm wide; lateral sepals obliquely ovate-falcate, 15–20 mm long, 7–9 mm wide; petals oblanceolate, obtuse, 11–13 mm long, 2–3 mm wide; lip with a short claw at the base, 3-lobed in the middle, 13–17 mm long, 12 mm wide, side lobes erect, subquadrate, midlobe much larger than side lobes, quadrate, margins frilled, 10 mm long and wide, with clavate hairs centrally; column 1.6 cm long.

In upland forest where there is frequent mist; 2000 m; flowering January to April.

Only recorded in Kenya from the Kinangop; also known in the southern highlands of Tanzania and in Malawi.

Polystachya holstii Kraenzlin

Plants epiphytic, glabrous. Pseudobulbs clustered, ovoid or conical, 1–3 cm long, 8–10 mm in diameter, covered in scarious white sheaths. Leaves 2–3, suberect, linear to oblanceolate, minutely apiculate, to 6–11 cm long, 9–12 mm wide. Inflorescence terminal, erect, bearing 3–9 flowers close together at the apex, bracts ovate, acuminate. Flowers densely pubescent, with red-purple sepals, lip cream, yellow at the apex, callus yellow spotted purple; dorsal sepal ovate, acuminate, 9–11 mm long, 4–5 mm wide; lateral sepals obliquely ovate-triangular, acuminate, 10–12 mm long, 6–8 mm wide, mentum to 6 mm high; petals oblanceolate, obtuse, 8 mm long, c. 2 mm wide; lip 3-lobed, 7–8 mm long, 5 mm wide, side lobes obscure, subelliptic, midlobe ovate, subacute; callus absent; column very short, c. 0.5 mm long.

Polystachya holstii   BOB CAMPBELL

Only known from montane forest on the Chyulu hills; 1200–1500 m; flowering in January.

Also recorded from forests and on introduced trees on hills in the Lushoto district of northern Tanzania.

Polystachya lindblomii Schlechter

Plants epiphytic, erect or pendulous, eventually forming a large branching mass. Stems very slender, narrowly cylindric throughout their length,

Polystachya lindblomii   BOB CAMPBELL

each new growth 7–9 cm long, arising from the centre of the previous growth, leafy in the apical part. Leaves linear, grass-like, acute, 5–11 cm long, 2–4 mm wide. Inflorescence terminal on each growth, much shorter than the leaves, unbranched with 4–8 flowers. Flowers yellowish green with mauve lip, ovary hairy; dorsal sepal ovate, acuminate, 3–5 mm long, 2 mm wide; lateral sepals obliquely ovate, 7–9 mm long, 4–5 mm wide, forming a broad mentum 4–5 mm high that is rounded at the apex; petals linear to oblong-elliptic, 3 mm long, 1 mm wide; lip 3-lobed in the apical half, 6 mm long, 4 mm wide, side lobes rounded, midlobe much larger than side lobes, broadly ovate, apiculate, callus a fleshy transverse ridge between the side lobes; column 2 mm long.

A distinctive leafy epiphyte in forests and at forest margins; most common west of the Rift Valley but also recorded from isolated hills in Masai and Kajiado districts; 1000–2330 m; flowering in July and August.

Also recorded from northern Tanzania and Uganda, and in Ethiopia, Zaïre, Mozambique, Malawi and Zimbabwe.

Polystachya modesta Reichenbach f.

Plants epiphytic or rarely lithophytic, 10–20 cm high. Pseudobulbs slender, conical-cylindric or ovoid-conical, 1–10 cm high, growing close together on a basal rhizome, purple or yellow. Leaves 4–5, lanceolate or oblanceolate, acute or subacute, thin, 7–15 cm long, 1–2 cm wide, dark

Polystachya modesta   BOB CAMPBELL

green edged with purple. Inflorescence as long as the leaves, with short side branches, to 20 cm long, with flowers borne in short dense clusters on the sheath-covered branches. Flowers small, bright yellow-green, pale green, pale yellow, pink or purple; dorsal sepal ovate, apiculate, 2–3.5 mm long, 1–2 mm wide; lateral sepals obliquely triangular, acute, 3–5 mm long, 2.5 mm wide, mentum conical, to 3 mm high; petals linear to oblanceolate, acute, 3 mm long, 1 mm wide; lip 3-lobed in the middle, 3–5 mm long, 2–3.5 mm wide, side lobes narrowly elliptic, rounded, shorter than midlobe that is rounded and fleshy, callus a cushion of mealy hairs near the base; column 1.5 mm long.

Usually epiphytic on old trees and bushes in riverine forest and in patches of forest on hills; recorded from several of the hills in Teita district; 500–1200 m; flowering in December.

Also recorded from Uganda and Tanzania, and widespread in tropical Africa westwards to the Ivory Coast and south to Zambia, Malawi and Zimbabwe.

Robust specimens are sometimes confused with *Polystachya tessellata* but the flowers of that species always have a fleshy callus along the centre of the lip which is usually white.

Polystachya pachychila Summerhayes

Plants epiphytic. Pseudobulbs clustered, narrowly cylindric, dark green, 2–15 cm long, *c.* 2 mm in diameter. Leaf single, elliptic to ovate, obtuse, auriculate at the base, 3–13 cm long, 1.5–3 cm wide. Inflorescence terminal, branched, longer than the leaf, bearing up to 60 flowers not all open at once, sparsely hairy, bracts inconspicuous. Flowers yellow or yellowish green, spotted with purple; dorsal sepal oblong-lanceolate, apiculate, 4–5 mm long, 2–2.5 mm wide; lateral sepals oblique, triangular, 4–7 mm long, 3–6 mm wide, mentum ovoid, up to 6 mm high; petals linear to spathulate, obtuse, 3–6 mm long, up to 1.5 mm wide; lip fleshy, distinctly 3-lobed, 4–7 mm long, 2–6 mm wide, side lobes erect, rounded below, acute above, midlobe fleshy, linear, truncate; column *c.* 2 mm long.

Only collected once in Kenya, at Kaptagat, in 1962; 1900 m; flowered in cultivation in August.

Also recorded in Zaïre.

Polystachya piersii Cribb

Plants epiphytic, up to 22 cm high, usually robust. Pseudobulbs slender, conical-cylindric or ovoid-conical, 3–4 cm high, growing close together on a basal rhizome. Leaves 2, narrowly oblanceolate, subacute, 12–18 cm long, 1–2 cm wide, dark green,

Polystachya piersii   BOB CAMPBELL

high; petals narrowly elliptic, obtuse, 7–8.5 mm long, *c.* 2 mm wide; lip 3-lobed, *c.* 8 mm long, 5 mm wide, side lobes erect, rounded, midlobe ovate, acute, callus between the side lobes fleshy, pubescent or papillose; column 1.5 mm long.

Only known from small areas of forest on Mt Nyiru and the Ndotos Mts in the Northern Frontier district; 2500–2700 m; flowering in August and January.

Not known elsewhere.

Polystachya polychaete Kraenzlin

Plants epiphytic, erect, 14–45 cm high. Pseudobulbs narrowly conical, 8–10 cm high, up to 1 cm wide. Leaves 3–4, suberect, ligulate, unequally bilobed at the apex, lobes round, 12–18 cm long, 8–22 mm wide. Inflorescence erect to 25 cm long, cylindric, densely many flowered, arising from within a long, compressed sheath, bracts narrow and pointed, bristle-like, 3–8 mm long. Flowers very small, white or cream; dorsal sepal ovate-triangular, acuminate, 2 mm long, 1 mm wide; lateral sepals ovate, triangular, acuminate, 3 mm long, 2 mm wide, mentum short and rounded; petals narrowly elliptic, acute or acuminate, 1.5 mm long, 0.7 mm wide; lip 3-lobed in basal half, 2 mm long and wide, side lobes upright or reflexed, midlobe

sometimes purplish. Inflorescence longer than the leaves, to 15 cm long, with 5–8 flowers on a hairy peduncle, bracts ovate, falcate. Flowers rather fleshy, softly hairy on outer surface, white or cream or pale green, lip white with a pink margin; dorsal sepal elliptic, subacute, 10 mm long, 5 mm wide; lateral sepals obliquely ovate-triangular, acute, 11–12 mm long, 7 mm wide, mentum conical, to 5 mm

Polystachya polychaete   ERIC LA CROIX

quadrate or oblong, apiculate, lacking a callus; column minute.

Only recorded once in Kenya, in the forest on Maungu hill, Teita district; *c.* 900 m; flowering in December.

Also recorded in Tanzania and Uganda and westwards throughout equatorial Africa as far as Sierra Leone.

Polystachya simplex Rendle

Plants epiphytic or lithophytic, erect or pendulous, eventually forming a large branching mass. Stems slender, cylindric or fusiform, each new growth 3–20 cm long, arising from the centre of the previous growth, leafy in the apical part. Leaves elliptic, acute, 5–15 cm long, 1.5 cm wide, larger leaves at the apex, often with wavy margins. Inflorescence at the tip of the young growth, shorter than the leaves, branching or unbranched, with many flowers close together. Flowers green or yellowish green, tinged with brown or purple, lip yellow with purple markings; dorsal sepal ovate-lanceolate, acute or acuminate, 5 mm long, 2 mm wide; lateral sepals obliquely ovate-triangular, acuminate, 5 mm long, 3 mm wide, forming a narrow mentum 2.5 mm high; petals linear or lanceolate, 4 mm long, 1 mm wide; lip 3-lobed in the middle, 5 mm long, 4 mm wide, side lobes elliptic, small, midlobe quadrate-ovate, acuminate or apiculate, with a slight fleshy thickening between the side lobes; column 1.2 mm long.

On trees and rocks in dry highland forests; recorded from Mt Kenya, Aberdare Mts, Mt Elgon,

Polystachya simplex   BOB CAMPBELL

and in many forests west of the Rift Valley; 2000–2350 m; flowering in May and June, and also in September and October.

Also recorded in Tanzania, Uganda, Zaïre, Malawi and Zimbabwe.

Polystachya spatella Kraenzlin

Plants epiphytic, erect or pendulous, eventually forming a large branching mass. Stems slender, narrowly cylindric or slightly enlarged about the middle, each new growth 10–12 cm long, arising from the centre of the previous growth. Leaves lanceolate, acute or unequally bilobed at the apex with rounded lobes, 3–8 cm long, 3–6 mm wide. Inflorescence terminal on each growth, shorter than the leaves, unbranched with 2–8 flowers.

Polystachya spatella   BOB CAMPBELL

Flowers yellowish green with mauve anther cap, lip brighter than the other tepals, ovary smooth; dorsal sepal concave, ovate-lanceolate, acuminate, 4.5 mm long, 2 mm wide; lateral sepals obliquely ovate, 5 mm long and wide, forming a mentum 5 mm high that is rounded at the apex; petals oblanceolate, acute, 4 mm long, 1 mm wide; lip 3-lobed in the apical half, 7–9 mm long, 5 mm wide, side lobes rounded, midlobe quadrate, apiculate, slightly pubescent, callus fleshy; column 2.5 mm long.

Common in all the highland forests on both sides of the Rift Valley; 2000–2800 m; flowering in April, and also in August and September.

Also recorded from northern Tanzania, Uganda and Zaïre.

Polystachya steudneri Reichenbach f.

Plants epiphytic, 10–20 cm high. Pseudobulbs very slender, narrowly conical, 2–5 cm high. Leaves erect, linear or narrowly oblong-lanceolate, obscurely bilobed at the apex, up to 12 cm long, 5–12 mm wide, deciduous. Inflorescence forming

Polystachya steudneri   BOB CAMPBELL

after the leaves have fallen, branched, enclosed by straw-coloured sheaths. Flowers yellowish green or almost white, spotted and lined with red; dorsal sepal lanceolate, 3–6 mm long, 1.5 mm wide; lateral sepals obliquely ovate-lanceolate, 4 mm long, 2 mm wide, mentum short to 2 mm long; petals oblong-lanceolate, acute, 3 mm long, 0.6 mm wide; lip 3-lobed, 3 mm long, 2 mm wide, side lobes small at

right angles to midlobe that is ovate, callus on claw of lip, obconical, fleshy; column minute.

On trees and old bushes in deciduous woodland; in the drier parts of the central, west and southern Kenya highlands; 1500–2300 m; flowering in November through to January, also recorded in July.

Also recorded from Uganda, Ethiopia, Sudan, Cameroon and Nigeria.

Polystachya teitensis Cribb

Plants epiphytic to 7 cm high. Pseudobulbs clustered, conical, 1.5 cm long, 0.6 mm in diameter. Leaves 2–3, narrowly elliptic-lanceolate or oblanceolate, acute, 3 cm long, 7 mm wide. Inflorescence terminal, erect, bearing 3–4 flowers close together at the apex, bracts lanceolate, acuminate. Flowers pubescent, sepals and petals dull yellow, purplish towards the base, lip white, side lobes faintly striped purple, callus yellow; dorsal sepal ovate, acuminate, *c.* 7 mm long, *c.* 4 mm wide; lateral sepals obliquely and broadly ovate, acuminate, 6–7 mm long, 5 mm wide, mentum to 4 mm high; petals oblong to oblanceolate, obtuse, 5 mm long, 1.5 mm wide; lip 3-lobed, shortly clawed, 5 mm long, 4 mm wide, side lobes rounded, erect, very short, midlobe fleshy, ovate, subacute; callus fleshy, raised, pubescent; column short, purple and yellow.

Polystachya teitensis   BOB CAMPBELL

Only known from montane forest in Teita district, from Mt Kasigau and from Maungu hill; 800–900 m; flowering in May.

Not known elsewhere.

Polystachya tenuissima Kraenzlin
Syn. *Polystachya inconspicua* Rendle
Plants small, epiphytic, glabrous. Pseudobulbs clustered, narrowly cylindric, dark green, 1–6 cm long, up to 2 mm in diameter. Leaf single, linear, fleshy, cuneate at the base, retuse or obtuse, 2–14 cm long, 2–7 mm wide. Inflorescence terminal, branched, as long as the leaf, bearing up to 40 flowers but usually less than 10, bracts inconspicuous. Flowers yellow to yellowish green, column and lip side lobes tinged purple; dorsal sepal elliptic to ovate-triangular, apiculate, 1.5–4 mm long, 1–2 mm wide; lateral sepals oblique, triangular, 2–4 mm long, 2–6 mm wide, mentum cylindric, to 5 mm high, sometimes bilobed at the tip; petals narrowly oblanceolate or linear, subacute to obtuse, 2–3 mm long, up to 1.5 mm wide; lip strongly recurved, 3-lobed in the apical third, 3–7 mm long, 1–4 mm wide, side lobes erect, oblong to ovate, midlobe subquadrate, fleshy, callus obscure at base of midlobe; column to 1 mm long.

Epiphytic in highland forests, Ngong hills and many forests west of the Rift Valley; 1700–2500 m; flowering in April and May.

Also recorded on Mt Kilimanjaro in Tanzania, and in Uganda, Zaïre, Cameroon, Ghana and Ivory Coast.

Recent collections from the Saiwa Swamp National Park seem to indicate that *P. tenuissima* and *P. inconspicua* may be different from each other and both represented in Kenya. *Polystachya inconspicua* is shorter than *P. tenuissima*, with shorter leaves and smaller inflorescences which have fewer but larger flowers.

Polystachya tessellata Lindley
Plants epiphytic or rarely lithophytic, 10–60 cm high, usually robust. Pseudobulbs slender, conical-cylindric or ovoid-conical, 5–15 cm high, growing close together on a basal rhizome. Leaves 3–5, oblanceolate or elliptic, obtuse or rounded, thin, 12–25 cm long, 1–4 cm wide, dark green, purplish. Inflorescence much longer than the leaves, with short side branches, up to 40 cm long, with many flowers borne in short dense clusters on the sheath-covered branches. Flowers small, bright or creamy yellow, pale green, pink or purple, usually with a white lip; dorsal sepal oblong-elliptic, acute, 3–

Polystachya tessellata   BOB CAMPBELL

4 mm long, 2 mm wide; lateral sepals obliquely ovate, apiculate, 3–5 mm long, 3 mm wide, mentum conical, to 3.5 mm high; petals ligulate to spathulate, apiculate, 2–3.5 mm long, 1 mm wide; lip 3-lobed at or above the middle, 3–5 mm long, 2.5–4 mm wide, side lobes oblong, subacute or obtuse, shorter than the rounded midlobe that has wavy margins, callus a fleshy and hairy ridge, rounded at the apex and tapering towards the base; column 2 mm long.

In warmer forests near the coast and in west Kenya; sea level to 1650 m; flowering in August and September.

Also recorded in Tanzania and Uganda, and widespread in tropical Africa westwards to Sierra Leone and south to South Africa (Natal).

American botanists have proposed that this species should be considered conspecific with the widespread *Polystachya concreta*, but specimens of New World plants that I have grown together with African plants seem to be different in a number of small features. Small plants of *Polystachya tessellata* can be confused with *P. modesta*, but the shape of the lip and its callus are always good distinguishing characters.

Polystachya transvaalensis Schlechter
Syn. *Polystachya nigrescens* Rendle
Plants epiphytic, glabrous, 10–30 cm tall. Pseudobulbs clustered, slender, covered with loose tubular sheaths and leaf bases that become brown or black with age, to 25 cm long, 2–5 mm in diameter.

Polystachya transvaalensis   BOB CAMPBELL

Leaves 4–6, widely spaced, spreading, ligulate or elliptic-lanceolate, fleshy, rounded or obtuse, 4–10 cm long, 5–10 mm wide. Inflorescence erect, as long as or slightly shorter than the leaves, unbranched or with few weak branches, 5–15 cm long. Flowers glabrous and shiny, pale green, yellow or cream, suffused with brown or red, petals and lip white or cream with reddish markings; dorsal sepal ovate, acute or subacute, 5–8 mm long, 2–4 mm wide; lateral sepals obliquely triangular, acute or acuminate, 8–11 mm long, 6–9 mm wide, mentum cylindric-conical, 5–9 mm long; petals oblanceolate, subacute, 5–6 mm long, 1–2 mm wide; lip obscurely 3-lobed in the apical half, 6–10 mm long, 6–8 mm wide, side lobes rounded, midlobe broadly triangular, callus a single rounded swelling in the centre; column 2.5 mm long.

On trees and bushes in upland forests and forests on hills that are sometimes mist-covered; widespread from Teita hills, Chyulu hills and at higher

altitudes throughout the southern half of the country, including Mt Kenya and Aberdare Mts; 1200–3350 m; flowering in April and May.

Also recorded from Uganda, Tanzania, westwards to Zaïre and south to South Africa (Transvaal and Natal).

This species is sometimes confused with *Polystachya bennettiana* when not in flower but is easily recognised by its smaller inflorescences with shiny, not hairy, flowers. It can be distinguished from *Polystachya albescens* by the rounded, not pointed leaves.

Polystachya vaginata Summerhayes
Plants epiphytic or lithophytic, erect, to 30 cm high. Stems close together, often forming long chains, swollen at the base to form a round or conical pseudobulb with one scar, 1–3 cm high, very slender above, deciduous in dry season. Leaves 2–4, ligulate-linear, almost grass-like, rounded or obscurely bilobed at apex, 10–25 cm high, 3–5 mm wide. Inflorescence usually much longer than the leaves, simple or with a few branches, covered with flattened sheaths, 7–30 cm high, each branch with 2–5 flowers. Flowers cream or straw coloured, turning brown, densely hairy on the outer surface, lip white; dorsal sepal lanceolate or oblong-lanceolate, acute, 6–9 mm long, 2–4 mm wide; lateral sepals obliquely and narrowly triangular, acuminate, 8–11 mm long, 5 mm wide, mentum cylindric-conical, rounded, 4 mm long; petals obliquely oblanceolate, acute, 6–8 mm long, 2 mm wide; lip recurved, 3-lobed at or above the middle,

Polystachya vaginata   BOB CAMPBELL

Rangaeris amaniensis BOB CAMPBELL

7–9 mm long, 5–6 mm wide, side lobes small, erect, hairy in front, midlobe ovate, apiculate, densely hairy in centre; column 2 mm long.

Epiphytic on trees in deciduous woodland and on hills in the drier parts of the country; recorded from Naromoru, Endau hill, Ngong hills, and other parts of southern and eastern Kenya; 1000–1650 m; flowering at different times throughout the year.

Also recorded in Tanzania, Malawi and Zimbabwe.

This species has often been misidentified as *Polystachya shega* and *Polystachya isochiloides*, both of which are known only from Tanzania.

Rangaeris Summerhayes

Many people do not realise that the name of this genus is nearly an anagram of *Aerangis*. The generic name was invented by the Kew botanist Victor Summerhayes in 1936 when he wanted to move

Aerangis muscicola away from *Aerangis*, where it had previously been placed on account of its conspicuous white flowers. The plants are very different, with their stiff narrow leaves, V-shaped in cross section, and in the flowers the two pollinia are each borne on a separate stipe but attached to a single large viscidium, instead of a shared stipe as in *Aerangis*. He somewhat hesitantly placed *Aerangis brachyceras* in this genus too. However, that species has green flowers with a quite different appearance and it has now been transferred to the genus *Cribbia*.

Rangaeris muscicola

BOB CAMPBELL

Summerhayes looked at the genus *Rangaeris* again in 1949 when he transferred *Leptocentrum amaniense* to it. In the recent account of *Rangaeris* in the *Flora of Tropical East Africa*, Orchidaceae, Part 3 (1989), Phillip Cribb has added to the genus the curiously flowered Tanzania species previously known as *Leptocentrum schliebenii*. Altogether, six species of *Rangaeris* are now recognised, two of which occur in Kenya.

Both the Kenya species are easy to maintain in cultivation, but they do not seem to flower at all regularly. *Rangaeris muscicola* plants are usually found in areas of high humidity, often with their roots in a dense growth of moss as the specific epithet implies. *Rangaeris amaniensis*, however, is found in quite dry places in the highlands of Kenya, and its thick roots and somewhat succulent leaves enable it to withstand long periods of dryness.

CULTIVATION

The differences in the native habitats of these two species need to be borne in mind in their cultural regime. Both grow well as mounted plants, or established in a well-drained medium in a basket. It seems to be very important to prevent the roots being saturated with water for too long. Air movement and excellent drainage is the key. In the wild *R. amaniensis* grows in much stronger light than *R. muscicola*, which is often found in very shady situations.

Key to the species of *Rangaeris*
Stems long;   lip 10–24 mm long, obscurely
    3-lobed, spur 8–16 cm long . . . **R. amaniensis**
Stems short;   lip 8 mm or less long, entire, ovate,
    spur 5–7 cm long . . . . **R. muscicola**

Rangaeris amaniensis (Kraenzlin)
Summerhayes
Plants erect epiphytes or lithophytes often branching from the leafless part and forming dense clumps. Stems 15–45 cm long, curved or pendent when very long but usually upright, bearing thick roots along their length and leaves in the upper part. Leaves in two rows, folded, ligulate, with unequal rounded lobes at the apex, 4–8 cm long, 1–2 cm wide. Inflorescences arching away from stem, 6–10 cm long, bearing 5–12 flowers and blackish bracts. Flowers white, green on the outer surface and in the spur, fading to yellow or orange, very variable in size; dorsal sepal lanceolate, acuminate, 1–2.5 cm long, 3–6 mm wide; lateral sepals similar,

oblique; petals lanceolate, acuminate, shorter and narrower than sepals, 1–2 cm long, 2–4 mm wide; lip rhombic, somewhat 3-lobed in the middle, side lobes quadrate or rounded, midlobe lanceolate, 10–24 mm long, 5–11 mm wide, spur very slender, 8–16 cm long; column 4–5 mm long.

Epiphytic in bright situations in highland forest and also on isolated trees, even in Nairobi, occasionally on rocks; widespread in the central parts of Kenya, recorded from Mt Kulal, Marsabit, Timau, Chyulu hills, Mbololo hill, Ngong hills, Loita hills and Mara river areas; 1000–2300 m; flowering in April and May, also in October and November.

Also recorded from Tanzania, northern Uganda, Ethiopia and Zambia.

Rangaeris muscicola (Reichenbach f.)
Summerhayes
Plants erect epiphytes or lithophytes. Stems short, usually not more than 6 cm long, upright, bearing thick roots at the base and two rows of closely overlapping leaves. Leaves usually 4–8, arranged in a fan shape, folded, narrowly ligulate or linear, with unequal rounded lobes at the apex, dark green, 6–20 cm long, 6–12 mm wide. Inflorescences arching away from stem or almost erect, 6–20 cm long, bearing 10–16 flowers in two rows and blackish bracts. Flowers white, sometimes with a pinkish orange spur, fading to yellow or orange, very variable in size; dorsal sepal ovate, acute, 7–9 mm long, 2–4 mm wide; lateral sepals similar, slightly narrower, oblique; petals obliquely elliptic or lanceolate, reflexed, acute, shorter and narrower than sepals, 6–8 mm long, 1.5–3 mm wide; lip entire, broadly ovate, acute, 6–9 mm long, 4–7 mm wide, spur very slender, 5–7 cm long; column 3–4 mm long.

Epiphytic in humid forests, usually growing amongst mosses on well-shaded branches, occasionally lithophytic; known from the warmer forests in central Kenya, including Ngong hills, around Nairobi, Ndau hill near Kitui, Kericho and Mt Elgon; 1200–2200 m; flowering in April and May, also in November.

Recorded from Tanzania and Uganda, also widespread westwards as far as Sierra Leone and south to South Africa (Natal).

Solenangis Schlechter

This genus contains only five species in tropical Africa, one of which is also widespread in the islands of the western Indian Ocean including Madagascar. They all have rather long stems and, with the aid of their long roots that are often branched and curled, have adopted a scandent habit. The leaves are small or absent. The flowers are rather varied, very small and insignificant or quite attractive, but they all have a pollinarium in which the two pollinia are borne on a single stipe attached to a fairly large viscidium.

The name is derived from two Greek words *solen* (pipe) and *angos* (vessel) and refers to the large spur at the base of the lip. In some species the lip blade is so insignificant and the rest of the flower so small that the flower at first sight seems to consist only of a spur.

CULTIVATION

These species grow easily in a suitable environment that is warm and humid throughout the year. They can be mounted on a piece of bark but seem to grow and flower just as well when attached to a wire frame or other support. They flourish in strong light and where there is good air movement, and need to dry out well between waterings.

Key to the species of *Solenangis*

1　Plants leafless; spur curved, swollen at the
　　　　apex . . . . **S. aphylla**
　　Plants with leaves; spur conical or
　　　　slender 2

2　Leaves very narrow, less than 2 cm long;
　　　　lip entire, 3 mm long . . . . **S. conica**
　　Leaves more than 5 mm wide, 1–3 cm
　　　　long; lip strongly 3- lobed at the apex,
　　　　10 mm long . . . . **S. wakefieldii**

Solenangis aphylla (Thouars) Summerhayes
Plants scandent or pendent, climbing amongst twigs and branches by means of the curled roots. Stems slender, up to 40 cm long, bearing roots throughout their length but no leaves. Inflorescences many, at intervals along the stem, 1–2.5 cm long, bearing 8–16 flowers close together. Flowers white tipped with reddish brown and spur brownish; dorsal sepal elliptic, obtuse, 2–3 mm long; lateral sepals oblique, elliptic, obtuse, 2.5–3 mm long; petals linear-oblong, acute or obtuse, 2.5–3 mm long; lip concave, obscurely 3-lobed, side lobes erect, midlobe ovate, obtuse, 3 mm long, 2 mm wide, spur strongly curved and swollen at the apex, 4–5 mm long; column 2 mm long.

Epiphytic in thickets and bush near the coast and

in the Boni forest; sea level to 300 m; flowering in September and October.

Also recorded from Tanzania, Zanzibar, Mozambique, Zimbabwe, Madagascar and the Mascarene islands.

Solenangis aphylla　　　　　　　BOB CAMPBELL

Solenangis conica (Schlechter) L. Jonsson
Plants dwarf, rather insignificant, scandent epiphytes, climbing by prominent greyish roots. Stems slender, 4–22 cm long. Leaves few, towards the stem apex, narrow, iris-like and slightly flattened, 13–16 mm long, 0.5–1.5 mm wide. Inflorescences usually several, arising below roots, 10–14 mm long, bearing 2–4 flowers. Flowers white or greenish white, spur green at tip; dorsal sepal ovate, 2–3 mm long, 1.3 mm wide; lateral sepals similar; petals linear, subacute, 2.5 mm long, 0.7 mm wide; lip concave, ovate, 3 mm long, 2 mm wide, spur conical, 1–2 mm long; column minute.

Twig epiphyte in montane forest with the roots and stems shrouded in lichens; so far only recorded from Ol Doinyo Orok west of Namanga; 1800 m; flowering in May.

Also recorded from Tanzania, Malawi, Zimbabwe and Mozambique.

Solenangis wakefieldii (Rolfe)
　　　　　　　　　　　　Cribb & J. Stewart
　　Syn. *Tridactyle wakefieldii* (Rolfe) Summerhayes
Plants scandent, with elongated stems and conspicuous whitish, branching, curled roots. Stems upright or pendent, 20–100 cm long. Leaves spaced 1–3 cm apart and usually opposite a root,

Solenangis conica ERIC LA CROIX

lanceolate or ovate, unequally acutely bilobed at the apex, 1.5–3 cm long, 0.5–1.3 cm wide. Inflorescences spreading, 1–several, 4–6 cm long, with 4–6 well-spaced flowers. Flowers white, sometimes with greenish spur; dorsal sepal oblong-elliptic, obtuse or apiculate, 3 mm long, 1–2 mm wide; lateral sepals oblong-elliptic, oblique, subacute, 4–4.5 mm long, 1.5 mm wide; petals oblique, oblong-lanceolate, 3.5 mm long, 1.5 mm wide; lip

Solenangis wakefieldii BOB CAMPBELL

narrow in the basal part and 3-lobed in the apical third, 10 mm long and wide, side lobes reflexed or spreading, linear, 4–5 mm long, midlobe lanceolate, acute 3 mm long, spur slender, pendent, 6–7 cm long; column 1 mm long.

Scrambling in coastal and lowland bush; first collected near Mombasa; sea level to 300 m; flowering in September through to November.

Also recorded in Tanzania and Zanzibar.

Sphyrarhynchus Mansfeld

This monotypic genus with an almost unpronounceable name was known only from northern Tanzania until recently when it was discovered on the eastern slopes of the Aberdare Mts. Each plant has only a few small, glaucous leaves above a mass of flattened roots that are green when wet. They can hardly be distinguished from the two small species of *Angraecopsis* except when flowering. The flowers are unexpectedly large, glistening white with a green flash on the surface of the lip. Usually there are a few flowers on each of several or many inflorescences so that the tiny plant appears to be covered in a ball of flowers. The generic name is derived from two Greek words *sphyra* (hammer) and *rhynchos* (snout or beak) and refers to the shape of the rostellum at the apex of the column: in side view the rostellum resembles a minute hammer.

The species is named in honour of H.J. Schlieben, a German plant collector who discovered it in Tanzania in 1935, and who later lived in South Africa where he also made many interesting collections.

CULTIVATION

This species is easily maintained in cultivation if collected on the small branches on which it is found. It has also been raised from seeds, at the Royal Botanic Gardens, Kew, where it surprised everyone in the laboratory by flowering while it was still in the flask. The young seedlings are best established on pieces of cork oak bark or on small pieces of hard wood. Since it is a montane species the plants thrive where there is a drop in temperature to cool conditions at night.

Sphyrarhynchus schliebenii Mansfeld
Plants minute, epiphytic, with a very short stem and many conspicuous flattened roots. Leaves 3–5,

fleshy, linear, falcate, greyish green, 2–4 cm long, 2–5 mm wide. Inflorescences usually several, 1–3 cm long, bearing 3–10 flowers. Flowers variable in size, the apical ones usually largest, glistening white with a dark green mark on the lip; dorsal sepal elliptic or lanceolate, acute, 5–15 mm long, 2–4 mm wide; lateral sepals similar, oblique; petals oblong, obtuse, 6–14 mm long, 2–4 mm wide; lip oblong or oblanceolate, subacute, 4–6 mm long, 2–4 mm wide, spur clavate, 5–8 mm long; column minute.

Only one record from the eastern slopes of the Aberdare Mts above Thika; 1600 m; flowering in October.

Also recorded from Mt Meru in Tanzania.

Stolzia Schlechter

This genus of small creeping epiphytes was named in honour of Adolf Stolz, a German missionary who lived in southwest Tanzania for many years, and who made many important orchid collections around Tukuyu where he was based. All the species of *Stolzia* are small, creeping or upright epiphytes which produce chains of small pseudobulbs that appear to creep over the surface of branches and rocks. Each pseudobulb bears one or two leathery leaves at its apex, and an inflorescence arises between them. Ten species have been described from Tanzania but only one from

Sphyrarhynchus schliebenii   BOB CAMPBELL

Kenya. It is the most widespread of all the species and is easily recognised by its single bright red or orange flower that is almost stemless and borne between the leaves. From a little distance the plants resemble a mossy carpet and are sometimes confused with small plants of *Peperomia* species when not in flower.

CULTIVATION

Small mats of the creeping stems of this orchid are not difficult to establish on a piece of bark or tree fern fibre. However, they need cool, humid conditions and are not easy to keep alive if there is continuous hot weather. They are not difficult to maintain under glass in cool conditions. They respond well to frequent misting and thrive in a shady position.

Stolzia repens (Rolfe) Summerhayes

A creeping epiphyte forming a dense mat of several intertwined prostrate stems, usually only 1–2 cm high. Pseudobulbs elongated, prostrate, swollen towards the apex which bears 2 or 3 leaves, 2–4.5 cm long, 3–6 mm wide, each new pseudobulb arising near the apex of the preceding one. Leaves usually 2, elliptic, obovate or rounded, 0.5–1.4 cm long, 3–8 mm wide. Inflorescence terminal, between the leaves, bearing 1 small flower on a very short peduncle. Flower yellow, orange or red, striped with red or brown; dorsal sepal oblong-ligulate or lanceolate, acute, 7 mm long, 3 mm

Stolzia repens   BOB CAMPBELL

wide; lateral sepals similar but oblique, 6 mm long, 3 mm wide; petals falcate-lanceolate, acute, 5 mm long, 2 mm wide; lip fleshy, tongue-like, acute, 2 mm long, 1 mm wide; column very small.

Throughout the highland forests as an epiphyte on mossy branches and on rocks, usually in shade; 1900–2830 m; flowers from April to June and occasionally at other times throughout the year.

Widespread in tropical Africa: known from Uganda, Ethiopia, and throughout Tanzania, Malawi and in Zimbabwe, as well as westwards to Zaïre, Cameroon, Nigeria and Ghana.

Triceratorhynchus Summerhayes

This is another monotypic genus characterised by a distinctive rostellum structure that becomes visible (with a magnifying glass) when the anther cap and pollinia are removed. The rostellum has three distinct prongs or horns that protrude both up and down, the centre one shorter than the other two. Summerhayes coined the name for the genus from three Greek words that allude to this structure, *tri* (three), *keras* (horn) and *rhynchos* (beak or snout).

Apart from this curious structure, the small green flowered plants closely resemble some of the smaller species of *Angraecum* and *Angraecopsis*. The first description was made in 1951, although plants had been collected nearly 20 years earlier. They have been collected rather rarely and have probably been overlooked in the warm forests where they occur. The species has not yet been brought into cultivation.

Triceratorhynchus viridiflorus Summerhayes

Plants miniature, epiphtyic, with numerous elongated roots. Stems very short, less than 1 cm long. Leaves suberect or spreading, linear, falcate, rather obscurely lobed at the apex, 1–5 cm long, 1–3 mm wide. Inflorescences arching or horizontal, longer than the leaves, to 6 cm long with up to 9 flowers. Flowers green or yellowish green; dorsal sepal linear-lanceolate, acute, 4–5 mm long, 1 mm wide; lateral sepals obliquely linear-lanceolate, falcate, acute, 5–6 mm long, 1 mm wide; petals lanceolate, acuminate, 4–5 mm long, 1 mm wide; lip concave, obscurely 3-lobed, ovate-lanceolate, acuminate, 4–5 mm long, 3.5 mm wide, fleshy towards the apex, spur curving up above the ovary, slender, tapering, 5–8 mm long; column minute.

Twig and branch epiphyte in the warmer forests;

recorded only from Kakamega; 1500–1600 m; flowering in June.

Also recorded from the Budongo forest in Uganda.

Tridactyle Schlechter

The flowers of *Tridactyle* species are among the least showy of the African epiphytic orchids. Usually ochre brown, yellow or green, rarely white, they are also rather small and mostly in few-flowered inflorescences. A few species have an entire lip with a pair of auricles on either side of the spur opening at the base, but typically the lip is 3-lobed. The generic name alludes to this feature – from the Greek words *tri* (three) and *daktylos* (finger).

The plants of nearly all the species have long, woody stems covered in the remains of old leaf bases, often branched and growing in rather untidy clumps. A few are neat plants with upright stems, at least when young. Some species are widespread in Kenya and indeed throughout Africa, while others are very localised in their distribution. About 45 species have been described and to date 10 are recorded in Kenya

CULTIVATION

All these species grow easily in cultivation whether they are mounted on a piece of bark or placed upright in a basket or pot of free-draining compost. Mature plants are often hard to establish and it is best to start with seedlings or young plants. Providing the best conditions for their healthy growth depends on trying to emulate the environment in their native habitats. Some knowledge of the alti-

Tridactyle bicaudata   BOB CAMPBELL

tude and climatic conditions where they occur is particularly helpful.

Key to the species of *Tridactyle*

1 Leaves terete or cylindrical, pointed 2
  Leaves flat or folded, unequally bilobed
    at the apex 3

2 Leaves very slender, 1–1.5 mm in diameter,
    sharply pointed at the apex; spur less
    than 8 mm long . . . . *T. filifolia*
  Leaves short and blunt, 2–4 mm in
    diameter; spur usually more than 8 mm
    long . . . . *T. tridentata*

3 Leaves yellowish green with dark green
    spots or markings . . . . *T. tanneri*
  Leaves plain green 4

4 Racemes of 2–4 flowers, or flowers borne
    singly on the woody stem 5
  Racemes axillary, bearing 4–25 flowers . . 7

5 Lip entire, or with a very short tooth on
    each side of the central lobe . . . .
    . . . . *T. anthomaniaca*
  Lip 3-lobed 6

6 Spur of lip slender, 9–12 mm long . . . .
    . . . . *T. scottellii*
  Spur of lip inflated at the middle,
    6–7 mm long . . . . *T. nigrescens*

7 Leaves long and grass-like; racemes
    2–5 cm long, bearing 4–9 flowers . . . .
    . . . . *T. cruciformis*
  Leaves not grass-like, thick and stiff;
    racemes 5–12 cm long, bearing 8–25
    flowers 8

8 Lateral lobes of lip longer than midlobe,
    much fringed at apex . . . . . . *T. bicaudata*
  Lateral lobes of lip shorter than midlobe,
    entire or slightly fringed 9

9 Sepals and petals 8–10 mm long; spur
    narrow, 14–27 mm long . . . . *T. furcistipes*
  Sepals and petals 5–6 mm long; spur
    slender 12–15 mm long . . . . . . *T. tricuspis*

Tridactyle anthomaniaca (Reichenbach f.)
                Summerhayes
Plants epiphytic usually pendent in large masses with verrucose roots. Stems slender, woody, to 45 cm long, producing branches at right angles to

the main stem. Leaves fleshy, linear or narrowly oblong, unequally obtusely bilobed, olive green, 4–8 cm long, 6–20 mm wide. Inflorescences very short, up to 1 cm long, bearing 2–3 flowers. Flowers ochre or dirty orange; dorsal sepal oblong or elliptic, obtuse, 4–6 mm long, 1.5–2.5 mm wide; lateral sepals similar but oblique at the base; petals lanceolate, acute, 4–5 mm long, 1–1.8 mm wide; lip with fleshy auricles at the base by the spur mouth, entire, lanceolate, acute, 3–6 mm long, 2 mm wide, spur slender, S-shaped or straight, 10–16 mm long; column 1–2 mm long.

Tridactyle anthomaniaca   BOB CAMPBELL

Epiphytic in the lower, warmer forests; recorded from Kakamega and Sagala hill in Teita district; 750–1650 m; flowering in March and April.

Also recorded from Tanzania and Uganda, and westwards to Sierra Leone, south to Malawi, Mozambique, Zambia and Zimbabwe.

Tridactyle bicaudata (Lindley) Schlechter

Plants epiphytic, upright or pendent, often forming large clumps with slightly verrucose roots. Stems woody, 10–80 cm long, leafy only in the upper part, roots mainly from the base. Leaves linear, straight or falcate, sometimes folded, unequally roundly bilobed at the apex, 8–14 cm long, 8–15 mm wide. Inflorescences spreading, 3–12 cm long, bearing 8–25 flowers in two rows. Flowers ochre-orange or greenish yellow; dorsal sepal oblong-ovate, acute or apiculate, 4–6 mm long, 1.5–3 mm wide; lateral sepals obliquely ovate, acute or apiculate, 5–6.5 mm long, 2.5–3.5 mm wide; petals lanceolate, acute or obtuse, 4 mm long, 1 mm wide; lip with rhombic auricles on either side of the spur mouth, 3-lobed in the upper part, the side lobes longer than the midlobe and fringed, 3–6 mm long

8–12 mm wide, spur straight, narrow, 10–16 mm long; column 1–1.5 mm long.

Epiphytic or lithophytic in a wide range of undisturbed habitats throughout the country, one of the commonest epiphytic orchids; sea level to 2350 m; flowering March to April and September to November.

Also recorded in Uganda and Tanzania; widespread throughout tropical Africa, westwards as far as Sierra Leone, and south to South Africa (E. Cape and Natal).

Tridactyle cruciformis Summerhayes

Plants epiphytic usually pendent in large masses with verrucose roots. Stems slender, woody, to 60 cm long, usually upturned at the apex. Leaves grass-like, linear, unequally acutely bilobed, 7–23 cm long, 1–2.5 mm wide, glossy green. Inflorescences 2–5 cm long, bearing 5–9 flowers. Flowers pale green or greenish yellow, browning with age; dorsal sepal ovate-elliptic, obtuse, 2–3 mm long, 1.5 mm wide; lateral sepals similar but slightly longer; petals linear, acute or obtuse, 2–3 mm long, 0.5–1 mm wide; lip strongly 3-lobed at the middle, side lobes spreading, narrower than the midlobe, acute, 2–2.5 mm long, 1.8–3 mm wide, spur slender, incurved, 11–13 mm long; column 1 mm long.

Epiphytic in forest patches on Chyulu hills and in Teita hills; 1200–2200 m; flowering in January.

Also recorded from Tanzania, in Lushoto district.

Tridactyle cruciformis   BOB CAMPBELL

Tridactyle filifolia (Schlechter) Schlechter
Syn. *Tridactyle tridentata* (Harvey) Schlechter var. *subulifolia* Summerhayes

Plants pendent epiphytes with long slender stems, single or forming untidy clumps, rooting at the

Tridactyle filifolia   BOB CAMPBELL

base. Stems branched, 10–100 cm long, rather slender. Leaves suberect or falcate, terete or grooved on the upper surface, sharply pointed, 3–12 cm long, 1–2 mm in diameter. Inflorescences very short or sessile, 2–8 mm long with 2–3 flowers. Flowers small, dingy white or ochre; dorsal sepal lanceolate, acute, 2–3 mm long; lateral sepals obliquely ovate, acute, 2–3 mm long; petals linear-lanceolate, smaller than the sepals; lip with 2 auricles or side lobes at the base on either side of the spur mouth and 3-lobed at the apex, lobes entire, 2–3 mm long, 1–2 mm wide, spur slender, incurved, 6–7 mm long; column minute.

Epiphyte of large branches of trees in the warmer forests; only recorded from Kakamega; 1650 m; flowering in October.

Also recorded from Uganda and Tanzania; widespread in tropical Africa from Ethiopia westwards to Sierra Leone and south through Zaïre to Zambia and Malawi.

This species was formerly treated as a variety of *Tridactyle tridentata* and some authors question its distinctness from that species. In Kenya the two species do seem to be quite different.

Tridactyle furcistipes Summerhayes
Plants epiphytic, usually upright, often forming large clumps. Stems woody, 10–20 cm long, leafy only in the upper part, rooting from the base. Leaves linear, straight or falcate, sometimes folded, unequally roundly bilobed at the apex, 11–18 cm long, 8–15 mm wide. Inflorescences spreading, 4–11 cm long, bearing 8–20 flowers in two rows. Flowers greenish white or dirty cream fading to

ochre-orange; dorsal sepal lanceolate, acuminate, 9–12 mm long, 2–4 mm wide; lateral sepals lanceolate, falcate, acuminate, 10–12 mm long, 2–3.5 mm wide; petals lanceolate, acuminate, 8.5–10 mm long, 2–3 mm wide; lip with rhombic auricles on either side of the spur mouth, 3-lobed in the upper part, the side lobes shorter than the midlobe, entire or fringed or forked at the tip, 9–12.5 mm long, 4–6 mm wide, spur straight, narrow, 14–27 mm long; column 2–3 mm long.

Epiphytic in highland forests and scrub at the upper edge of forests and forest margins; recorded from Cherangani hills, Aberdare Mts, Mt Kenya, Karissia hills, Loita hills, and the highest parts of the Mau and Tinderet forests; 2300–2850 m; flowering in April and July.

Also recorded from a few places in Uganda and Tanzania.

This species resembles *Tridactyle bicaudata* vegetatively but has much larger flowers and is usually found at higher altitudes.

Tridactyle furcistipes   BOB CAMPBELL

Tridactyle nigrescens Summerhayes
Plants epiphytic usually pendent in masses with smooth roots. Stems slender, woody, to 30 cm long, drying black. Leaves fleshy, drying black, linear, unequally acutely bilobed, 3–7 cm long, 1–3 mm wide. Inflorescences very short, 5–6 mm long, bearing 2–3 flowers. Flowers pale green or greenish yellow becoming dirty orange with age; dorsal sepal elliptic, obtuse, 3–4 mm long, 1.5–2 mm wide; lateral sepals oblong-ovate, obtuse, 3–4 mm long, 2 mm wide; petals lanceolate, acute, 3–4 mm long, 1–1.3 mm wide; lip with auricles at

the base by the spur mouth, strongly 3-lobed at the apex, side lobes longer than the midlobe and lacerate at the apex, 2.6–4 mm long, 2 mm wide, spur slender, slightly inflated in the middle, 6–7.5 mm long; column 1–1.5 mm long.

Only recorded in dry highland forest on the Cherangani hills; 2200 m.

Also recorded from Uganda and Zaïre.

Tridactyle scottellii (Rendle) Schlechter

Plants epiphytic usually pendent in large masses with smooth roots. Stems slender, woody, to 60 cm long. Leaves grass-like, linear, unequally obtusely bilobed, 7–18 cm long, 3.5–6 mm wide. Inflorescences very short, 3–4 mm long, bearing 1–3 flowers. Flowers greenish yellow becoming dirty orange with age; dorsal sepal ovate-elliptic, acute, 4–6 mm long, 1.5–2.5 mm wide; lateral sepals similar but oblique at the base; petals lanceolate, acute, 4–5 mm long, 1–1.8 mm wide; lip with fleshy auricles at the base by the spur mouth, strongly 3-lobed at the apex, side lobes longer than the midlobe, 4–5 mm long, 6–7 mm wide, spur slender, straight, 9–12 mm long; column 1.5–2 mm long.

Widespread epiphyte in highland forests: 2200–3000 m; no definite flowering season.

Also recorded from Uganda, Zaïre and Rwanda.

Tridactyle scottellii   BOB CAMPBELL

Tridactyle tanneri Cribb

Plants small epiphytes with long smooth roots. Stems short, 1–4 cm long, usually erect. Leaves linear, unequally bilobed and toothed at apex, with darker green spots or markings on pale or mid-green background, 6–10 cm long, 6–10 mm wide. Inflorescences arching or pendent, 2–5 cm long,

bearing 2–8 flowers. Flowers green or dull yellow, scabrid on the outer surface; dorsal sepal oblong, acute, 7 mm long, 3 mm wide; lateral sepals obliquely oblong-lanceolate, acuminate, 8–9 mm long, 2.5 mm wide; petals lanceolate, acuminate, 7 mm long, 2 mm wide; lip obscurely 3-lobed in the middle, 8–9 mm long, 3–4 mm wide, auriculate at the base, spur pendent, curved at the tip, 18–20 mm long.

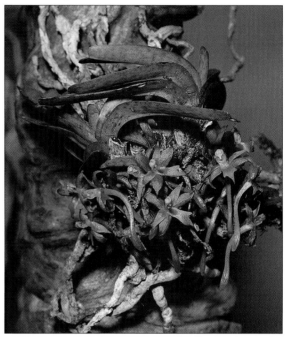

Tridactyle tanneri   BOB CAMPBELL

Epiphytic on tree trunks in deep shade in warm evergreen forest; only known from some of the hills in Teita district; 1200–1450 m; flowering in December and January.

Also recorded in Tanzania, in Lushoto district.

With its pendent inflorescences, flowers with scabrid outer surface and Y-shaped stipes, this species might be more appropriately placed in the genus *Ypsilopus*.

Tridactyle tricuspis (Bolus) Schlechter

Plants usually small epiphytes growing in tangled clumps with smooth roots. Stems upright, short, 1–10 cm long. Leaves linear, arcuate, in two rows, unequally rounded bilobed at the apex, conduplicate, 8–15 cm long, 8–12 mm wide. Inflorescences below the leaves, spreading or suberect, 4–15 cm long. Flowers 7–30, pale green to yellow-brown in two rows; dorsal sepal lanceolate, acuminate, 6–7.5 mm long, 2–2.5 mm wide; lateral sepals obliquely lanceolate, acuminate, 6–7.5 mm long, 2 mm wide; petals lanceolate, acuminate, 5–6.5 mm long, 1.5–2 mm wide; lip 3-lobed in the apical half, cuneate at base and auriculate, 5–8 mm long, 3.5–5 mm wide, side lobes short, slender, erose or bifid at tip, mid-lobe triangular, longer than side lobes, spur slender, 12–15 mm long; column 2–2.5 mm long.

In forest and bush on hills, so far only recorded in Kenya from the Loita hills; *c.* 2000 m; flowering in April.

Also recorded from Tanzania and southwards throughout eastern Africa to South Africa (Transvaal, Natal and E. Cape), as well as Zaïre.

Tridactyle tricuspis   JOYCE STEWART

Tridactyle tridentata (Harvey) Schlechter
  Syn. *Tridactyle teretifolia* Schlechter
Plants erect or pendent epiphytes, single or forming untidy clumps, rooting at the base. Stems branched, 10–50 cm long, robust and covered with rugulose sheaths. Leaves suberect or falcate, terete

Tridactyle tridentata   BOB CAMPBELL

or cylindric but grooved on the upper surface, pointed, dull olive green, 6–10 cm long, 2–4 mm in diameter. Inflorescences short, 2–3 cm long with 4–5 flowers. Flowers small, green to yellow or ochre; dorsal sepal oblong-elliptic, obtuse, 4–5 mm long; lateral sepals obliquely ovate, acute, 4–5 mm long; petals falcate, lanceolate, narrower than the sepals, 3–4 mm long; lip with 2 auricles or side lobes at the base on either side of the spur mouth and 3-lobed at the apex, lobes entire, side lobes equal to or shorter than the midlobe, 4–5 mm long, 3–4 mm wide, spur slender, incurved, 6–9 mm long; column 1–2 mm long.

Epiphytic on branches of large trees in the warmer forests and woodlands; recorded from the Kakamega forests; *c.* 1600 m; flowering in October.

Also recorded in Tanzania and Uganda; widespread along the eastern side of Africa, southwards to South Africa (Natal and E. Cape where it is lithophytic) and in Zaïre.

This species is extremely variable throughout its range. The plants always look more succulent and robust than those of *Tridactyle filifolia* which has sometimes been treated as a variety of *Tridactyle tridentata*.

Ypsilopus Summerhayes

Summerhayes used the Greek word for the letter 'y', *ypsilon*, when he named this genus of small epiphytic orchids, an allusion to the Y-shaped stipe that holds the two pollinia at right angles to the viscidium. Four species are now recognised, each rather different from the others in vegetative appearance and flowers, but all having the pollinarium he described. They all occur in Tanzania, but so far only two species have been recorded in Kenya.

Forested areas where there is a prolonged dry season are the best places to look for these orchids. The plants have short stems with rather thick roots spreading widely over the host tree and often penetrating into the bark. The plants of both the Kenya species are pendent, and it is at first a surprise to find them hanging below the branches of forest trees including *Podocarpus* and *Juniperus procera*, but probably they have access to more rainwater in this position.

CULTIVATION

Both species grow well mounted on a piece of bark. When being watered, they need a good soaking and then a dry period before being watered again. They grow best in good light where there is plenty of air movement and seem to do best where there is a pronounced drop in temperature at night.

Key to the species of *Ypsilopus*

Inflorescences with 2–10 white flowers, leaves
grass-like . . . . *Y. longifolius*
Inflorescences with 1–2 green flowers, leaves
iris-like . . . . *Y. viridiflorus*

Ypsilopus longifolius (Kraenzlin) Summerhayes
    Syn. *Ypsilopus graminifolius* (Kraenzlin)
                    Summerhayes
Plants pendent with long white roots spreading from a short stem. Leaves folded, linear, acute, greyish green, 5–25 cm long, 3–6 mm wide. Inflorescences usually several, pendent or arching, 3–8 cm long, each bearing 2–10 flowers. Flowers white with greenish tips to the tepals, scabrid on the outer surface; dorsal sepal ovate, acute, 6–7 mm long, 2–3 mm wide; lateral sepals oblique, ovate-lanceolate, acute, 6–9 mm long, 2–3 mm wide; petals slightly reflexed, lanceolate, acuminate, 5.5–6.5 mm long, 2–3 mm wide. Lip slightly recurved, ovate to rhombic, obscurely 3-lobed in the middle, acuminte, 6–8 mm long, 2–4 mm wide, spur slender, cylindric, 3–4 cm long; column *c.* 2 mm long.

Epiphytic on trunks and larger branches of trees in highland forests, especially rough barked trees, and on *Grevillea* and other trees in plantations; recorded throughout the highlands including north of the Aberdare Mts, Karissia hills, around Mt Kenya, Nairobi, and Ngong hills; 1450–2400 m; flowering in March and April.

Also recorded from Tanzania.

Ypsilopus viridiflorus Cribb & J. Stewart
Pendent epiphyte with a short stem and extensive grey roots. Leaves with the upper surfaces fused thus appearing bilaterally compressed, iris-like, linear and tapering, 4–25 cm long, 2–5 mm wide. Inflorescences single or several, each with 1–2 flowers, 2–6 cm long. Flowers pale green or yellowish green, scabrid on the outer surface; dorsal sepal lanceolate, acuminate, 7–9 mm long, 1.5–2 mm wide; lateral sepals similar, oblique at the base; petals linear-lanceolate, acuminate, 6–8 mm long, 1.5–1.8 mm wide; lip deflexed, entire, lanceolate, acuminate, 7–8 mm long, 2 mm wide, spur slender, curved or straight, 15–18 mm long; column 1 mm long.

Epiphytic on branches in mixed evergreen forest; only recorded so far from Mt Kasigau and in the Mbololo hills in Teita district; 1500–2100 m; flowering in May.

Also recorded from Tanzania.

Ypsilopus longifolius   BOB CAMPBELL

Ypsilopus viridiflorus   BOB CAMPBELL

Part II Orchid Lianes

Vanilla Miller

The name *Vanilla* is derived from a Spanish word *vanilla* (little pod) referring to the bean-like fruit of this orchid. It was probably the fruits that became known first because a substance derived when they are fermented has long been used as a flavouring, particularly in Mexico. Today the commercial product is important in several parts of the world, particularly Madagascar, Réunion, Puerto Rico and other parts of the Caribbean, and is chiefly obtained from cultivated *Vanilla planifolia*, a native of Mexico.

Vanilla planifolia: the species grown commercially for flavouring.   JOYCE STEWART

This genus of scrambling, terrestrial or epiphytic lianes is distributed throughout the tropical parts of the world. There are approximately 100 species but only 15 are recorded in Africa, four of them in Kenya.

CULTIVATION

Vanilla plants are easy to maintain in a warm greenhouse. They need to be able to put out roots into a rich but well drained compost in a large container. With support from a cane or wires the stems will quickly grow up towards the light. If there is plenty of space they will branch and form a dense growth immediately below the roof. It is only when the stems have achieved their full length that flower-bearing side branches develop and hang down into the greenhouse. Although each flower lasts only a few days, there is usually a succession of *Cattleya*-like flowers. These may be followed by a bunch of green fruits resembling french beans if the flowers are pollinated.

Vanilla planifolia: young fruits developing.
JOYCE STEWART

Key to the species of *Vanilla*
1   Plants apparently leafless, stems reddish . . . . .
    . . . . *V. roscheri*
    Plants bearing conspicuous leaves, stems
    green 2

2 Sepals and petals less than 3 cm long,
    leaves up to 15 cm long and 5 cm wide . . . .
    . . . . *V. ramosa*
  Sepals and petals more than 5 cm long;
    leaves often over 15 cm long and 6 cm
    wide   3

3 Sepals and petals more than 7 cm long;
    lip bearing a dense tuft of fine hairs on
    its centre . . . .   *V. imperialis*
  Sepals and petals up to 6 cm long; lip
    bearing a crest of *c*. 12 rows of
    transverse, branching scales below the
    column . . . .   *V. polylepis*

Vanilla imperialis Kraenzlin

Epiphytic, glabrous, leafy liane. Stems often many metres long, up to 2.5 cm in diameter, dull bluish green, succulent, with a single large leaf at each node, opposite to or subtending a root. Leaves green, succulent, elliptic-oblong to ovate, apiculate or subobtuse, 12–25 cm long and 8–12 cm wide, upper leaves smallest. Inflorescences axillary with many flowers opening successively, each lasting 1–3 days. Flowers pale green, white, or cream, lip heavily marked with purple streaks; sepals and petals subequal, elliptic-lanceolate, acute, fleshy, up to 8 cm long and 1.8 cm wide; lip funnel shaped up to 6 cm long, basal part adnate to the column for 4 cm, the basal part hairy on the inner surface, bearing a dense tuft of fine hairs, margins undulate.

Scrambling up tree trunks and through the canopy of forest trees; recently discovered in west Kenya; 900–1200 m.

Vanilla imperialis   BOB CAMPBELL

Also known in Tanzania and Uganda, and recorded westwards through Zaïre, Cameroon, Ghana and Ivory Coast as far as Sierra Leone, and south to Angola.

Vanilla polylepis Summerhayes

Terrestrial or epiphytic, glabrous, leafy liane. Stems often several metres long, up to 2.5 cm in diameter, succulent, with a single large leaf at each node, opposite to or subtending a root. Leaves green, succulent, elliptic-lanceolate to oblong, shortly acuminate, 10–21 cm long and 3–8 cm wide, upper leaves smallest. Inflorescences axillary with many flowers opening singly and each lasting 1–3 days. Flowers pale greenish white, lip paler with rosy-maroon streaks towards the apex, yellow near the base; sepals oblanceolate, obtuse, fleshy, *c*. 6 cm long; petals elliptic-lanceolate, slightly longer than sepals; lip funnel shaped up to 6 cm long, basal part adnate to the column for 3 cm, margins undulate, bearing crests of numerous and various scales and papillae.

Among riverside bushes and trees, on cliffs and scrambling over rocks near rivers, usually in deep shade and flowering when the tip of the vine reaches strong sunlight; near Thika at about 1500 m; flowering from September to January.

Also known from similar habitats in Zaïre, Malawi, Zambia, Zimbabwe and Angola.

Vanilla ramosa Rolfe

Epiphytic, glabrous, leafy liane. Stems often several metres long, up to 7 mm in diameter, succulent, dull green, with a single leaf at each node, opposite to or subtending an adventitious root. Leaves fleshy or leathery, elliptic or elliptic-oblong, rounded at the base, shortly acuminate at the apex, 8–16 cm long and 3–6 cm wide. Inflorescences axillary, frequently branched, densely many flowered. Flowers white, cream or pale yellow, lip marked rosy mauve to purple; sepals all similar, oblong-elliptic to lanceolate, up to 3 cm long and 1.2 cm wide; petals similar but shorter and narrower; lip distinctly 3-lobed, up to 2.5 cm long and 2.7 cm wide, midlobe bearing a series of lamellae and a raised keel in the basal part, side lobe margins adnate to the column throughout their length.

Not yet recorded in flower from Kenya, but a sterile specimen collected on the forest margin at 350 m in the Shimba Hills is almost certainly this species.

Widespread in Africa, in forest, dense scrub on coral rock and in plantations; sea level to 900 m; usually flowering from September to February (in

Vanilla polylepis   ERIC LA CROIX

Tanzania). Also recorded on the west coast of Africa from Ghana, Nigeria and southwards to Gabon.

Vanilla roscheri Reichenbach f.

Terrestrial or scrambling, glabrous liane with long brownish stems and short roots at the nodes. Stems often channelled on either side, brownish green, of indeterminate length, with a brown vestigial leaf up to 3 cm long arising at each node. Inflorescences terminal or axillary, bearing up to 35 flowers that open in succession. Flowers large and conspicuous, white or pale pink; dorsal sepal lanceolate oblong, subobtuse, up to 8 cm long and 2.5 cm wide, lateral sepals similar but slightly narrower; petals elliptic-oblong to ovate, up to 8 cm long and 3.5 cm wide; lip white with pink or yellow throat, entire, trumpet shaped, up to 8 cm long and 5 cm wide, margins undulate, adnate to the sides of the column in the basal part, bearing 2–3 rows of hairy crests.

A scrambler in coastal bushland, over coral rock, at the edge of mangrove swamps and in the open, evergreen scrub some distance inland from the coast including Tsavo National Park; usually below 750 m; flowering from September to December.

Also known from Tanzania and Mozambique. This species is very similar to *Vanilla phalaenopsis*, which was described earlier from the Seychelles.

Vanilla roscheri   BOB CAMPBELL

Part III Terrestrial Orchids

About half of the orchids of Kenya grow in the ground, with their roots hidden from view among the rocks, soil and other plants. Some are visible all year round, but many have a short growing season when their aerial parts appear and a long dormant season when their tubers or pseudobulbs are quite invisible.

A few have prostrate stems that creep over the surface of the ground and root into the soft substratum of the forest floor below. Every year or growing season a dormant bud on the horizontal rhizome begins to grow. It produces an upright leafy stem that flowers at its apex, then shrivels and dies with or without forming fruits. *Platylepis* and *Cheirostylis* have this habit of growth.

Many terrestrial plants have subterranean tubers or fleshy rhizomes from which the plants produce a new shoot each year when temperature and moisture conditions are favourable. The shoots are usually upright and solitary but each bears many flowers. The huge genus *Habenaria* shares this habit with the brightly coloured species of *Satyrium* and *Disa*. Sometimes the flowering shoot is accompanied by a sterile leafy shoot, but both are ephemeral, disappearing after a few short weeks of life. Species of *Eulophia* regularly produce two shoots from each underground rhizome or pseudobulb, one leafy and the other flowering. In *Nervilia* also, two shoots are produced, but they never appear together and it may be quite difficult to recognise the flowers and leaves belonging to the same species after an interval of several weeks or months before they each appear.

Other terrestrial species have a tufted habit of growth, with a rosette of leaves that last for more than one season. The large plicate leaves of *Calanthe* are always somewhat evergreen.

Epipogium roseum and a few species of *Eulophia* lack green leaves of any kind and are often referred to as saprophytes. They live with a fungal partner throughout their life and have lost their chloroplasts and ability to photosynthesise. Thus the plants are pinkish brown or greyish white in colour, lack leaves, and have a very short life above the ground. They are quite hard to find in shady forests.

The terrestrial orchid genera can be identified from the artificial key that follows. A few species are occasionally epiphytic, and some of the epiphytes may fall from a branch and continue life on the ground. If you cannot identify a particular plant in the key below, turn to the key for the epiphytic orchids on page 4.

Key to the genera of terrestrial orchids

1 Plants without a perennial base formed
    by pseudobulbs 2
   Plants with a group of perennial
    pseudobulbs at ground level or below
    the surface 23

2 Leaves green and present at or just after
    flowering 3
   Leaves absent or not green or appearing
    a long time after flowering 27

3 Plants with creeping stems, rooting at
    the nodes and becoming leafy in the
    terminal part 4
   Plants not creeping, stems leafy from
    the base and upright above the
    underground tuber or rhizome 7

4 Flowers purplish or green, lip large . . . .
    . . . . *Malaxis*
   Flowers white, green and white, or
    brown and white, lip small 5

5 Inflorescence dense, sepals glandular-
    hairy on the outside, 7–9 mm long . . . .
    . . . . *Platylepis*
   Inflorescence slender, sepals may be
    hairy but not glandular, less than
    5 mm long 6

6 Flowers white; sepals *c.* 5 mm long . . . .
    . . . . *Cheirostylis*
   Flowers green and white, sepals *c.*
    2 mm long . . . . *Zeuxine*

7 Flowers without a spur 8
   Flowers with a spur on the lip, dorsal
    sepal or lateral sepals 9

8   Flowers pink or purple . . . . *Brachycorythis*
     Flowers greenish or yellowish brown . . . .
     . . . . *Epipactis*

9   Spur present on dorsal sepal 10
     Spur or spurs present on lip or lateral
        sepals 11

10   Flowers white . . . . *Brownleea*
     Flowers pink, yellow, or red but not
        white . . . . *Disa*

11   Lip with one or two spurs 12
     Lip not spurred but sometimes saccate
        at the base 21

12   Lip uppermost in the flower, with two
        spurs . . . . *Satyrium*
     Lip on the lower side of the flower,
        with a single spur 13

13   Flowers green, white, yellow or orange . . 14
     Flowers pink or mauve, if white then
        flushed with mauve 18

14   Lateral sepals and front lobe of petals
        joined to lip and stigmatic arms . . . .
     . . . . *Bonatea*
     Lateral sepals free from petals and lip
        or not united at the same time 15

15   Stigmas simple, each on a separate
        stalk 16
     Stigmas bilobed . . . . *Roeperocharis*

16   Flowers bright yellow or orange . . . .
     . . . . *Platycoryne*
     Flowers green or green and white or
        white 17

17   Flowers on one side of the spike, close
        together . . . . *Holothrix*
     Flowers arranged all round the
        inflorescence, lax or dense . . . *Habenaria*

18   Leaves basal, 1–2 19
     Leaves all round the stem 20

19   Petals free, longer than sepals, usually
        divided into several lobes . . . . . *Holothrix*
     Petals fused to column at base, usually
        shorter than sepals and hidden inside
        dorsal sepal . . . . *Cynorkis*

20   Stem and outer surface of flowers with
        pin-shaped glands . . . . *Cynorkis*
     Stem, leaves and flowers smooth or
        velvety-hairy but not glandular . . . .
     . . . . *Brachycorythis*

21   Ovary not twisted, lip uppermost . . . .
     . . . . *Satyrium*
     Ovary twisted, dorsal sepal uppermost . . 22

22   Lateral sepals each with a spur or sac . . . . . .
     . . . . *Disperis*
     Lateral sepals not spurred or saccate . . . .
     . . . . *Brachycorythis*

23   Column united to the lip for most of its
        length . . . . *Calanthe*
     Column not united to the lip 24

24   Flowers with a distinct spur at the base
        of the lip 25
     Flowers without a spur 26

25   Lip 3-lobed, side lobes usually upright
        on either side of column . . . . . . *Eulophia*
     Lip 4-lobed . . . . *Oeceoclades*

26   Pseudobulbs flat, underground; grassland
        plants . . . . *Pteroglossaspis*
     Pseudobulbs conical, above ground,
        forest plants . . . . *Liparis*

27   Plant without chlorophyll; lip shortly
        spurred . . . . *Epipogium*
     Plant with chlorophyll but the single leaf
        appearing long after the inflorescence;
        lip without a spur . . . . *Nervilia*

Bonatea Willdenow

The species of *Bonatea* are conspicuous green
flowered orchids that are usually found in grassland in sheltered places, often associated with rocks
or bushes. Their tall leafy stems arise from a group
of swollen tuberous roots. The flowers resemble
those of *Habenaria*, to which they are undoubtedly
closely related. They differ from that huge genus in
having the lateral sepals and the lower lobe of the
bilobed petals all united to the lip and to the stigmatic arms. This gives them a characteristic appearance which is further enhanced by the large,
dark green, 3-lobed rostellum that forms the major
part of the column.

The genus was named by the German botanist C.L. Willdenow in honour of Guiseppe Antonio Bonato, professor of botany at Padua in Italy in 1805.

CULTIVATION

These delightful orchids with their leafy stems and unusual flowers are easy to grow in a sandy, well-drained soil mix. Whilst the stems are leafy and flowering, they need to be kept well-watered and fed. As soon as the leaves begin to turn brown they should be dried off gradually. No further water should be given until the new shoots arise from near the base of the old stems, even though there will usually be an interval of several months before this happens.

Key to the species of *Bonatea*
1 Spur over 7 cm long, usually much longer . . . . ***B. steudneri***
   Spur less than 7 cm long, usually much shorter 2

2 Side lobes of rostellum slender, much longer than the hooded midlobe . . . . ***B. volkensiana***
   Side lobes of rostellum equalling or shorter than the midlobe 3

3 Spur 4.5–6 cm long; no tooth in the mouth of the spur . . . . ***B. rabaiensis***
   Spur 2.5–3.5 cm long; distinct tooth at the mouth of the spur . . . ***B. tentaculifera***

Bonatea rabaiensis (Rendle) Rolfe
Terrestrial herb 25–50 cm high. Stem erect, leafy throughout. Leaves 8–10, oblanceolate, lanceolate or elliptic, acute, the largest 6–12 cm long, 3–4 cm wide, the lower and upper ones bract-like. Inflorescence 5–12 cm long, usually with 3–7 flowers, bracts thin. Flowers green and white; dorsal sepal erect, ovate, incurved, 17–20 mm long, 13 mm wide; lateral sepals deflexed, united to the lip for *c.* 10 mm, obliquely ovate-lanceolate, acuminate, to 20 mm long, 10 mm wide; petals bipartite nearly to the base, upper lobe erect, adhering to the dorsal sepal, linear, up to 20 mm long, lower lobe adnate to the lip for about 7 mm, curved outwards, linear, 25–30 mm long; lip deflexed, 3-lobed above a narrow basal part 10–15 mm long, midlobe shorter and wider than side lobes, spur swollen in the apical half, 5–6 cm long.

At forest margins and in bushland on sandy soil or associated with rocks; only known from the Shimba hills, the Rabai hills, and from the Sokoke forest; sea level to 300 m; flowering in May and June.

Also recorded in Tanzania.

Bonatea steudneri (Reichenbach f.) Durand & Schinz
Syn. *Bonatea kayseri* (Kraenzlin) Rolfe
Bonatea ugandae Summerhayes
Terrestrial herb 25–125 cm high. Stem erect, leafy throughout. Leaves 10–20, the middle ones ovate-elliptic or lanceolate, acute, enfolding the stem at the base, 7–20 cm long, 3–5 cm wide, the upper and lower ones smaller. Inflorescence cylindrical or corymbose, 5–30 cm long and bearing 3–30 large flowers, bracts leaf-like. Flowers green and white; dorsal sepal erect, convex, elliptic-lanceolate, acuminate, 2–3 cm long, 1–2 cm wide; lateral sepals deflexed, oblique, lanceolate, acuminate, united along the upper margin to the lip for 1–2 cm, 2–3 cm long, 1–1.5 cm wide; petals bipartite almost to the base, the upper lobe linear, slightly curved, adhering to the edge of the dorsal sepal, lower lobe adnate to the lip for 1–2 cm then curving downwards and outwards, narrowly linear or filiform, 3–7 cm long; lip 3-lobed above a narrow base 1.5–3 cm long, midlobe usually sharply bent in the middle, 2–3.5 cm long, 1–3 mm wide, side lobes spreading, long and filiform, 2.5–9 cm long, 1–2 mm wide, spur dependent, swollen in the apical part, 10–20 cm long.

Bushland and scrub, at the edges of thicket and on rocky slopes, widespread in many of the drier parts of the country, often collected around Nairobi; 1700–2700 m; flowering in May to July.

Also recorded in Uganda and Tanzania; widespread throughout eastern Africa from Sudan and Somalia to eastern Zaïre and south to Zimbabwe, also in Arabia and Yemen.

Bonatea tentaculifera Summerhayes
Terrestrial herb at least 60 cm high. Stem erect, leafy throughout. Leaves 7 or more, the middle ones lanceolate-elliptic, shortly acuminate, largest 12 cm long, 5 cm wide, grading into the bracts. Inflorescence cylindrical, 25 cm long, densely many-flowered, bracts leafy. Flowers green; dorsal sepal erect, convex, elliptic-lanceolate, acute, 17 mm long, 8 mm wide; lateral sepals obliquely lanceolate, acute, upper margin adnate to lip for 5 mm, 18 mm long, 6–7 mm wide; petals bipartite nearly to base, upper lobe erect, adhering to dorsal sepal, curved, nearly 2 cm long and 6 mm wide at

middle, lower lobe united to the lip for 3–4 mm, then spreading, becoming filiform, to 5.5 cm long; lip 3-lobed above a narrow base 4 mm long, midlobe deflexed, ligulate, obtuse, 2 cm long, 2.5 mm wide, side lobes narrow, spreading, to 6.5 cm long 1 mm wide, spur dependent, slightly swollen in the apical half, 2.5–3 cm long.

Only ever collected once, in Nairobi City Park; 1500 m; flowering in April.

Not known elsewhere.

Bonatea volkensiana (Kraenzlin) Rolfe

Terrestrial herb 20–70 cm high. Stem leafy throughout. Leaves 10–16, lanceolate or oblong-lanceolate, acute, the largest 6–11 cm long and 2–4 cm wide, the lower and upper ones smaller. Inflorescence cylindrical, 4–18 cm long, rather dense, bearing 3–25 flowers, bracts leaf-like, thin. Flowers green or green and white; dorsal sepal erect, convex, elliptic-lanceolate, acuminate, 1.5–2.5 cm long, 1–1.5 cm wide; lateral sepals deflexed,

Bonatea steudneri

BOB CAMPBELL

obliquely obovate, acuminate, 1.4–2.4 cm long, 8–12 mm wide, upper margin adnate to lip for 4–7 mm; petals bipartite nearly to base, upper lobe erect, adhering to dorsal sepal, linear, 1.2–2 cm long, 1.5–2 mm wide, lower lobe narrowly linear, adnate to lip for 4–7 mm, apical part curved upwards and outwards, 2.5–4.5 cm long, 1 mm wide; lip 3-lobed above the narrow base 1–1.5 cm long, midlobe linear, 1.5–3 cm long, 1–3 mm wide, side lobes diverging, narrower, 2–4.5 cm long, spur cylindrical, slightly swollen in apical half, 3–4.5 cm long.

In bush or rocky grassland, widespread in some of the drier parts of Kenya, sometimes with *Bonatea steudneri*; 1700–2400 m; flowering in May and June, sometimes in January and March.

Also recorded in Tanzania.

Brachycorythis Lindley

The genus *Brachycorythis* currently consists of about 35 species mostly in tropical and South Africa and a few in Asia. It was first described by John Lindley in 1838. He derived the name from two Greek words *brachys* (short) and *korys* (helmet), in allusion to the sometimes hooded appearance of the upper part of the flower. Not all the flowers demonstrate this characteristic very well. They do have a characteristic lip, however, that is boat-shaped in the basal part (the hypochile), sometimes with a spur, and flattened out in the upper part (epichile) which in all the Kenya species has three lobes. They are all brightly coloured, in various shades of pink or mauve, and all except *Brachycorythis kalbreyeri* are grassland plants. This one exception is unusual in the genus, not only for being a forest species, but also because it often grows epiphytically.

CULTIVATION

None of the grassland species of *Brachycorythis* has been maintained in cultivation for very long, but *B. kalbreyeri* is a very welcome addition to many collections. Because it dies down after flowering and fruiting, great care is needed during the dormant period so that the thick woolly tubers do not rot from too much moisture or shrivel from getting too dry. As soon as the new shoot appears each year, the plants should be watered and fed with dilute fertiliser. They need a fairly open but moisture-retentive compost, similar to that used for many

epiphytes. In the forests where this species grows temperatures are cool at night but warm by day.

Key to the species of *Brachycorythis*

1 Leaves hairless 2
  Leaves covered with short hairs . . . .
  . . . . *B. pubescens*

2 Base of lip forming a spur 5–10 mm long . . . .
  . . . . *B. tenuior*
  Base of lip boat-shaped or with a sac but
    not spurred 3

3 Dorsal sepal 4–5 mm long; upper part of
    the lip with a conical thickening just in
    front of the basal part . . . . . *B. buchananii*
  Dorsal sepal 5–14 mm long; upper part of
    lip without a conical thickening but
    with a raised midrib 4

4 Leaves ending in a very fine point; basal
    part of lip 1.5–2.5 mm long . . . .
  . . . . *B. pleistophylla*
  Leaves with a short point; basal part of
    lip 3.5–6 mm long 5

5 Flowers 20–100 in a dense spike; lip
    12–16 mm long . . . . *B. ovata*
  Flowers 3–10, rarely up to 20, in a loose
    spike; lip 15–25 mm long . . . *B. kalbreyeri*

Brachycorythis buchananii (Schlechter) Rolfe
Terrestrial herb 20–50 cm high, slender, arising from narrowly ellipsoid tuberous roots. Leaves numerous, lanceolate, 4 cm long, 1 cm wide, decreasing in size up the stem and grading into the bracts. Inflorescence slender, densely many-flowered, to 14 cm long, bracts lanceolate. Flowers small, pink, mauve or purple; sepals lanceolate-elliptic, laterals slightly oblique, 4–6 mm long; petals obovate or semiorbicular, a little longer than the sepals and much wider; lip hypochile boat-shaped with triangular sides, 1.5–2.5 mm long, epichile transversely elliptic or reniform, 3-lobed, the side lobes longer than the midlobe, callus small, in front of the hypochile, total length 2.5–3.5 mm, width 4–5.5 mm; column 2 mm long.

In grassland and swamps; only recorded in western Kenya, near Kakamega; 1700–2200 m; flowering in July.

Also recorded from Uganda, Tanzania, westwards to Zaïre and Nigeria and southwards to Malawi, Zambia, Zimbabwe and Angola.

Brachycorythis kalbreyeri Reichenbach f.
Epiphytic or terrestrial herb 15–40 cm high, arising from a thick cylindrical root or tuber that is densely covered with hairs. Stem glabrous or with few hairs in the lower part where it is spotted purple. Leaves up to 15, alternate, lanceolate to broadly lanceolate, acute, 10 cm long, 2.5 cm wide, thin. Inflorescence lax with up to 20 large flowers, bracts leafy. Flowers lilac or mauve rarely whitish, yellow at the base of the lip; dorsal sepal elliptic, subacute, 15 mm long; lateral sepals obliquely ovate, obtuse, to 18 mm long, narrower than the dorsal; petals held forwards, broadly obliquely ovate, 10–15 mm long; lip hypochile boat-shaped, *c.* 6 mm long with straight margins, epichile nearly orbicular, 3-lobed in the upper part, the midlobe small and pointed, much smaller than the wide, deflexed side lobes, total length 15–20 mm; column stout, 4 mm long.

Epiphytic on mossy tree trunks and branches and on rotten logs and fallen branches on the forest floor; in riverine forest in west Kenya from the Cherangani hills south to Sotik; 2000–2350 m; flowering in April to July.

Also recorded from northern Tanzania and from Uganda westwards across equatorial Africa to Sierra Leone.

Brachycorythis kalbreyeri

BOB CAMPBELL

Brachycorythis ovata Lindley
　　ssp. *schweinfurthii* (Reichenbach f.)
　　　　　Summerhayes
　　Syn. *Brachycorythis ugandensis* Schlechter
　　Brachycorythis grandis Kraenzlin
　　　var. *ugandensis* Braid

Terrestrial herb 40–100 cm high, arising from fleshy cylindrical roots. Leaves numerous, lanceolate, acute, the middle ones to 8 cm long, 2.5 cm wide, decreasing in size upwards and merging into the bracts. Inflorescence lax to dense, with rather large flowers, up to 35 cm long, bracts leaf-like. Flowers purple and mauve, sometimes pale; dorsal sepal elliptic, obtuse or rounded, 5–9 mm long; lateral sepals obliquely ovate, subacute, 6–11 mm long; petals erect on each side of column, oblong-ovate, truncate, 5–9 mm long; lip hypochile boat-shaped, curved, 4–6 mm long, epichile obovate, 3-lobed in the upper part with a central keel running into the midlobe, side lobes longer than the upcurved midlobe, total length 12–16 mm long; column 3–4 mm long.

Grassland; only known from west Kenya around Mt Elgon, in the Cherangani hills and Kakamega; 2000–2550 m; flowering in May.

Brachycorythis pleistophylla　　　　ERIC LA CROIX

Also recorded from Uganda and Sudan and westwards to Senegal.

The typical subspecies is shorter in growth with denser inflorescences. It also has smaller flowers in which the midlobe of the lip is as long as or longer than the side lobes. This form only occurs in South Africa. There is a third subspecies, ssp. *welwitschii*, which is found in central Africa, Zaïre, Zambia, Malawi, Zimbabwe and Angola. Geerinck (1984) has 'lumped' all these subspecies.

Brachycorythis pleistophylla Reichenbach f.
Terrestrial herb 25–100 cm high, arising from a thick fleshy tuber. Leaves numerous, lanceolate to narrowly lanceolate, acuminate, the middle ones to 6 cm long, 1.5 cm wide, decreasing in size upwards and grading into the bracts. Inflorescence somewhat lax, up to 35 cm long with many flowers, bracts lanceolate. Flowers lilac or purple, often white or yellow in the centre; sepals elliptic or narrowly ovate, 6–9 mm long; petals held forwards on either side of the column, almost orbicular, 6–9 mm long and slightly narrower in width; lip hypochile shortly boat-shaped, 2–3 mm long with triangular side lobes, epichile elliptic or almost orbicular, 3-lobed, the midlobe tooth-like and much smaller than the rounded side lobes, total length 7–13 mm, width 6–12 mm; column 2 mm long.

In grassland and at the edges of deciduous woodland; only recorded from Mt Elgon and from Sagala and Mbololo hills in Teita district; 1000–2700 m; flowering in April (Mt Elgon) and October to November (Teita district).

Also recorded in Tanzania, Uganda, westwards as far as Nigeria and southwards to South Africa (Transvaal) and Angola; also recorded from Madagascar.

Brachycorythis pubescens Harvey
Terrestrial herb 25–80 cm high, arising from ellipsoid tubers. Leaves numerous, lanceolate, acuminate, those in the middle of the stem 6 cm long, 2.5 cm wide, gradually decreasing towards the bracts, densely velvety hairy. Inflorescence densely many-flowered, up to 35 cm long, bracts similar to leaves. Flowers in shades of pink or purple, orange in the centre; dorsal sepal elliptic, obtuse, 4.5–7.5 mm long; lateral sepals ovate or elliptic, slightly longer than dorsal, all the sepals hairy on the outer surface; petals erect on each side of column, obliquely elliptic, rounded, 4–6 mm long; lip hypochile rounded, 2–3 mm long, margins angular, epichile bent downwards, wedge-shaped, 3-lobed

at the apex, 5–10 mm long, 6–14 mm wide, the lobes similar; column stout, 2.5–4 mm long.

In grassland and open woodland in several parts of western Kenya; 2000–2700 m; flowering in May to July.

Also recorded from Tanzania and Uganda and widespread in many parts of tropical Africa and as far south as South Africa (Transvaal and Natal).

Brachycorythis pubescens   ERIC LA CROIX

Brachycorythis tenuior Reichenbach f.

Terrestrial herb to 55 cm high, arising from an ellipsoid tuber. Leaves numerous, lanceolate, acute, up to 5.5 cm long and 1.5 cm wide, decreasing in size up the stem and grading into the bracts. Inflorescence dense, to 14 cm long, many-flowered, bracts leaf-like. Flowers purple or pale violet, often with darker spots and callus on the lip white with purple spots; dorsal sepal elliptic, 5–9 mm long; lateral sepals obliquely ovate or oblong, 6–10 mm long; petals oblong, twisted, 5–9 mm long; lip hypochile forming a curved cylindrical spur, 5–10 mm long, epichile 3-lobed, with a fleshy, raised midlobe and thin, wing-like lateral lobes, 5–10 mm long, 3–7 mm wide, callus of two raised ridges; column slender 4–6 mm long.

In long grass, swampy areas and cleared woodland; only recorded from Kakamega and from Machakos district; 1300–1700 m; flowering in July (Kakamega) and in December (Machakos).

Also recorded in Uganda and Tanzania and widely distributed throughout tropical Africa as far south as South Africa (Transvaal and Natal).

Brownleea Lindley

This is a small genus of terrestrial orchids with only about seven species, in the eastern parts of Africa, and in Madagascar. *Brownleea parviflora* is the most widespread but curiously disjunct in its distribution. It has been found on Mt Cameroon, and on Mt Nyiru in the Northern Frontier Province of Kenya. Elsewhere it is more common, from the highlands of Tanzania, through Malawi to Zambia, Zimbabwe, Swaziland, Lesotho and South Africa (Transvaal, Natal and Cape Province).

The inflorescences and flowers resemble those of the genus *Disa* in having conspicuous sepals, the dorsal one spurred, but the petals are fused to the dorsal sepal in *Brownleea* and the lip is minute, often upcurved over the front of the column.

CULTIVATION

This species has been collected only once in Kenya and is not known in cultivation.

Brownleea parviflora Lindley

Terrestrial herb 20–60 cm high, arising from ellipsoid tubers. Stem erect, slender, bearing 2–5 leaves, usually 3. Leaves erect, narrowly lanceolate, the largest 7–12 cm long, 1–2 cm wide. Inflorescence cylindrical, 3–16 cm long with many flowers, bracts narrowly lanceolate, 1–3.5 cm long, the upper ones smaller. Flowers white to pale lilac or pale mauve, sometimes dotted with purple; dorsal sepal erect or incurved, lanceolate, 3–5 mm long, narrowing into a spur which is recurved at the back, the spur cylindrical 4–7 mm long; lateral sepals spreading downwards, oblong-lanceolate, acute, joined together at the base, 3–4 mm long, 1.5–3 mm wide; petals erect, adhering to the dorsal sepal along their margins, obliquely triangular-quadrate, 2–4 mm long, 2 mm wide; lip very small, linear, acute, turned up in front of the stigma, 1 mm long; column very short.

Upland grassland, especially in damp places; Mt Nyiru; 1700 m; flowering in July.

Widespread in eastern Africa from Tanzania south to South Africa (Cape Province) and on Mt Cameroon.

Calanthe R. Brown

This is a large genus of about 150 species that occur in Asia, and a single species that is widespread in Africa. They are almost all terrestrial plants in forest habitats and the large plicate leaves are often damaged by molluscs or insects. The name refers to the pretty flowers of many of the species – from the Greek *kalos* (beautiful) and *anthos* (flower).

Many of the plants are large or of medium size, herbaceous, with erect ovoid pseudobulbs arising one in front of the other and held at or near the surface of the soil by numerous hairy roots. The leaves surround the pseudobulb at the base of the petiole and are expanded to form a broad lamina in the upper part. Sometimes they are very large. The inflorescence is usually single and arises from the base of the pseudobulb. The flowers are borne in the axils of pretty, pale green bracts. The 3-lobed lip is fused to the column at its base.

CULTIVATION

Easily maintained in cultivation provided it is correctly grown as a terrestrial plant of the shaded forest floor with good drainage. In well-grown plants the leaves are smooth and shiny and make attractive specimens even when not in flower. The plants need plenty of water and weak fertiliser during the growing season, i.e. when new leaves are elongating and the flowering shoot is developing, and rather less afterwards. They should not be allowed to dry out completely.

Calanthe sylvatica (Thouars) Lindley
Syn. *Calanthe corymbosa* Lindley
Calanthe volkensii Rolfe

A large, erect, terrestrial herb up to 65 cm tall. Pseudobulbs cylindrical-conical, 2–5 cm high and 1.5 cm in diameter, often borne in rows which become obvious after the leaves have rotted. Leaves 3–5, erect or spreading, lanceolate to elliptic-oblong, acute, 15–45 cm long, 5–13 cm wide, dark green above, often plicate, petiole 4–25 cm long. Inflorescence erect, up to 60 cm long, with a stout hairy peduncle and usually many flowers close together near its apex. Flowers white to rose purple, usually with a darker lip bearing a white or orange callus in front of its fusion with the column, column white, the flowers fading to orange as they age, sometimes turning pale turquoise blue if damaged; dorsal sepal lanceolate to narrowly elliptic, acute, 1.3–3.5 cm long; lateral sepals similar but oblique; petals elliptic or oblanceolate, 1–3 cm long; lip 3-lobed, with 2–4 cm spur at the base, side lobes auriculate, 5–7 mm long, midlobe much larger, obovate or flabellate, emarginate, callus of 3 ridges, fleshy, 3–7 mm long.

Robust plants of the forest floor, often near rivers; in all the highland forests of Kenya including the Chyulu hills; 900–2750 m; flowers in June and July and in December.

This widespread but very variable species occurs throughout Africa and in Madagascar, the Comoro Islands and the Mascarenes.

Cheirostylis Blume

This is a small genus of about 20 species that are found in the warmer forests of Asia and Australia. Three species have been described in Africa, one of which extends to Madagascar, and only one of these has so far been found in Kenya. All the plants have creeping stems with short upright parts that bear the leaves and inflorescences. They are rather similar to *Platylepis* and *Zeuxine* and have sometimes been misidentified as one of these.

The name is derived from two Greek words *cheir* (hand) and *stylis* (style) and refers to part of the tiny column that bears a fanciful resemblance to a hand.

CULTIVATION

Unknown in cultivation but it should not be difficult to grow in the same way as *Platylepis glandulosa*, which the author maintained for several years.

Cheirostylis lepida (Reichenbach f.) Rolfe
Perennial herb up to 20 cm high, stems creeping at the base. Leaves thin, ovate, acute, rounded at the base, up to 5 cm long, 2.5 cm wide, petiole shorter than the lamina, widening at the base to sheath the stem. Inflorescence a terminal raceme, dense, up to 20 small white flowers; bracts glabrous, slightly longer than the hairy ovary. Flowers less than 5 mm long; sepals acute; petals obovate, acute; lip slightly longer than the tepals, saccate at the base with 2

---

hooked calli, bilobed at the apex; column up to 2 mm long.

In dense shade, in leaf mould and litter on damp places of the forest floor; only known in Kenya from the Teita hills; *c.* 900 m; flowering in September.

Widespread but nowhere common, from Nigeria to Ethiopia, and also in Uganda and Tanzania.

Cynorkis Thouars

Most of the 125 species of *Cynorkis* are found in Madagascar and other islands of the western Indian Ocean. Only about 17 have been recorded in Africa, four of these in Kenya. Our species are instantly recognisable by their small lilac flowers that are glandular on the outer surface. The stems and bracts are also sparsely covered with pin-shaped glandular hairs. The single leaf or small group of radical leaves lack these hairs and are often quite shiny. The leaves appear, followed shortly by the inflorescence, during the rainy season. This may vary from year to year in date and intensity, so it is not always easy to find the plants, whether in leaf or in flower. Usually they grow terrestrially but some species become epiphytic on moss-covered branches in areas of high rainfall. *Cynorkis kassneriana*, for example, is often found on the trunks and branches of trees as well as amongst mosses on rocks in Kericho district. They

Calanthe sylvatica

BOB CAMPBELL

are all moisture-loving plants. Since the plants are all deciduous, and disappear from view completely during the dry season, it is possible that further species may yet be found in Kenya.

CULTIVATION

Several of these species have been maintained in cultivation for a number of years. They need a loose, open compost with good drainage and some feeding during the short season of active growth. After flowering, when they die down, the compost should be kept dry so that the hidden tubers do not perish.

Key to the species of *Cynorkis*
1 Spur straight or only slightly curved   2
   Spur markedly curved and much swollen
      at the apex . . . .   *C. uncata*

2 Lip entire, or obscurely 3-lobed at the
      apex only, sometimes with a very small
      lobule on each side at the base   3
   Lip distinctly 3-lobed about half way
      along . . . .   *C. kassneriana*

3 Lip quite entire . . . .   *C. anacamptoides*
   Lip 3-lobed at the apex and with distinct
      lobules at the base . . . .
   . . . .   *C. buchwaldiana* ssp. *braunii*

Cynorkis anacamptoides Kraenzlin
Terrestrial herb 10–60 cm high. Stem slender, erect, glandular-pubescent in the upper part, with 2–6 leaves at the base and smaller ones above. Leaves lanceolate, acute, up to 13 cm long, 8–18 mm wide, glabrous. Inflorescence many flowered, bracts glandular becoming smaller upwards. Flowers pink, mauve or purple; dorsal sepal ovate, very convex, 3 mm long; lateral sepals spreading, obliquely oblanceolate, 3.5–5 mm long; petals lanceolate, curved, cohering to the edge of the dorsal sepal, 3–4 mm long; lip ligulate, obtuse, 3–5 mm long, 1 mm wide, spur cylindrical, 3–5 mm long, slightly swollen in the apical half; column short.

In grassland on moorland and in bogs, marshes, swamps and by streams in highland rain forest; western Kenya and the slopes of the Aberdare Mts; 1850–3350 m; flowering more or less throughout the year.

Also recorded from Uganda and Tanzania; widespread in tropical Africa from Ethiopia across to Cameroon and south to Zimbabwe and Angola.

Cynorkis anacamptoides   BOB CAMPBELL

Cynorkis buchwaldiana Kraenzlin ssp. *braunii*
   (Kraenzlin) Summerhayes
   Syn. *Cynorkis braunii* Kraenzlin
Terrestrial herb 8–40 cm high, arising from small ellipsoid tubers. Stem slender, erect, with 2, rarely 3 leaves at the base and several glandular sheaths above. Leaves erect or spreading, lanceolate or elliptic, acuminate, 3–14 cm long, 1–3.5 cm wide, glabrous. Inflorescence lax with 3–30 flowers, rachis glandular hairy, bracts lanceolate, sparsely hairy. Flowers pink, mauve or purple, base of lip paler with dark spots; dorsal sepal ovate, 3–3.5 mm long; lateral sepals semiorbicular, obtuse, 4–5 mm long; petals ovate, 3–4 mm long; lip cuneate, shortly 3-lobed at the apex, midlobe equalling the side lobes, 6–8 mm long, with short rounded lobes on each side at the base, spur incurved, slender, 5–8 mm long; column *c.* 1.5 mm long.

In mountain forest; only known in Kenya from Mt Kasigau and Vuria peak in Teita district; 1700–2200 m; flowering in July to October.

Also recorded from Tanzania in the Usambara and Uluguru Mts.

Cynorkis kassneriana Kraenzlin
Terrestrial or sometimes epiphytic herb 15–50 cm high, arising from ellipsoid root tubers. Stem slender, erect, with a single leaf at the base, rarely 2, and several sheaths above. Leaf erect or spreading, lanceolate or oblanceolate, acute, 4–20 cm long, 1–4 cm wide, glabrous, sometimes mottled in several shades of green. Inflorescence densely flowered, 3–10 cm long, with 3–22 flowers, rachis glandular

hairy, bracts lanceolate, glandular-ciliate. Flowers lilac or pinkish purple; dorsal sepal very convex, ovate, 5–7 mm long; lateral sepals spreading, obliquely ovate or lanceolate-ovate, obtuse, 6–8 mm long; petals obliquely lanceolate, acute, 4–7 mm long; lip ovate or broadly lanceolate in outline, 3-lobed at about the middle, 5–8 mm long, 2–5 mm wide, the midlobe triangular and much longer than the side lobes, spur constricted in the middle and swollen at the apex, 6–9 mm long; column short and stout.

Mossy banks by streams, forest floor, and epiphytic on moss-covered trunks and branches; 2200–2800 m; flowering in September to November.

Also known from Tanzania, Uganda, Ethiopia, west to Zaïre and south to Malawi, Zimbabwe and South Africa (Transvaal).

Cynorkis kassneriana   BOB CAMPBELL

Cynorkis uncata (Rolfe) Kraenzlin
Terrestrial herb 10–35 cm high, arising from ellipsoid tubers. Stem sometimes prostrate at first, then erect, bearing 2 leaves and several sheaths above. Leaves spreading, lanceolate, elliptic or ovate, apiculate, 3.5–16 cm long, 1–5 cm wide, glabrous. Inflorescence rather lax, 3–17 flowers, glabrous, bracts lanceolate. Flowers pink, mauve or purple; dorsal sepal elliptic-ovate, obtuse, convex, 5 mm long; lateral sepals obliquely ovate, 4–6 mm long; petals obliquely ovate, acute, 4–6 mm long, 4 mm

wide; lip transversely elliptic from a narrow base, 3-lobed in front, 8–14 mm long and wide, side lobes large and rounded, midlobe smaller, spur strongly incurved with a wide mouth and swollen apex, 8 mm long; column stout, 2 mm long.

Shady paths and banks in highland forest, and among rocks; only known in Kenya on Maungu and Sagala hills in Teita district; 900–1650 m; flowering in May and June.

Also recorded from Tanzania.

Disa Bergius

The name of this genus was derived from Swedish folklore when the attractive South African species *Disa uniflora* was named. It has the largest flower in the genus and the bright red flower has attractive net-like markings on the inner surface of the dorsal sepal. This striking feature reminded the Swedish botanist Bergius of the tale of Disa, a beautiful lady, who appeared wrapped in a fishing net when invited to appear before the King 'neither naked nor clothed'.

Disa is one of the most striking of the terrestrial orchid genera in Africa because nearly all the species are brightly coloured. The plants have one or more tubers and fleshy roots, from which arise a leafy flowering stem and sometimes a separate leafy shoot adjacent to the main stem. The leaves are at the base of the stem in a rosette and sometimes along the stem, grading into the bracts. The flowers have a characteristic shape with three large sepals, the dorsal one usually bearing a spur. The petals are small, sometimes bilobed, and tucked inside the dorsal sepal. The lip is small and narrow, hanging vertically below the column which has a conspicuous stigma just below the anther.

Widespread in Africa south of the Sahara, including Madagascar and Réunion, with one species extending into the Arabian peninsula; approximately 120 species, the greatest proportion of them endemic in Cape Province, South Africa.

CULTIVATION

None of the Kenya species of *Disa* has been maintained in cultivation, either in a pot or in garden conditions, for more than one or two seasons. Great care must be taken to ensure the correct underground conditions of moisture or dryness for the seasonal growth of the plant.

Disa scutellifera

K.O.S.

Key to the species of *Disa*

1   Plants with fewer than 8 rather large
flowers . . . . **D. erubescens**
Plants with a dense spike of many
flowers 2

2   Flowers yellow or orange . . **D. ochrostachya**
Flowers pink, red or purplish, bright or
dull 3

3   Anther erect; spur pendent at the base . . . 4
Anther reflexed to a horizontal position;
spur horizontal or ascending at the
base 6

4   Petals entire, simple . . . .
. . . . **D. fragrans** ssp. **deckenii**
Petals bilobed 5

5   Posterior petal lobe narrow and linear . . . . . .
. . . . **D. scutellifera**
Posterior petal lobe ovate or lanceolate,
acute . . . . . **D. welwitschii** ssp. **occultans**

6   Flowers bright pink or magenta . . **D. stairsii**
Flowers dull mauve or dirty white
mottled with purple 7

7   Spur straight, inflated, short and wide . . . . . .
. . . . **D. aconitoides** ssp. **goetzeana**
Spur curved and slender, at least in the
upper half 8

8   Flowers basically dull purplish red; lip
linear, similar in colour to the rest of
the flower . . . . **D. hircicornis**
Flowers basically white mottled with
purple; lip elliptic-spathulate, white . . . .
. . . . **D. perplexa**

Disa aconitoides Sonder ssp. *goetzeana* (Kraenzlin) Linder

Plants usually slender, 25–60 cm high. Leaves cauline, lanceolate to narrowly ovate, 4–8 cm long, and sometimes also 2 on a separate sterile shoot. Inflorescence narrow with 15–70 dull flowers, pale mauve or dirty white heavily marked with darkish mauve. Flowers facing down at an angle of 45°; dorsal sepal ovate to elliptic, dominated by the deep and laterally flattened, horizontally carried spur 4–6 mm long; lateral sepals narrowly oblong, acute, keeled on the back with a short apiculus, spreading horizontally forwards, 5–7 mm long; petals erect, oblong, 3.5–5 mm high; lip narrowly elliptic, rounded on the upper surface, extending forward, about 5 mm long.

In grassland, often among scattered bushes in areas that were formerly forested; in the highlands west of the Rift Valley; 2100–2800 m; flowers between March and June.

Recorded from a wide range of habitats in the uplands of Tanzania, Uganda and Ethiopia as well as Kenya. This orchid was previously known as *Disa goetzeana* and as *Disa concinna* in Kenya; the latter is now recognised as another subspecies of *Disa aconitoides* in the highlands of Zimbabwe, Zambia and Malawi. *Disa aconitoides* ssp. *aconitoides* is restricted to South Africa.

Disa erubescens   K.O.S.

Disa erubescens Rendle
Plants slender, 40–90 cm high. Leaves 2–3, on a separate sterile shoot, up to 30 cm long, 2 cm wide; cauline leaves shorter and narrower, imbricate, grading upwards into the bracts; the lower sheaths on both shoots spotted with red. Inflorescence lax with 3–8 (rarely 12) bright orange red flowers of distinctive character. Flowers large, 3–6 cm in diameter; dorsal sepal spathulate with a shallow galea at the end of a narrow, erect claw, 11–26 mm long, galea 12–24 mm long, spotted with red or purple on the inner surface, facing downwards with slender, ascending spur 8–16 mm long; lateral sepals

obliquely oblong, spreading upwards, 17–35 mm long; petals bilobed, the lobe tips often yellow with red spots, anterior lobe ovate, spreading from either side of the anther, posterior lobe longer, linear and curved in the upper half, ascending, inside the galea; lip linear, acute, 9–20 mm long.

In short upland grassland particularly where drainage is poor, and in swamps; throughout the highland areas of Kenya west of the Rift Valley; 1550–2800 m; flowers in June and July.

Widespread in montane areas of tropical Africa and Kenya to Nigeria and Sudan to Zimbabwe.

Disa fragrans Schlechter ssp. *deckenii*
    (Reichenbach f.) Linder
Plants short but robust, 5–50 cm high. Leaves usually 2, on a separate sterile shoot, narrowly elliptic, 7–20 cm long, 1–3 cm wide; cauline leaves wider and imbricate, 3–10 cm long and grading upwards into the bracts. Inflorescence dense, with 10–150 bright pink, rose, or crimson flowers. Flowers small, about 8 mm in diameter; dorsal sepal erect, with incurved margins, with a cylindrical spur 4–6 mm long; petals entire, lanceolate, acute, erect

Disa fragrans ssp. *deckenii*   D.J. WARREN-GASH

with the tips curved over the anther; lip ligulate, pendent, scarcely 1 mm wide.

Grassy glades at the upper edges of forest and among *Erica arborea*, and in stony and rocky places on hilltops; widespread, but not common, in the Kenya highlands; 2100–3300 m; flowers from June to October.

Formerly known as *Disa deckenii*, this subspecies of *Disa fragrans* occurs on the higher mountains of eastern Africa: Kivu, in Zaïre, Kilimanjaro, the uplands of Kenya, the peaks in the Karamoja district of Uganda, the Imatong mountains of Sudan and the Ethiopian highlands.

Disa hircicornis Reichenbach f.

Plants slender to robust, 30–85 cm high. Leaves 2, on a separate sterile shoot, up to 30 cm long and 2 cm wide; cauline leaves lanceolate, acute; all leaves mottled or barred with red to some extent. Inflorescence dense with 16–70 pale pink to dull red or dusky purple flowers, bracts usually longer than the flowers and reflexed at their apices. Flowers medium size, 10–12 mm in diameter, facing down at an angle of 45°; dorsal sepal elliptic to ovate with a distinctive spur that has a large conical base but soon tapers to a slender cylinder and is

sharply decurved in the slender part, 8–13 mm long; lateral sepals usually deflexed, oblong, apiculate; petals erect, obovate-oblong, the apex curved over the column; lip linear, pendent, up to 5 mm long.

Wet grassland and swamps, often near streams in the Kitale area; 950–2550 m; flowers from June to September.

Widespread in the montane zones of Africa from Kenya and Nigeria southwards to Natal.

Disa ochrostachya Reichenbach f.

Plants slender or robust, 35–100 cm high. Leaves 2–3, reddish, on a separate sterile shoot, 15–20 cm long, up to 4 cm wide; the cauline leaves narrower and gradually decreasing in size as they approach the bracts. Inflorescence dense, with 50–200 bright yellow or yellow mottled with orange flowers. Flowers about 10 mm in diameter; dorsal sepal erect or curved to face downwards, with a narrow,

Disa hircicornis   K.O.S.

Disa ochrostachya   ERIC LA CROIX

sometimes apically inflated spur 7–12 mm long; petals erect, unequally 2-lobed at or above the middle; lip linear, pendent, up to 9 mm long.

Upland grassland and grassy forest glades; in the highlands west of the Rift Valley; 1450–2650 m; flowers in July and August.

Widely distributed in the montane regions of Africa south of Sudan and reaching as far south as the eastern highlands of Zimbabwe.

Disa perplexa Linder

Plants slender to robust, 30–90 cm tall. Leaves cauline, lanceolate, sheathing. Inflorescence dense with many dull white, purple mottled flowers, often overtopped by the bracts. Flowers medium size, 8–12 mm in diameter, facing down; dorsal sepal elliptic to ovate with a distinctive spur that is at first horizontal from a small conical base, then decurved and cylindrical, 9–11 mm long; lateral sepals spreading, oblong, obtuse; petals oblong, erect, included in the galea; lip white, elliptic-spathulate, 3–5 mm long.

Wet grassland and swamps, only known from two localities in the Kitale area; c. 2000 m; flowers in June.

Widespread in eastern Africa from Kenya south to Zimbabwe and one collection from Cameroon; apparently rather rare.

Disa scutellifera A. Richard

Plants robust, 25–75 cm high. Leaves 2–4, on a separate, sterile shoot, up to 20 cm long, 2 cm wide; cauline leaves smaller and with the upper part forming an ovate, acute blade, the lower part sheathing, grading upwards into the bracts. Inflorescence dense, with 14–80 pink flowers, sometimes spotted with darker colour. Flowers up to 2 cm in diameter; dorsal sepal up to 10 mm long, shallowly hooded, sometimes white with purple spots, spur pendent, 4–14 mm long; lateral sepals obliquely oblong, spreading sideways and upwards; petals bilobed, the anterior lobe ovate, spreading on the sides of the anther, the posterior lobe slightly longer, linear, erect inside the galea; lip linear, pendent, 6–10 mm long.

Damp grassland and grassy, rocky slopes; in the highlands west of the Rift Valley and on Mt Kenya; 1800–2400 m; flowers mainly in June and July with some specimens collected in flower in May and August.

Widely distributed in the highlands of northeastern Africa, in the mountains of Ethiopia, the Imatong mountains of Sudan and the peaks of the Karamoja district of Uganda as well as Kenya.

Disa scutellifera   K.O.S.

Disa stairsii Kraenzlin

Plants robust, to 90 cm high, without tubers and with no separate leafy shoot beside the flowering stem. Leaves cauline, sometimes several forming a rosette at the base of the stem and surrounded by the narrower ones of other young shoots, up to 30 cm long and 4 cm wide. Inflorescence thick and dense with many pink, crimson or purplish flowers partly hidden among the reddish bracts. Flowers medium size, 12–20 mm in diameter; dorsal sepal erect with a deep galea, margins incurved, with a slender spur 16–20 mm long; lateral sepals oblong, rounded, margins incurved; petals erect, oblong-lanceolate; lip narrowly oblong, 7.5–9 mm long.

Occasionally epiphytic, usually terrestrial in the bamboo and ericoid vegetation of high mountains, often in swamps; 2100–3750 m; flowers throughout the year.

Only known from the high mountains of eastern Zaïre, Uganda and northern Tanzania as well as Kenya.

Disa welwitschii Reichenbach f. ssp. *occultans* (Schlechter) Linder

Plants very variable in size, slender to robust, 20–95 cm high. Leaves 2–4, on a separate sterile shoot, up to 30 cm long, 1–4 cm wide; cauline leaves smaller and sheathing; both shoots have small basal

Disa stairsii   HERMANN MEYER

Disa welwitschii ssp. *occultans*   ERIC LA CROIX

leaves or sheaths that are striped or blotched with red. Inflorescence dense with 20–100 pink, carmine or magenta flowers that are sometimes spotted with deeper colour. Flowers small to medium size, 5–15 mm in diameter; dorsal sepal 5–13 mm high, erect, narrow, with a slender or slightly inflated spur 4–8 mm long; lateral sepals narrowly ovate, spreading, 5–13 mm long; petals bilobed, the anterior lobe ovate, spreading, the posterior lobe as long as or up to one-third longer than the anterior and lanceolate or oblanceolate; lip linear, pendent, 4–12 mm long.

Damp grasslands and swamps; in the highlands of Kenya west of the Rift Valley; 1500–2000 m; always at lower altitudes than *Disa scutellifera* with which it has often been confused; flowers between June and August.

Widely distributed in the montane areas of tropical Africa, from Kenya south to Zambia and westwards as far as Liberia. Previously known in East Africa under the names *Disa occultans* and *Disa subaequalis* in Kenya and *Disa tanganyikensis* in Tanzania.

Disperis Swartz

The little plants of the genus *Disperis* are amongst the easiest of African orchids to recognise but are rather rarely collected. All the species produce leaves, flowers, fruits and seeds, and die down again within a very short period, usually during the rains. In Kenya they are nearly all forest or woodland plants, growing in mossy, shady places, sometimes as epiphytes. They have delicate dark green leaves that are often deep purple on the lower surface and sometimes attractively veined with silver. In the flowers the dorsal sepal and petals cohere along their edges to form a shallow or peaked hood, on the top of the flower, while the lateral sepals each have a conspicuous pouch. It is this feature that gave the Swedish botanist Olof Swartz the inspiration for the name of the genus, from the two Greek words *dis* (twice) and *pera* (pouch). Overall, the flowers appear triangular in shape, and come in a variety of colours from white, through pink and carmine and sometimes yellow. The most intriguing feature of all is the lip that curves back over the column and lies tucked into the hood of the dorsal sepal. Sometimes the lip ends in a curious linear appendage that lies parallel with the main blade of the lip.

About 75 species of *Disperis* are now recognised and the genus is distributed throughout Africa from Togo to Ethiopia and south to Cape Province, South Africa. Nearly half the species are

South African, where many of the species grow in grasslands and are vegetatively rather different from the forest species. Of the eight species recorded from Kenya only one (the inconspicuous *Disperis pusilla*) is a grassland species. The genus is also represented in the Mascarene Islands, India and New Guinea.

CULTIVATION

Several species have been kept alive for a number of seasons with the small underground tubers buried in a loose, open compost that resembles the humus of the forest floor. Over-watering when the plants are dormant must be avoided. When a number of tubers are planted together in a shallow pan a very attractive flowering can be achieved.

Key to the species of *Disperis*

1   Leaves opposite   2
     Leaves 1 or absent, or arranged
         alternately along the stem   4

2   Dorsal sepal and petals forming a short,
         rounded hood but never a spur . . . .
         . . . . **D. dicerochila**
     Dorsal sepal extended into a long
         narrow spur   3

3   Lip elongated, reaching the end of the
         spur where it is recurved and
         terminates in a flattened appendage,
         9 mm long, which nearly reaches the
         spur opening . . . . **D. nemorosa**
     Lip 8–15 mm long but not reaching the
         end of the spur, terminating in a
         recurved, fringe-like apex . . **D. anthoceros**

4   Leaf single or absent   5
     Leaves 2–4, alternate   6

5   Plant hairy, leaf single . . . . **D. pusilla**
     Plant hairless, leaf absent . . . . **D. aphylla**

6   Flowers white, tinged with pink or green . . . .
         . . . . **D. kilimanjarica**
     Flowers deep rose pink or magenta   7

7   Dorsal sepal and petals forming a rather
         open, saucer-shaped hood . . . .
         . . . . **D. reichenbachiana**
     Dorsal sepal and petals extended into a
         long narrow spur . . . . **D. egregia**

Disperis anthoceros Reichenbach f.

Herb 8–30 cm tall, arising from a single oblong tuber. Leaves 2, opposite, sheathing at the base, truncate or cordate above the sheath, ovate, 1–4 cm long, 1–3 cm wide, purple beneath. Inflorescence erect with 1–3 flowers, bracts leaf-like *c.* 1 cm long and wide. Flowers white tinged green or pale pinkish; dorsal sepal forming a long slender, vertical spur up to 2 cm long, greenish; lateral sepals sometimes pink-spotted, obliquely obovate, 6–15 mm long, 3–10 mm wide, united to the middle, bearing conical sacs to 1.5 mm deep; petals narrow and falcate, auriculate at the base; lip elongate, linear, 8–15 mm long, not reaching the apex of the spur, appendage short and fringed.

Found in the ground litter of evergreen forest and conifer plantations, also in bamboo forest; often in dense colonies but not common, in western Kenya; 2700–3000 m; flowering in June and July.

Also recorded in Uganda and Tanzania, westwards to Rwanda, Burundi, Zaïre and Nigeria, north to Sudan and Ethiopia and south to Malawi,

Disperis anthoceros   ERIC LA CROIX

Zambia, Zimbabwe and South Africa (Transvaal and Natal).

Disperis aphylla Kraenzlin

Herb 8–16 cm tall, arising from 1–2 densely hairy small tubers. Leaf absent but one or two sheaths present near the base of the stem, occasionally with one small ovate leaf, purplish beneath. Inflorescence erect with 2–6 flowers, bracts leaf-like, 4–8 mm long. Flowers white, sometimes tinged pink or green; dorsal sepal forming a spur with petals, 3–4 mm long; lateral sepals sometimes tinged pink, irregularly ovate, 3–4 mm long, 2–3 mm wide, free, with small sacs to 1 mm deep; petals irregularly triangular; lip slender with antler-shaped appendages near the apex.

Only known from leaf litter in dense evergreen forest in Kakamega and the Shimba hills; 330–1700 m; flowering in May to July.

Also recorded from Uganda, Zaïre, Cameroon and Angola.

Disperis dicerochila Summerhayes

Herb 6–25 cm tall, arising from a small ellipsoid or round tuber. Leaves 2, opposite, sheathing at the base, rounded or cordate above the sheath, ovate or ovate-lanceolate, 1.5–5 cm long, 1–3 cm wide, often purplish beneath. Inflorescence erect with 1–3 flowers, bracts leaf-like, lanceolate. Flowers white, tinged rose or purple, or entirely magenta;

dorsal sepal 7–10 mm long, forming an open boat-shaped hood with the petals; lateral sepals rhomboid-ovate, 7–10 mm long, 4–7 mm wide, free, with obtuse sacs 1.5–2 mm deep; petals elliptic or curved, 7–10 mm long; lip linear, with 2 2-lobed appendages at the apex.

In leaf litter and on mossy branches, also on rocks, in rain forests and plantations; Aberdare Mts and west of the Rift Valley; 2200–2830 m; flowering in June, also recorded in December.

Also recorded from Uganda, Ethiopia and the southern highlands of Tanzania, westwards to Rwanda, Burundi, and Zaïre, southwards to Malawi, Zambia and Zimbabwe.

Geerinck (1984) records *Disperis thomensis* from Kenya but I have not seen Kenya material of this species. It is widespread in West Africa and is much smaller than *Disperis dicerochila* with white flowers and deeper sacs on the lateral sepals.

Disperis egregia Summerhayes

Herb 8–18 cm tall. Leaves 2, distinctly alternate but close together on the stem, sheathing at the base, ovate, 2–5 cm long, 1.5–4 cm wide. Inflorescence erect, bearing 3 flowers in narrowly ovate, leaf-like bracts. Flowers bright rose pink; dorsal sepal joined to the petals and forming a curved, helmet-like spur 12 mm long; lateral sepals joined for more than half their length, 8–10 mm long, 12 mm wide, with conical sacs 5 mm deep; petals irregularly 3-lobed, 12 mm long, 6 mm wide; lip 10 mm long, slender, with a carrot shaped apical appendage.

Disperis dicerochila   BOB CAMPBELL

Disperis egregia   BOB CAMPBELL

On mossy rock faces in forest; only known from isolated hills in Teita district; 900–1050 m; flowering in May and June.

Only known elsewhere in Tanzania, in the Usambara Mts.

Disperis kilimanjarica Rendle
Herb 7–12 cm tall, arising from a small ovoid tuber and spreading by underground shoots which produce more tubers. Leaves 2, alternate, sheathing at the base, cordate above the sheath, ovate, 1.2–3 cm long, 1–2 cm wide. Inflorescence short, erect with a single flower in a leaf-like bract. Flower white tinged green, or green and dull mauve, margined with pink or mauve along the edge of the hood; dorsal sepal hooded, forming a short, wide mouthed spur with the petals, 8–16 mm long, narrowed upwards; lateral sepals obliquely ovate, 6–12 mm long, 4–5 mm wide, free, with sacs 2 mm deep; petals irregularly oblong, 8 mm long, 4 mm wide; lip 6 mm long, widened towards the apex and bearing a ligulate appendage below its recurved tip.

Dense shade of evergreen forest, on branches covered with mosses and liverworts or in leaf litter; epiphytic on stunted trees and bushes on the Ngong hills and also on the Aberdare Mts, Mt Elgon and Mt Kenya; 2300–3000 m; flowering in July to October.

Also known elsewhere from the Uganda side of Mt Elgon, Mt Kilimanjaro in Tanzania, the montane forests of Rwanda, Burundi, Malawi and Zambia.

Disperis kilimanjarica　　　　　　BOB CAMPBELL

Disperis nemorosa Rendle
Herb 8–28 cm tall, arising from 1 or 2 small oblong tubers, spreading by tuber-producing underground stems. Leaves 2–4, opposite, sheathing at the base, cuneate to truncate above the sheath, ovate, 2.5–7 cm long, 2–4 cm wide. Inflorescence erect, with 1–4 flowers, bracts leaf-like, ovate or ovate-lanceolate. Flowers white or white and mauve; dorsal sepal joined with petals to form a very slender, horizontal spur, 10–15 mm long; lateral sepals free, irregularly oblong, oblique, 7–8 mm long, with sacs 1–1.5 mm deep; petals rounded, auriculate at the base; lip long and slender, with a long appendage directed back towards the mouth of the spur, appendage enlarged and papillose at the apex.

Mossy places and leaf litter on the floor of cool, shady forests; widespread in Kenya, in the bamboo zone on Mt Kenya and the Aberdare Mts, in the Chyulu and Teita hills, and in western Kenya; 1800–2830 m; flowering in July and September.

Also recorded in Uganda, Tanzania, Malawi and Zambia.

Disperis pusilla Verdcourt
Herb 2–4 cm tall, arising from a small round tuber, the whole plant densely covered with short papilla-like hairs. Leaf 1, sheathing at the base, cordate above the sheath, ovate, 6–8 mm long. Inflorescence erect, bearing 1 flower in a leaf-like bract. Flower yellow, yellowish brown or red; dorsal sepal and petals forming an open hood 8 mm long; lateral sepals semicircular, 6 mm long, with sacs less than 1 mm deep; petals oblong-linear, falcate, 8 mm long; lip expanded to form a triangular limb with narrow tip.

Grassland, especially in boggy places; only known from a collection on the Cherangani hills; 2700 m; flowering in May.

Also recorded from Tanzania, Zaïre and Zambia.

Disperis reichenbachiana Reichenbach f.
Herb 8–25 cm tall, arising from small ellipsoid to globose tubers. Leaves 2–4, alternate, ovate, elliptic-ovate or lanceolate-ovate, cordate, mostly purple beneath and often with silvery venation. Inflorescence erect with 1–5 flowers held horizontally, bracts elliptic, leaf-like. Flowers mauve or magenta sometimes marked with yellow; dorsal sepal joined to petals to form an open, obovate or rhomboid hood c. 1 cm long; lateral sepals obliquely oblong, 4–10 mm long, 4–5 mm wide, free or united for about a quarter of their length, with

shallow sacs to 1 mm deep; petals triangular-elliptic, 8–10 mm long; lip white or yellowish 6.5–8 mm long, sharply bent back on itself near the base and bearing a stout 2-lobed appendage at the bend.

Disperis reichenbachiana   BOB CAMPBELL

In leaf mould on the forest floor and in rock crevices in grassland and bush; widely scattered in Kenya; 1500–2330 m; flowering in May to July.

Also known from Uganda and Tanzania; widespread in tropical Africa, westwards to Rwanda, Burundi, Zaïre and Sao Tome, and southwards to Zambia, Zimbabwe and Angola.

Epipactis Zinn

Most of the species in this genus are rather robust, terrestrial herbs with long inflorescences above tall leafy stems. About 25 species have been recognised in the temperate regions of the world, including three in the cooler parts of the mountains of eastern Africa. The most widespread of these, *Epipactis africana*, is the only one so far recorded from Kenya.

The name *Epipactis* is an ancient Greek word for which *helleborine* is an alternative. The type of the genus, and a common species in Europe, is *Epipactis helleborine*, the broad-leaved helleborine.

CULTIVATION

Some of the European and Chinese species are grown without difficulty as potplants. Maintained in a suitable soil mix, with proper attention to a resting period or winter conditions, they make attractive specimens in an alpine house and sometimes outside. A few hybrids have also been created and are easily grown. Because of its great length the African species would be rather difficult to manage in a pot, but plants might succeed in frost-free gardens.

Epipactis africana   BOB CAMPBELL

Epipactis africana Rendle

An erect terrestrial herb up to 3.5 m tall, covered with brownish hairs in most parts. Stem up to 1 cm thick at the base, 2 cm thick in the middle, purplish or bluish green. Leaves arranged along the stem, at intervals of 5–10 cm, lanceolate to ovate, strongly veined, up to 20 cm long, 9 cm wide, the lowermost reduced to sheaths, uppermost bract-like. Inflorescence elongate, with several or many flowers. Flowers hanging, not very conspicuous, greyish purple on the outer surface, greenish yellow within, some orange-brown on the lip; dorsal sepal lanceolate, acuminate, 2 cm long; lateral sepals oblique, ovate, acuminate, slightly longer; petals lanceolate to ovate, up to 2.5 cm long, with a warty, keeled midvein on the outer surface; lip up to 2.5 cm long, hypochile concave, warty, bearing long side lobes, epichile broadly ovate, acute, margins upturned, the warty callus on the midline extending to the base.

In evergreen and bamboo forests on the mountains, also among *Pteridium*, *Erica* and patches of coarse grass by mountain streams; recorded from Mt Elgon, the Cherangani hills, Mau forests, Aberdares and Mt Kenya; 2300–3750 m; flowers between October and January.

Widespread in the highlands of eastern Africa, from Zaïre eastwards to Ethiopia and south to Malawi.

Epipogium R. Brown

Only two species are known in this curious genus, one of which is distributed throughout the temperate parts of Europe and Asia and the other is found in the tropics of the Old World. The plants lack chlorophyll and spend the whole of their lives in close association with mycorrhizal fungi. They have sometimes been called saprophytes, but may be more accurately described as parasites upon their associated fungi. The name is derived from two Greek words *epi* (on) and *pogon* (beard), referring to the turned up lip that has a fanciful resemblance to a beard.

The leafless plants are a dull pinkish-brown colour and bear a few sheath-like, brownish leaves towards the base. The flowers are usually nodding, white or pinkish and sometimes spotted in a darker colour. They are often self-pollinated at an early age and the ovary swells up to become a conspicuous part of the flower. Seeds are dispersed within a few days.

CULTIVATION

Unknown and rather unlikely considering the very short life of the flowering stage of these plants.

Epipogium roseum (D. Don) Lindley
Plants growing from a tuberous horizontal rhizome, which is ovoid, composed of many nodes and up to 5 cm long. Flowering scape to 60 cm, fleshy, brownish below, white above. Inflorescence up to 20 cm long, many flowered, bracts ovate, up to 1.5 cm long. Flowers creamy white to dull, dirty pink, with small purplish or pinkish spots, rather drooping and not opening fully; sepals lanceolate, acute, up to 1 cm long; petals similar to the sepals but shorter; lip as long as the tepals, broadly ovate, bearing two verrucose crests from the base to near the apex, margins upturned near the base, spur broad, *c.* 4 mm long; column very short.

Forest floor, often in leaf litter in deep shade; only known at present from Mt Elgon; flowering in

March. This species is notoriously little known because of the very short time in which the flowering stems complete their life cycle above the ground: only a few days are required for the development of the scape, flowering, and the release of seeds. It will almost certainly be found in other suitable localities in due course.

Widespread in the warm tropics from West Africa to the Indo-Malaysia region, Australia and the New Hebrides.

Eulophia Lindley

Syn. *Lissochilus* Lindley

This well-known genus was established by John Lindley in 1821. The name refers to the crest or hairs on the lip that are a conspicuous feature in many of the species. It is derived from two Greek words *eu* (well or good) and *lophos* (plume). Robert Brown had proposed the name *Lissochilus* two years earlier for *Eulophia speciosa* and other species in which the sepals are much smaller than the petals and usually reflexed behind the flower. Many discussions have taken place about the distinctness of the two genera. Now and for about the last 100 years, authors have included *Lissochilus* in *Eulophia* and there is international agreement that this treatment should be followed even though the name *Lissochilus* was actually published earlier. Geerinck has gone further in his account of the orchids of Rwanda (1988), also including *Oeceoclades* and *Pteroglossaspis* in *Eulophia*. I have followed Cribb (1989) in keeping these three genera separate.

Eulophia is a large genus with representatives distributed worldwide. They occur in the Caribbean, and tropical parts of the Americas, in Australia, and throughout tropical and subtropical parts of Asia. Most of the 250 species are to be found in Africa, with a few in Madagascar, and 31 have so far been recorded in Kenya. Many have colourful flowers that show up well among the grasses with which they mostly grow. Being essentially a tropical genus, most of the species are found at low and medium altitudes, below 2200 m. (The terrestrial orchids with brightly coloured flowers at higher altitudes are usually species of *Disa* and *Satyrium*.)

Eulophia is also a very diverse genus. Most species have green leaves but these are not always present at flowering time. They are usually associated with the growth of a new pseudobulb, which may be underground or upright at or just above the soil surface. Some species have a slender rhizome underground, which grows from year to year, but in others there are chains of pear shaped or flattened pseudobulbs. Each new shoot bears two or more leaves and is separate from the flowering stem that arises from the mature pseudobulb, either alongside the leaves, or before or after they have developed fully. The inflorescence is usually simple and upright, up to 100 cm tall, but it can be much taller in the robust *Eulophia horsfallii* and taller still and branching in the dry-country species, *Eulophia petersii*. The flowers are also extremely varied, in colour, size and shape. Almost every colour is represented. At the apex of the column, under the easily-moved anther cap, there are always two bright yellow pollinia attached by a short stipe to a large sticky viscidium. The complete pollinarium is very similar to that of the genus *Cymbidium*, to which *Eulophia* is probably rather closely related.

CULTIVATION

The Kenya species of *Eulophia* can be divided into two groups from the cultivation viewpoint. Those that have pseudobulbs above the ground are amongst the easiest of terrestrial orchids to grow and flower. These include the first seven species listed in the key below. They require only a loose, well-drained compost in a suitable container and some attention to with-holding water when the plants are clearly at 'rest'. Under these conditions the development of large plants that flower at their usual season every year is assured. The remaining species are much more difficult, chiefly because they have underground chains of pseudobulbs or rhizomes and it is very difficult to know whether these are 'resting' or about to start into new growth. Such plants are easily over-watered and killed off, but some meticulous growers have been able to maintain these species for a number of seasons. I have had some success with *Eulophia cucullata*, *E. speciosa*, *E. milnei* and *E. subulata*, but lost them all within five years of bringing them into cultivation. Continued vigilance is difficult, and there are also accidents.

Some of the swamp-growing species, notably *Eulophia horsfallii* and *Eulophia latilabris*, are easier because they require a constant supply of water. Some very spectacular container-grown plants of these species have been seen at orchid shows in Nairobi at various times.

Key to the species of *Eulophia*

1 Plants with conspicuous ovoid, conical or cylindric pseudobulbs above the ground 2
Plants with a rhizome or chain of pseudobulbs underground 8

2 Leaves thick, tough and leathery with a serrated edge 3
Leaves thin, plicate at least when young, edge entire 5

3 Inflorescence usually a tall branching panicle; sepals bent back away from the column or rolled up from the apex . . . . *E. petersii*
Inflorescence usually simple or with one branch; sepals erect or spreading 4

4 Leaves 6 or more; sepals and petals 19–25 mm long . . . . *E. taitensis*
Leaves usually 4; sepals and petals 10 mm long or smaller . . . . *E. serrata*

5 Sepals and petals similar; lip pink or whitish 6
Sepals about half as long as petals; lip yellow 7

6 Lip pale pink, white at the base . . . . *E. guineensis*
Lip white or greenish white, flushed mauve, faintly veined with purple or with purplish hairs . . . *E. tanganyikensis*

7 Leaves never more than 2 cm wide . . . . *E. stenophylla*
Leaves 4–10 cm wide . . . . *E. streptopetala*

8 Sepals bent back along the ovary or spreading away from the petals 9
Sepals not bent back, usually similar to the petals and held close to them 20

9 Petals yellow, green or brownish 10
Petals pink or mauve 15

10 Sepals about half as long as petals 11
Sepals nearly as long or longer than the petals 13

11 Flowers bright yellow, sometimes with a
    little red or purple marking on the lip
    which lacks a spur . . . . *E. speciosa*
    Flowers reddish or brownish yellow,
    veined or lined with red on the inner
    surface of the petals 12

12 Spur 12–16 mm long . . . . . *E. orthoplectra*
    Spur 8–9 mm long . . . . . . *E. schweinfurthii*

13 Petals 16–25 mm long; plants of swampy
    places . . . . *E. angolensis*
    Petals less than 10 mm long; plants of
    dry grassland and rocky places 14

14 Petals less than 5 mm long; spur 1 mm
    long or less . . . . *E. parvula*
    Petals 6–8 mm long; spur 1.5–2.5 mm
    long . . . . *E. pyrophila*

15 Sepals and petals very similar 16
    Sepals much narrower than petals 17

16 Lip with numerous longitudinal ridges
    divided like teeth . . . . *E. cristata*
    Lip with thickened veins but no distinct
    raised ridges . . . . *E. livingstoniana*

17 Robust plants with flowering stems over
    1 m tall 18
    Flowering stems less than 90 cm tall 19

18 Lip distinctly 3-lobed; petals longer than
    wide . . . . *E. horsfallii*
    Lip indistinctly 3-lobed; petals round,
    or wider than long . . . . *E. latilabris*

19 Lip bearing two square thickenings in
    the throat . . . . *E. cucullata*
    Lip bearing 3 or more low keels along
    the midlobe . . . . *E. calantha*

20 Plant a leafless, whitish or greyish
    saprophyte, without leaves . . . .
    . . . . *E. galeoloides*
    Plants green or purplish with normal
    green leaves 21

21 Flowers pink, mauve or white . . . .
    . . . . *E. montis-elgonis*
    Flowers yellowish, greenish, brownish,
    or of mixed colours 22

22 Sepals and petals similar in colour, clear
    pure yellow 23
    Sepals and petals of different colours,
    or not clear yellow 25

23 Flowers small, widely spaced along a
    lax raceme . . . . *E. milnei*
    Flowers large, close together at the top
    of the raceme 24

24 Lip with deep red or brownish papillae . . . .
    . . . . *E. zeyheri*
    Lip with yellow or orange papillae . . . .
    . . . . *E. subulata*

25 Petals white . . . . *E. stachyodes*
    Petals white with reddish stripes, or
    greenish, brownish or yellowish 26

26 Petals cream or pale yellow with red
    stripes or veins . . . . *E. clitellifera*
    Petals not striped or veined in a different
    colour 27

27 Sepals and petals greenish, lip green or
    mauve 28
    Sepals brown or brownish, petals cream
    or yellow 29

28 Petals 15–20 mm long . . . . . *E. adenoglossa*
    Petals 8–12 mm long . . . . *E. kyimbilae*

29 Petals more than 9 mm long 30
    Petals less than 8 mm long 32

30 Inflorescence stalk entirely covered with
    overlapping chaffy sheaths . . . .
    . . . . *E. odontoglossa*
    Inflorescence stalk not entirely covered,
    sheaths not overlapping 31

31 Petals ovate, tapering to a bluntly
    pointed apex . . . . *E. ovalis*
    Petals oblong to elliptic-oblong or
    slightly obovate-oblong, pointed or
    blunt . . . . *E. clavicornis*

32 Petals 5 mm long or less; spur 1 mm
    long . . . . *E. parvula*
    Petals 6–8 mm long; spur 1.5–2.5 mm
    long . . . . *E. pyrophila*

Eulophia adenoglossa (Lindley) Reichenbach f. Plants 45–75 cm tall. Underground organ a chain of ovoid or ellipsoid pseudoulbs. Leaves 2–3, appearing with the flowers, plicate, erect, linear, 18–40 cm long, 5–8 cm wide. Inflorescence up to 75 cm high, with many flowers. Flowers green, sepals and petals yellowish green, lip green or pale purple with dark purple venation on the side lobes and purple papillae; dorsal sepal lanceolate, acute, 15–25 mm long, 4–6 mm wide; lateral sepals lanceolate, acute, 17–28 mm long, 5–7 mm wide; petals narrowly oblong, obtuse, 15–21 mm long, 4–5 mm wide; lip 3-lobed, 20 mm long, 10 mm wide, side lobes rounded, midlobe almost quadrate, callus of 2 ridges terminating in papillae, spur incurved, 2–5 mm long; column 8 mm long.

In grassland and on rocky ground, only in Kavirondo district; 1330–1700 m; flowering in April.

Also recorded in Tanzania, westwards to Ghana and southwards to South Africa (Natal).

bearing many roots. Leaves 2–4, present with the flowers, plicate, erect, linear-lanceolate, 50–120 cm long, 1–4 cm wide. Inflorescence usually simple, erect, with many flowers borne over a long period. Flowers spreading or almost pendent, with purplish-brown sepals and yellow petals and lip; dorsal sepal erect, ligulate-spathulate, obtuse, 16–27 mm long, 5–7 mm wide; lateral sepals similar but somewhat reflexed, 16–25 mm long, 5–7 mm wide; petals parallel to and hiding column, elliptic, rounded at apex, 16–25 mm long, 9–14 mm wide; lip 3-lobed, saccate at base, 16–25 mm long, 10–16 mm wide, side lobes elliptic, rounded, midlobe oblong or obovate, callus of 3 tall ridges becoming flexuous in front; column 9–11 mm long.

In marshes, swamps and seasonally flooded grasslands; widespread; sea level to 2500 m; flowering from March to July.

Also recorded from Uganda and Tanzania, and throughout Africa, westwards from Kenya to the Gambia and south to South Africa (Natal).

Eulophia adenoglossa   ERIC LA CROIX

Eulophia angolensis   K.O.S.

Eulophia angolensis (Lindley) Reichenbach f. Plants 60–200 cm tall. Underground organ a fleshy rhizome with many nodes, 1–5 cm in diameter and

Eulophia calantha Schlechter
Plants 20–75 cm high. Underground organ a chain of irregularly shaped pseudobulbs on a slender rhizome. Leaves 1–2, appearing after the flowers,

erect, linear, 25–40 cm long, 5 mm wide. Inflorescence with 3–7 flowers. Flowers white flushed with pinkish mauve, lip deep pink; dorsal sepal strongly reflexed, oblong-lanceolate, acuminate, 13–16 mm long, 3–4 mm wide; lateral sepals strongly reflexed, oblong, acuminate, 13–16 mm long, 3–4 mm wide; petals elliptic or obovate, 17–20 mm long, 8–10 mm wide; lip 3-lobed, curved in side view, 14–20 mm long, 9–14 mm wide, side lobes obliquely oblong, rounded, midlobe transversely oblong, obtuse, callus of 3–5 rugulose ridges slightly dilated towards the apex, spur conical, incurved, 5–7 mm long; column 7–8 mm long.

Eulophia calantha   ERIC LA CROIX

In marshes, swamps and seasonally wet grassland; only in a few areas west of the Rift Valley; 1300–2000 m; flowering April to July.

Also recorded in Uganda and Tanzania and in many parts of Africa westwards to Guinea and south to Angola and Malawi.

Eulophia clavicornis Lindley var. *nutans* (Sonder) A.V. Hall
Syn. *Eulophia nutans* Sonder
Plants 25–45 cm tall, arising from a chain of flattened underground pseudobulbs. Leaves arising with the flowers, 5–6, plicate, linear, 15–40 cm long, 3–8 mm wide. Inflorescence with few to many flowers, widely spaced. Flowers rather small, often self-pollinating and not opening fully, greenish brown with white petals and lip flushed purple or pink, callus yellowish green; dorsal sepal oblong elliptic, apiculate, 10 mm long, 3–4 mm wide; lateral sepals similar, oblique at the base, 11–12 mm long, 4–5 mm wide; petals elliptic, obtuse, 8–10 mm long, 3–5 mm wide; lip 3-lobed, 7–10 mm long, 5–9 mm wide, side lobes rounded, midlobe oblong, callus of 2 ridges becoming 4 rows of papillae in front, spur 2–3 mm long.

Grassland and bushland, especially where it is seasonally very dry; 1650–2200 m; flowering May to September, also in December.

Widespread in eastern Africa as far south as South Africa; also in Madagascar and Yemen. This species is sometimes confused with *Eulophia ovalis* ssp. *bainesii* but the flowers are only half as big and the lip has many more papillae.

Eulophia clitellifera (Reichenbach f.) Bolus
Plants 15–60 cm high. Underground organ a chain of more or less conical pseudobulbs with few roots. Leaves 3–5, appearing after the flowers, arranged in a fan, linear-lanceolate, smooth, 20–70 cm long, 7–9 mm wide. Inflorescence with few flowers, laxly arranged. Flowers dull, sepals brownish, petals and lip dirty white with dull red veins; dorsal sepal spreading, oblong-elliptic, obtuse, 5–6 mm long, 2.5–4 mm wide; lateral sepals similar, 6–9 mm long, 3–5 mm wide; petals spreading, ovate-ellip-tic to nearly circular, 7–10 mm long, 7–8 mm wide; lip 3-lobed, 6–10 mm long and wide, side lobes rounded or truncate, midlobe nearly circular, 6.5 mm long and wide, callus of 3–7 fleshy ridges, spur conical, 3–5 mm long; column 1–2 mm long.

In grassland, especially where it is seasonally burnt; only in a few areas west of the Rift Valley; 1500–2200 m; flowering April to May.

Also recorded from Uganda and Tanzania; widespread in Africa, westwards to Ghana and south to South Africa.

Eulophia cristata (Swartz) Steudel
Plants 60–130 cm tall. Underground organ consisting of potato-like pseudobulbs in chains on a slender rhizome. Leaves arising after the flowering stem, erect, plicate, lanceolate, acuminate, 40–70 cm long, 1–4 cm wide. Inflorescence with 10–30 flowers, laxly arranged. Flowers lilac or bright mauve with darker purple lip; dorsal sepal oblanceolate to narrowly elliptic, 14–25 mm long, 3–5 mm wide; lateral sepals similar but slightly larger;

petals elliptic, obtuse, 12–20 mm long, 6–10 mm wide; lip 3-lobed, 12–22 mm long, 10–14 mm wide, side lobes erect, semicircular, midlobe deflexed, convex, elliptic, crisped on the margin, callus of 2 raised, rounded, smooth ridges at base and 5–9 elongated, crenulate ridges in front, spur upcurved, 2–5 mm long; column 7–8 mm long.

In grassland, often where it is seasonally burnt; only recorded west of the Rift Valley; 1800 m; flowering in March.

Also recorded in Uganda and Sudan, westwards as far as Senegal and Gambia. This species is sometimes confused with *Eulophia livingstoniana*, which is similar in colour, but it is easily recognised by the crenulate ridges along the midlobe of the lip.

Eulophia cucullata (Swartz) Steudel

Plants 40–130 cm high. Underground organ a chain of pseudobulbs, irregularly shaped and held together on a slender rhizome. Leaves arising with or after the inflorescence, 3–4, plicate, erect, linear, 20–70 cm long, 1–2 cm wide. Inflorescence with 3–8 large flowers, widely spaced. Flowers showy, with rosy purple petals and lip, darker sepals; dorsal sepal erect or reflexed, lanceolate, acuminate, 14–25 mm long, 3–8 mm wide; lateral sepals erect or reflexed, obliquely lanceolate, acuminate, 14–25 mm long, 3–10 mm wide; petals flopping forward, elliptic or obovate, rounded, 15–24 mm long, 10–20 mm wide; lip 3-lobed, saccate at the base, 18–35 mm long, 20–40 mm wide, side lobes erect,

Eulophia cucullata

BOB CAMPBELL

rounded, midlobe emarginate, 10–12 mm long, 16–22 mm wide, callus of 2 square ridges in the throat; column white, 13–15 mm long.

In grassland, wooded grassland and in bush country; widespread in western Kenya including Turkana district, also at the coast; sea level to 2300 m; flowering March to April and in September.

Also recorded from Uganda and Tanzania; widespread throughout Africa, westwards to Sierra Leone and south to South Africa (Natal), also in Madagascar and the Comoro Islands. This species is very variable in the size of its flowers, but easily identified because they are few and showy.

Eulophia galeoloides Kraenzlin

Plants lacking chlorophyll, 6–100 cm tall. Underground organ a fleshy rhizome, 4–10 cm long, 4–16 mm in diameter. Inflorescence rather dense with 2-many flowers, pale buff in colour. Flowers white to pale brown with 2 dark red marks at the base of the lip and reddish hairs on side lobes; dorsal sepal erect, oblong-lanceolate, acute, 15–20 mm long, 4–7 mm wide; lateral sepals similar, oblique at the base, 15–25 mm long, 2–5 mm wide; petals oblong-spathulate, obtuse, 20–25 mm long, 4–7 mm wide; lip 3-lobed, 20 mm long, 12–14 mm wide, side

Eulophia galeoloides   ERIC LA CROIX

lobes rounded in front, midlobe elliptic, obtuse, callus of 3 fleshy ridges in basal part, spur conical 4–5 mm long, column 9–10 mm long.

In shade on the forest floor; only recorded from Kakamega; 1700 m; flowering in March.

Also recorded from Tanzania, Zaïre, Nigeria, Ghana and Sudan.

Eulophia guineensis Lindley

Syn. *Eulophia quartiniana* A. Richard
Eulophia guineensis Lindley var. *purpurata* Kotschy

Plants 30–65 cm tall, with squat or conical pseudobulbs 3–5 cm tall, 2–5 cm in diameter, glossy dark green. Leaves 3–4, developing after flowering, plicate, suberect, elliptic, acute, 10–35 cm long, 3–10 cm wide. Inflorescence erect, with 5–15 large flowers. Flowers showy, sepals and petals pale purplish brown, lip pale pinkish purple, white at the base; dorsal sepal reflexed, linear-lanceolate, acuminate, 16–26 mm long, 3–5 mm wide; lateral sepals similar, margins undulate; petals linear-lanceolate, acuminate, 15–25 mm long, 4–5 mm wide; lip 3-lobed at base, side lobes erect on either side of column, midlobe ovate, flat, 20–25 mm long, 15–30 mm wide, callus absent or present in the form of slightly raised ridges at the base only, spur slender, tapering from a wide mouth, 15–25 mm long; column short and broad, 4–5 mm long.

Eulophia guineensis   BOB CAMPBELL

Usually among rocks, growing in shade amongst bushes; only known near Mt Elgon and to the south and east of this mountain; 1650–2330 m; flowering in March to May.

Also recorded in Uganda and Tanzania; widespread throughout tropical Africa westwards to Sierra Leone and south to Malawi; also recorded from Yemen and Oman.

Eulophia horsfallii (Bateman) Summerhayes
Syn. *Eulophia porphyroglossa* (Reichenbach f.) Bolus
Eulophia elliotii Rendle

Plants very large, 1–3 m tall, arising from a fleshy, underground rhizome, 2–3 cm in diameter. Leaves 3–5, erect, lanceolate to oblanceolate, acute, 30–140 cm long, 2–15 cm wide, narrowing at the base into a long petiole. Inflorescence erect with 5–50 flowers, widely spaced. Flowers large, fleshy, sepals dull purplish brown, petals rosy purple, lip pink-purple with side lobes striped purple and yellow callus; dorsal sepal reflexed, oblanceolate, 17–26 mm long, 7–8 mm wide; lateral sepals similar, oblique at the base, 17–27 mm long, 7–8 mm wide; petals hiding the column, elliptic, obtuse, 20–35 mm long, 15–25 mm wide; lip 3-lobed, 20–40 mm long, 15–40 mm wide, side lobes erect, semicircular, midlobe elliptic-oblong with undulate margins, callus of three crests, spur conical 4–8 mm long; column purple, 10 mm long.

Eulophia horsfallii　　　　　BOB CAMPBELL

By streams, rivers and dams, also in swamps and marshy places, in the open and in forests; widespread in the highlands and also recorded from the Shimba hills; sea level to 2500 m; flowering in April, June and October to November.

Also recorded in Tanzania and Uganda; widespread throughout tropical Africa and south to South Africa (Transvaal and Natal).

Eulophia kyimbilae Schlechter
Plants 35–80 cm tall, arising from a chain of underground, conical pseudobulbs, each 1–2 cm tall. Leaves 4–5, present with the flowers, linear-lanceolate, acute, 30–55 cm tall, 2–16 mm wide.

Eulophia kyimbilae　　　　　ERIC LA CROIX

Inflorescence lax with few flowers that do not open widely. Flowers green, veined purple or brown, lip green at base and white or yellow in front; dorsal sepal linear-lanceolate, acute, 9–12 mm long, 2–3 mm wide; lateral sepals similar, oblique at the base, 9–17 mm long, 2–5 mm wide; petals narrowly elliptic, acute, 8–12 mm long, 3–5 mm wide; lip 3-lobed, 9–15 mm long, 6–10 mm wide, side lobes oblong, midlobe rounded, callus of 3 fleshy ridges changing to rows of papillae in front, spur cylindric, 1.5–2.5 mm long; column 4–6 mm long.

In seasonally wet grassland and at the forest edge; only recorded around the lower slopes of Mt Elgon; 1700–2100 m; flowering from March to June.

Also recorded in Tanzania and Uganda, Zambia, Malawi and Zimbabwe.

Eulophia latilabris Summerhayes

Plants robust, 75–120 cm tall, arising from chains of underground fleshy pseudobulbs, each 3–4 cm tall. Leaves arising after the flowers, 3–5, erect, lanceolate, 30–70 cm long, 4–8 cm wide Inflorescence stout, with many showy flowers. Flowers large, fleshy, somewhat pendent, sepals greenish purple, petals and lip pinkish mauve with darker veins and a bright yellow callus; dorsal sepal reflexed, obovate, apiculate, 20–25 mm long, 8–10 mm wide; lateral sepals similar, oblique at the base, 20–27 mm long, 10–15 mm wide; petals almost circular, hiding the column, 24–27 mm long, 28–30 mm wide; lip scarcely lobed at the sides, 27–35 mm long, 30–32 mm wide, callus of 5 ridges, spur conical 5–8 mm long; column 12–14 mm long.

In marshes, swamps and seasonally wet bogs; only recorded near Lake Victoria; 1500 m; flowering in April.

Eulophia latilabris   ERIC LA CROIX

Also recorded in Uganda and Tanzania; widespread across tropical Africa and south to Angola and Mozambique. This species is sometimes confused with *Eulophia horsfallii* but can be distinguished by its wider petals and the shape of the lip that is not 3-lobed.

Eulophia livingstoniana (Reichenbach f.) Summerhayes

Plants 50–100 cm high. Underground organ a cylindrical rhizome, irregular in shape and branching, up to 1 cm in diameter. Leaves arising after flowering, 3–6, linear, acute, 10–40 cm long, 5–15 mm wide. Inflorescence with few to many widely spaced flowers. Flowers pale to dark lilac sepals and petals, lip and column dark purple, side lobes of lip greenish yellow; dorsal sepal reflexed, lanceolate or oblanceolate, acute or obtuse, 15–20 mm long, 4–5 mm wide; lateral sepals reflexed, similar to dorsal sepal; petals erect, elliptic-obovate, obtuse, 15–20 mm long, 8–9 mm wide; lip 3-lobed, 12–18 mm long, side lobes erect, rounded, midlobe with reflexed sides, 8–12 mm long, callus almost non-existent except at the base, spur 3–7 mm long; column 7–9 mm long.

In grassland and deciduous woodland; widespread west of the Rift Valley and also near the coast in Kwale district; sea level to 2350 m; flowering in February and March.

Also recorded in Uganda and Tanzania; widespread throughout Africa and in Madagascar and the Comoro Islands. This species is similar in size and colouration to *Eulophia cristata,* but easily recognised by its smooth lip with its reflexed side lobes.

Eulophia milnei   ERIC LA CROIX

Eulophia milnei Reichenbach f.

Plants 25–50 cm tall, arising from a chain of ellipsoid underground pseudobulbs. Leaves 2–6, appearing after the flowers, linear, 10–30 cm long, 1–2 mm wide. Inflorescence slender with many small flowers, becoming closer together towards the top. Flowers small, bright yellow, sometimes with red at the base of the lip and on the side lobes; dorsal sepal oblong-lanceolate, 5–8 mm long, 2–3 mm wide; lateral sepals similar; petals oblanceolate, acute, 6–8 mm long, 2–3 mm wide; lip 3-lobed, 6–7 mm long, 4–5 mm wide, side lobes narrow, rounded in front, midlobe oblong, truncate or obtuse, callus with 2–3 basal ridges and few scattered papillae, spur 2–3 mm long; column 2–3 mm long.

In seasonally wet grassland and shallow swamps; only recorded near Broderick Falls; 960–2000 m; flowering in April.

Also recorded in Uganda and Tanzania; widespread in tropical Africa westwards to Sierra Leone and south to South Africa.

Eulophia montis-elgonis Summerhayes

Plants 30–100 cm tall, arising from a chain of irregular, underground pseudobulbs. Leaves 2–3, erect, linear, plicate, 30–60 cm long, 2–3 cm wide. Inflorescence many flowered at the top of the peduncle. Flowers pinkish purple or white with a purple lip; dorsal sepal ovate, acute, 15–18 mm long, 7–8 mm wide; lateral sepals ovate-elliptic, oblique, acute, 17–18 mm long, 8–10 mm wide; petals elliptic, obtuse, 13 mm long, 6 mm wide; lip 3-lobed, 13–14 mm long, 10–11 mm wide, side lobes rounded, midlobe subquadrate, callus of 2 ridges with 5 rows of papillae in front, spur 3 mm long; column 6 mm long.

Rocky hillsides and grassland around Mt Elgon and in the Cherangani hills; 2000–2350 m; flowering in June and July.

Also recorded in Uganda and Sudan.

Eulophia odontoglossa Reichenbach f.

Syn. *Eulophia shupangae* (Reichenbach f.) Kraenzlin
Eulophia johnstonii Rolfe

Plants 60–100 cm tall, arising from a chain of underground pseudobulbs. Leaves 5–6, erect, oblanceolate, plicate 40–70 cm long, 1–2 cm wide. Inflorescence slender with many flowers in a bunch at the top, entirely covered with overlapping papery sheaths. Flowers golden yellow with yellow-orange papillae on the lip; dorsal sepal ovate-elliptic, 9–12 mm long, 4–6 mm wide; lateral sepals

Eulophia montis-elgonis

ovate, oblique, 9–14 mm long, 4–5 mm wide; petals elliptic, oblique, obtuse, 8–12 long, 3–5 mm wide; lip 3-lobed, 8–12 mm long, 4–8 mm wide, side lobes rounded, midlobe oblong or subquadrate, truncate, callus of 2 basal ridges and many long papillae, spur conical, 1–3 mm long; column 4–5 mm long.

Eulophia odontoglossa   ERIC LA CROIX

Grassland, especially in rocky areas; 1650–2330 m; flowering in July and August.

Also recorded in Uganda and Tanzania; widespread throughout tropical Africa westwards to Sierra Leone and south to South Africa (Transvaal and Natal).

Eulophia orthoplectra (Reichenbach f.) Summerhayes

Syn. *Lissochilus saccatus* Rendle

Plants 60–100 cm tall, arising from a chain of flattened underground pseudobulbs. Leaves 2–4, appearing after or with the flowers, fleshy, conduplicate, linear, 18–50 cm long, 1–2 cm wide. Inflorescence slender, with 6–20 well spaced flowers. Flowers with reddish brown sepals, petals yellow lined with orange red, lip yellow with reddish brown side lobes; dorsal sepal reflexed, oblanceolate, 8–12 mm long, 4–6 mm wide; lateral sepals similar; petals elliptic-subcircular or ovate, 12–17 mm long, 13–19 mm wide; lip 3-lobed, 11–15 mm long, side lobes erect, rounded, midlobe convex, callus of 5 fleshy ridges, spur straight, 13–15 mm long.

In grassland, especially where it is seasonally moist; 1200–2350 m; flowering in November and January.

Also recorded in Uganda and Tanzania; widespread in tropical Africa, westwards to Nigeria and south to Zimbabwe. This species is very similar to *Eulophia schweinfurthii*, but has petals red or orange on the inner surface and a longer spur.

Eulophia ovalis Lindley ssp. *bainesii* (Rolfe) A.V. Hall

Syn. *Eulophia bainesii* Rolfe

Plants 12–35 cm tall, arising from a chain of conical underground pseudobulbs. Leaves 4–7, arising with the leaves, linear-lanceolate, plicate, 10–35 cm long, 4–20 mm wide. Inflorescence erect, with rather few flowers close together. Flowers with pale or greenish-brown sepals, pale yellow petals, lip yellow with purple-veined side lobes; dorsal sepal oblong-lanceolate, apiculate, 20–25 mm long, 3–6 mm wide; lateral sepals linear-lanceolate, acute, 20–22 mm long, 3–6 mm wide; petals elliptic, acute, 20–25 mm long, 8–9 mm wide, hiding the column; lip 3-lobed, 15–21 mm long, 10–15 mm wide, side lobes rounded, midlobe elliptic, callus of widely spaced papillae on veins, spur 3–4 mm long; column 3–5 mm long.

Grassland; only recorded from the Chyulu hills in Kenya; 1200 m; flowering in January.

Also recorded in Tanzania and southwards to South Africa.

Eulophia ovalis ssp. *bainesii*   BOB CAMPBELL

Eulophia parvula   ERIC LA CROIX

Eulophia parvula (Rendle) Summerhayes

Plants 20–60 cm high. Underground organ a chain of irregularly shaped, conical pseudobulbs, linked by a slender rhizome. Leaves up to 7, arising after the flowers, linear, acute, 10–30 cm long, 8–12 mm wide. Inflorescence with many small flowers, widely spaced. Flowers small, dull, yellow or greenish yellow, spotted or marked with brownish purple; dorsal sepal spreading or reflexed, oblong-elliptic, 4–6 mm long, 2 mm wide; lateral sepals similar; petals broadly ovate or nearly circular, 5 mm long, 4 mm wide; lip 3-lobed, 5–6 mm long, 6 mm wide, side lobes elliptic, acute, fused to the column in the basal half, midlobe rounded, 3–4 mm long, callus of 3–5 fleshy uneven ridges, spur conical, 1 mm long.

In grassland and bush country, often where there are seasonal fires; only recorded once in Kenya, in Kavirondo district (in 1894); 1570 m; flowering in January.

Also recorded in Uganda and Tanzania; widespread in Africa westwards to Nigeria and south to South Africa (Natal). Rather similar to *Eulophia pyrophila* but always distinguished by its smaller size.

Eulophia petersii Reichenbach f.

Syn. *Eulophia schimperiana* A. Richard

Plants large, 100–350 cm tall with cylindric or conical pseudobulbs, 6–30 cm high, greenish yellow, ribbed. Leaves 2–4, erect, fleshy or leathery, linear-ligulate, conduplicate, acute, 15–80 cm long, 1.5–6 cm wide, margins serrated. Inflorescence usually branched and very long, with many widely spaced flowers. Flowers fleshy, sepals and petals olive green sometimes veined red, lip white, veined red or purple; dorsal sepal erect, oblanceolate, recurved at the apex, 15–25 mm long, 4–5 mm wide; lateral sepals similar; petals oblanceolate or oblong, recurved at the apex, 15–18 mm long, 5–7 mm wide; lip 3-lobed 14–20 mm long, 8–15 mm wide, side lobes elliptic, midlobe circular or subquadrate, callus of 3 fleshy raised ridges, spur incurved, 4–6 mm long; column 8–9 mm long.

In dry bush country, often in sandy soil, also in rocky places; widespread in the drier parts of the country at low altitudes, including near the coast; sea level to 1800 m; flowering in May, August and November.

Also recorded in Uganda and Tanzania and from Sudan, Ethiopia and Zaïre south to Angola and South Africa (Natal); also recorded in Arabia.

Eulophia pyrophila (Reichenbach f.) Summerhayes

Plants 13–45 cm tall. Underground organ a chain of conical, upright pseudobulbs, each with terminal inflorescence. Leaves 4–5, arising after flowering, linear-lanceolate, acute, 5–15 cm long, 2–3 mm wide. Inflorescence with many small flowers, widely spaced. Flowers dull brown with lip cream or yellow, striped brown, and yellow callus; dorsal sepal oblong-elliptic, obtuse, 6–8 mm long, 2–4 mm wide; lateral sepals similar; petals elliptic or oblong-elliptic, 6–9 mm long, 4–6 mm wide; lip 3-lobed, 6–8 mm long, 5–7 mm wide, side lobes triangular, midlobe convex, elliptic, margin undulate, callus of 5–9 fleshy ridges on basal half of midlobe, spur conical, 1.5–2.5 mm long; column 2.5 mm long.

In short grassland and among rocks, usually where there are seasonal fires; widespread in Kenya eastwards as far as the Chyulu hills; 1000–2730 m; flowering January and March.

Also recorded in Uganda and Tanzania; widespread in Africa from Ethiopia westwards to Ivory Coast and south to South Africa. Sometimes confused with *Eulophia parvula*, but the flowers are usually slightly larger in all respects.

Eulophia schweinfurthii Kraenzlin
Syn. *Lissochilus johnstonii* Rolfe
Eulophia involuta Summerhayes

Plants 45–110 cm tall, arising from a chain of underground pseudobulbs. Leaves 1–2, arising after the flowers, succulent, conduplicate, linear, 21–38 cm long, 2–10 mm wide. Inflorescences 1–2, with widely spaced flowers. Flowers fleshy, sepals purplish brown, petals yellow with red veins within, lip yellow with reddish-purple side lobes and veins; dorsal sepal reflexed, oblong, apiculate, 9–10 mm long, 3–6 mm wide; lateral sepals similar; petals broadly ovate or circular, 11–17 mm long, 9–17 mm wide; lip 3-lobed, 14–16 mm long, 19–21 mm wide, side lobes round, midlobe convex, elliptic, callus of 3–5 verrucose ridges, spur conical, 8–9 mm long; column 3–5 mm long.

Grassland and bushland, especially on poor soils; 300–2100 m; flowering January to April.

Also recorded in Uganda and Tanzania; widespread in countries along the eastern side of Africa. This species is similar to *Eulophia orthoplectra*, but has slightly smaller flowers with a shorter spur and the petals completely veined with red on the inner surface. Geerinck (1988) treats the two species as one under *Eulophia orthoplectra*.

Eulophia serrata Cribb
Syn. *Eulophia stricta* Rolfe

Plants to 65 cm tall with slender cylindrical pseudobubs enclosed within the leaf bases. Leaves 3–4, fleshy, linear-lanceolate, acute, 14–30 cm long, 1.5–2 cm wide, with finely serrated margins. Inflorescence erect, with up to 20 widely spaced flowers. Flowers fleshy, dull green except for white lip, all parts with reddish veins; dorsal sepal erect, oblong-lanceolate, 10–12 mm long, 4 mm wide; lateral sepals similar; petals leaning forward, ovate, subacute, 7–8 mm long, 5 mm wide; lip 3-lobed, 9 mm long and wide, side lobes erect, rounded, midlobe transversely elliptic oblong with erose, undulate margins, spur 2–3 mm long; column 4–5 mm long.

In shallow sandy soils, over rocks, in bushland; only known so far from Kilifi district; 150–200 m; flowering in February.

Not known elsewhere.

Eulophia speciosa (Lindley) Bolus
Syn. *Lissochilus speciosus* R.Brown ex Lindley
Lissochilus wakefieldii Reichenbach f. & S. Moore
Lissochilus volkensii Rolfe

Plants 60–120 cm tall, arising from chains of irregular underground pseudobulbs. Leaves 3–6, arising after or with the flowers, fleshy, conduplicate, 30–65 cm long, 1–2 cm wide. Inflorescence very long and bearing many flowers over a long period. Flowers sweetly scented, sepals green, petals bright yellow, lip yellow with red or purple veins on side lobes; dorsal sepal reflexed, elliptic, 5–11 mm long, 2–4 mm wide; lateral sepals similar; petals spreading, elliptic-ovate, 11–18 mm long, 8–15 mm wide; lip 3-lobed, 12–16 mm long, 10–14 mm wide, side lobes rounded, reflexed, midlobe convex, callus of 3–5 low fleshy ridges, spur conical 1–3 mm long; column greenish 4–6 mm long.

In grassland, deciduous woodland, often on poor, rocky soils and in sand dunes; sea level to 2000 m; flowering throughout the year.

Also recorded in Uganda and Tanzania; widespread throughout Africa and in Arabia.

Eulophia speciosa   BOB CAMPBELL

Eulophia stachyodes Reichenbach f.
Syn. *Eulophia kirkii* Rolfe

Plants 30–80 cm tall, arising from chains of ellipsoid underground pseudobulbs. Leaves 4–5, arising with the flowers, lanceolate or oblanceolate, plicate, 17–100 cm long, 3–10 cm wide. Inflorescence with many well-spaced flowers. Flowers with dull greenish-bronze sepals and white petals, lip green with purple callus; dorsal sepal narrowly oblong, obtuse, 18–23 mm long, 2–5 mm wide; lateral sepals similar; petals elliptic-oblong, obtuse, 16–18 mm long, 6–8 mm wide; lip 3-lobed, 14–15 mm long, 9 mm wide, side lobes rounded, midlobe oblong with undulate margin, callus of 3 ridges becoming 3–5 rows of papillae, spur 4 mm long; column 6–7 mm long.

In grassland, bushland at woodland margins; 1830–2330 m; flowering in April and May.

Also recorded in Tanzania and Uganda; widespread in tropical Africa, west to Nigeria and south to Zimbabwe.

Eulophia stachyodes   ERIC LA CROIX

Eulophia stenophylla Summerhayes
  Syn. *Lissochilus micranthus* Kraenzlin
  Eulophia streptopetala Lindley var. *stenophylla*
    (Summerhayes) Cribb
Plants 50–80 cm tall, with conical pseudobulbs close together above the surface, 2.5–10 cm high, 1–4 cm in diameter, enclosed in leaf bases. Leaves 4–9, spreading, plicate, lanceolate, acuminate, 20–40 cm long, 1–2 cm wide. Inflorescence with many small flowers widely spaced. Flowers with small dull green or brown, tessellated sepals, bright

yellow petals, lip yellow with purple veins on side lobes; dorsal sepal oblanceolate to elliptic, acute or obtuse, 8–15 mm long, 3–5 mm wide; lateral sepals similar but longer; petals elliptic or obovate, 8–12 mm long, 6–8 mm wide; lip 3-lobed with the sides of the midlobe reflexed, 6–10 mm long, 5–10 mm wide, side lobes erect, rounded, midlobe erect, smooth, spur conical 3–4 mm long; column white, 3–5 mm long.

At forest margins and among bushes and scrub, also on rocky hillsides; widespread; 1400–2100 m; flowering throughout the year.

Also recorded from Uganda and Tanzania. This species is very similar to *Eulophia streptopetala* but is easily distinguished from that species by being much smaller in all respects.

Eulophia stenophylla   BOB CAMPBELL

Eulophia streptopetala Lindley
  Syn. *Lissochilus streptopetalus* (Lindley) Lindley
  Eulophia krebsii (Reichenbach f.) Bolus
  Eulophia grantii (Reichenbach f.) Summerhayes
  Eulophia paivaeana (Reichenbach f.)
    Summerhayes ssp. *borealis* Summerhayes
Plants 50–150 cm tall, with conical pseudobulbs close together above the surface, 2.5–10 cm high, 2–4 cm in diameter, enclosed in leaf bases. Leaves 4–9, spreading, plicate, lanceolate, acuminate, 40–65 cm long, 3–8 cm wide. Inflorescence with many flowers widely spaced, continuing to produce flowers over several months. Flowers with small

dull green or brown, tessellated sepals, bright yellow petals, lip yellow with purple veins on the side lobes; dorsal sepal oblanceolate to elliptic, acute or obtuse, 15–18 mm long, 6–10 mm wide; lateral sepals similar but longer; petals elliptic, round or obovate, 15–20 mm long, 10–17 mm wide; lip 3-lobed with the sides of the midlobe reflexed, 8–12 mm long, 7–12 mm wide, side lobes erect, rounded, midlobe erect, callus of 3–5 thickened, fleshy veins along the surface, spur concial 3–4 mm long; column white, 5–8 mm long.

Usually at forest margins or among bushes in scrub and grassland; widespread; 1200–2550 m; flowering in April to June.

Also recorded in Tanzania and Uganda; widespread throughout tropical and southern Africa; also in Arabia.

Eulophia streptopetala   HERMANN MEYER

Eulophia subulata Rendle
Plants 20–70 cm tall, arising from flattened, irregular pseudobulbs underground. Leaves arising with the flowers, 1–2, linear, acuminate, 15–40 cm long, 2–15 mm wide. Inflorescence erect with many flowers clustered together near the top. Flowers pale yellow with similar or darker yellow hairs on the lip; dorsal sepal lanceolate, acute, 19–21 mm long, 4–7 mm wide; lateral sepals oblong-lanceolate, oblique, 21–35 mm long, 8–11 mm wide; petals oblong, acute, 17–26 mm long, 3.5–8 mm wide; lip 3-lobed, 15–24 mm long, 10–13 mm wide, side lobes rounded, midlobe elliptic, callus of 2 ridges with a few papillae in front, spur 2.5–4 mm long; column 2–3 mm long.

In seasonally wet grassland, often flowering after burning; 1350–2000 m; flowering in September and October.

Also recorded in Uganda, Tanzania, Rwanda and Zaïre. Sometimes confused with *Eulophia zeyheri* which has a smilar inflorescence, but this species has smaller flowers that lack the dark colouration in the lip.

Eulophia taitensis Cribb & Pfennig
Plants 60–110 cm high with erect, cylindric pseudobulbs enclosed in the leaf bases, 7–22 cm long, 1.5–3 cm wide. Leaves 6–14, spreading, fleshy, conduplicate, linear, acute, 10–50 cm long, 1.5–3 cm wide, margins slightly rough. Inflorescence erect with 5–30 widely spaced flowers. Flowers fleshy, bright yellowish green, lip white or cream with yellow callus, veined with red; dorsal sepal spreading, oblanceolate, acute, 22–25 mm long, 4–8 mm wide; lateral sepals lanceolate or oblong-lanceolate, similar to the dorsal sepal; petals smaller than sepals, oblanceolate, 19–20 mm long, 4.5–9 mm wide; lip obscurely 3-lobed, 18–20 mm long, 15–17 mm wide, side lobes elliptic, midlobe quadrate, callus of 3 verrucose ridges; spur 3 mm long; column 11 mm long.

In thickets of *Acacia* and other shrubs on sandy soils, mostly near the coast and in Teita district; sea level to 1300 m; flowering in May and September.

Also recorded in Uganda and Tanzania; not known elsewhere.

Eulophia taitensis   HERMANN MEYER

Eulophia tanganyikensis Rolfe
Syn. *Eulophia chlorotica* Kraenzlin
Plants 40–60 cm tall, with small conical pseudobulbs 8–15 mm long, 10–20 mm in diameter, close together on a rhizome. Leaves 3–4, plicate, erect, linear, 40–100 cm long, 4 mm wide. Inflorescence slender with few to 10 flowers. Flowers not opening fully, sepals green tinged brown, petals white, lip white veined with purple and with red or purple papillae; dorsal sepal linear, acute, 13–17 mm long, 3 mm wide; lateral sepals similar; petals folded forward over the column, oblong, acute, 13–15 mm long, 5 mm wide; lip 3-lobed, 15–17 mm long, 13 mm wide, side lobes erect, elliptic or rounded, midlobe oblong or obovate with undulate margins, callus with 3 short fleshy ridges and 5–7 rows of

papillae, spur 3.5–5 mm long; column 5–6 mm long.

Damp grasslands; only known around Lake Victoria and in Kitale district; 1700–2300 m; flowering January to March.

Also recorded in Tanzania, and from Zaïre south to Malawi, Zambia and Zimbabwe.

Eulophia zeyheri Hooker f.

Plants 40–70 cm tall, arising from a chain of potato-like underground pseudobulbs. Leaves arising with or after the flowers, 2–3, lanceolate, acute, 30–50 cm long, 2–4 cm wide. Inflorescence dense with flowers very close together at the top of the peduncle. Flowers bright lemon yellow with a patch of dark reddish-brown hairs on the lip; dorsal sepal elliptic-lanceolate, acuminate, 28–36 mm long, 12–16 mm wide; lateral sepals similar but larger, to 40 mm long; petals elliptic-lanceolate, similar to sepals; lip 3-lobed, 23–26 mm long, 12–20 mm wide, side lobes small, rounded, midlobe semicircular obtuse or emarginate, callus of 2 ridges becoming rows of long papillae in front, spur 2–4 mm long; column 6–7 mm long.

Grassland and among scattered trees in grassland; 2000–2350 m; flowering April to June.

Also recorded in Tanzania and Uganda; widespread throughout tropical Africa, west to Nigeria and south to South Africa.

Eulophia zeyheri   ERIC LA CROIX

Habenaria Willdenow

Terrestrial orchids with green flowers nearly all belong to the genus *Habenaria*, or to its close relatives *Roeperocharis* and *Bonatea*. A few species of *Habenaria* have white flowers. There are also many that have green sepals while some or all of the other parts of the flower are white. All have rather narrow perianth parts, particularly the lip that is often divided into three lobes. The petals are also lobed in many of the species, with an upper lobe that adheres to the edge of the dorsal sepal and a lower lobe that hangs downwards in front of the lateral sepals or parallel with the side lobes of the lip. The name *Habenaria* is derived from the Latin word *habena* (reins), presumably in allusion to the long narrow shape of most of the parts of the flower.

The plants are also rather easily recognised, even when not in flower, by their densely leafy stems, or by two large basal leaves, flat on the ground and sheath-covered stems. In those species with many leaves, there are often a few sheaths at the base, then a group of large leaves, and the upper part of the stem is clothed with small leaves or sheaths that gradually intergrade into the bracts.

Habenaria is a large genus with more than 600 species distributed throughout the tropical and subtropical parts of the world. More than 100 have been recorded for East Africa, nearly half of them from Kenya. Thus it is the largest genus in the country so far as the number of species is concerned. But it is also one of the least frequently seen, at least today. Many of the grassland habitats have been so changed, either by grazing, draining or conversion to agriculture, that the places where these orchids used to grow have largely disappeared. Some of the highland and coastal habitats remain and are protected, and some rather spectacular species can be found in these areas by searching at the right time of year.

Because of the large number of species, I have divided them into five groups to make for easier identification. Even so, readers will find that some of the species with small green flowers are not easy to distinguish. I have tried to highlight the differences. First there is a key to the groups. Second, there are five keys to the small number of species that share some major characteristics.

The descriptions and details of each species are presented in alphabetical order, as for all the other genera in the book.

CULTIVATION

Very few of the species of *Habenaria* are in cultivation. When I lived on the outskirts of Nairobi, a plant of *Habenaria vaginata* came up year after year and flowered in my lawn where it was always welcome. Some of the forest-dwelling species from other parts of Africa have survived as potplants for several years but maintaining them is not easy. The most important requirement is to pay due regard to the changing seasons, in particular allowing the plants to die down after flowering and keeping them undisturbed for several months until the new shoots appear. Whilst in active growth they need frequent applications of rain water and dilute fertiliser.

Key to the groups of *Habenaria* dealt with in this book

1   Leaves 1–2, basal, orbicular or heart-shaped, appressed to the ground . . . . Group A
Leaves several or many, borne along the stem 2

2   Petals entire 3
Petals deeply two lobed 4

3   Side lobes of lip entire or absent . . . Group B
Side lobes of lip fringed or finely divided like a comb along the outer margin . . . . Group C

4   Lip with a short spur, always less than 3 cm . . . . Group D
Lip with a long spur, always more than 4 cm long, sometimes much longer . . . . Group E

Key to the species in Group A

Plants with one or two basal leaves appressed to the ground.

1   Petals entire . . . . *H. vaginata*
Petals 2-lobed 2

2   Side lobes of lip thread-like, much longer than the midlobe 3
Side lobes of lip equalling the midlobe or shorter 6

3   Spur over 5 cm long 4
Spur less than 4 cm long 5

4   Dorsal sepal 7–11 mm long; spur 5–7 cm long . . . . *H. subarmata*
Dorsal sepal 11–16 mm long; spur 8–18 cm long . . . . *H. armatissima*

5   Dorsal sepal less than 7 mm long; spur straight or slightly curved . . *H. trilobulata*
Dorsal sepal over 8 mm long; spur curved to form a loop . . . . *H. helicoplectrum*

6   Spur 10–17 cm long . . . . *H. macrura*
Spur 2–6 cm long 7

7   Spur slender or slightly thickened at apex . . . . *H. stylites*
Spur much swollen at the apex . . . . *H. lindblomii*

Key to the species in Group B

Plants with leaves along the stem, petals entire, side lobes of lip entire or absent.

1   Flowers green, green and white, or cream 2
Flowers white . . . . *H. zambesina*

2   Spur at base of lip 10 mm long or more . . 3
Spur at base of lip less than 10 mm long . . 7

3   Spur 10–15 mm long 4
Spur 15 mm long or more 5

4   Lip ligulate, entire; petals ovate . . . . *H. hologlossa*
Lip 3-lobed nearly to the base; petals broadly lanceolate . . . . *H. attenuata*

5   Dorsal sepal 9 mm long or more . . . . *H. epipactidea*
Dorsal sepal less than 9 mm long 6

6   Petals triangular to ovate, equalling the dorsal sepal; lobes of the lip ligulate . . . . *H. bracteosa*
Petals lanceolate, curved, adherent to the edge of the dorsal sepal; lobes of the lip narrow, linear . . . . . . *H. chlorotica*

7   Spur 5–7 mm long . . . . *H. eggelingii*
Spur 3 mm long or shorter 8

8   Spur scarcely 1 mm long; lip almost equally 3-lobed in the upper part . . . . *H. petitiana*
Spur 1.5–3 mm long; middle lobe of the lip twice as long as the recurved side lobes . . . . *H. peristyloides*

Key to the species in Group C

Plants with leaves along the stem, petals entire, side lobes of the lip fringed or finely divided like a comb along the outer margin.

1 Spur 10 cm or more in length   2
  Spur 5 cm or less in length   3

2 Dorsal sepal 1–2 cm long, obtuse . . . .
  . . . . *H. cavatibrachia*
  Dorsal sepal 3–4 cm long, acute . . *H. egregia*

3 Dorsal sepal less than 2 cm long   4
  Dorsal sepal 2 cm long or more   6

4 Stigmatic arms 2–4 mm long, slightly
    swollen in the upper part   5
  Stigmatic arms 9–20 mm long, the upper
    receptive part very much thickened . . . .
    . . . . *H. keniensis*

5 Dorsal sepal only slightly smaller than
    laterals; midlobe of lip tapering from
    the base . . . . *H. decorata*
  Dorsal sepal much smaller than the
    laterals; midlobe of lip with parallel
    sides . . . . *H. quartiniana*

6 Basal part of lip hairless; staminodes not
    stalked . . . . *H. macrantha*
  Basal part of lip somewhat hairy;
    staminodes stalked . . . . *H. splendens*

Key to the species in Group D

Plants with leaves along the stem; flowers white, green, or greenish white, petals deeply 2-lobed, lip with spur less than 3 cm long.

   Warning: the flowers of *H. cornuta*, *H. ndiana* and *H. altior* are often deformed or incompletely developed and may be difficult to identify using this key.

1 Flowers white, or white with a greenish
    spur   2
  Flowers green, or greenish white, or
    green with a white centre   3

2 Petal lobes papillose and ciliolate: lower
    petal lobe longer and wider than upper
    petal lobe . . . . *H. chirensis*
  Petal lobes not papillose or ciliolate;
    lower petal lobe shorter and narrower
    than upper petal lobe . . . . *H. kilimanjari*

3 Dorsal sepal erect, arching over the
    column   4
  Dorsal sepal bent back, exposing
    column   8

4 Lowermost bracts of inflorescence
    usually longer than pedicel and ovary . . . .
    . . . . *H. njamnjamica*
  Lowermost bracts of the inflorescence
    usually shorter than the pedicel and
    ovary   5

5 Lip entire or with only short teeth on
    either side of the midlobe; lower lobe
    of petals 2 mm long or less . . . *H. perrieri*
  Lip distinctly 3-lobed; lower lobe of
    petals more than 5 mm long   6

6 Lower lobe of petals curving upwards like
    a horn, 2–4 cm long . . . . *H. cornuta*
  Lower lobe of petals linear or lanceolate,
    less than 12 mm long   7

7 Side lobes of lip shorter than midlobe . . . . . .
    . . . . *H. tweedieae*
  Side lobes of lip longer than midlobe . . . . . .
    . . . . *H. malacophylla*

8 Petal lobes ciliate, papillose or hairy   9
  Petal lobes not ciliate, papillose or
    hairy   12

9 Upper lobe of petals densely hairy with
    fringed margins . . . . *H. altior*
  Upper lobe of petals papillose or ciliolate
    but not hairy   10

10 Lower lobe of petals equal to or shorter
    than upper lobe . . . . *H. thomsonii*
  Lower lobe of petals longer than upper
    lobe   11

11 Spur 10–16 mm long, twisted more than
    once . . . . *H. schimperiana*
  Spur 17–42 mm long, not or only slightly
    twisted . . . . *H. huillensis*

12 Dorsal sepal 8 mm long . . . . *H. linderi*
  Dorsal sepal 3–7 mm long   13

13 Spur twisted in the middle . . . . . *H. ndiana*
  Spur parallel to the ovary throughout its
    length   14

14   Ovary less than 5 mm long, borne on a
        long slender pedicel . . . *H. ichneumonea*
      Ovary 6–12 mm long, borne on a short
        stout pedicel . . . . *H. huillensis*

Key to the species in Group E

Plants with leaves along the stem; flowers white or green and white, petals deeply 2-lobed, lip with spur more than 4 cm long.

1   Spur 4–8 cm long   2
     Spur more than 10 cm long   4

2   Dorsal sepal reflexed, exposing column to
        view . . . . *H. plectromaniaca*
     Dorsal sepal erect, convex, surrounding
        the column   3

3   Dorsal sepal less than 2 cm long; lower
        petal lobe 2–4 cm long; spur parallel to
        the ovary . . . . *H. clavata*
     Dorsal sepal 2 cm long or longer; lower
        petal lobe 4–8 cm long; spur curved
        backwards to form a bow . . . . *H. laurentii*

4   Lower lobe of petals and side lobes of lip
        slender, 1 mm wide, petal lobe curving
        forward and upward like a horn . . . .
        . . . . *H. cirrhata*
     Lower lobe of petals and side lobes of lip
        broadly lanceolate or oblong-elliptic,
        2–6.5 mm wide   5

5   Lobes of lip 15–30 mm long; stigmas
        narrowly club-shaped, 8–12 mm long . . . . .
        . . . . *H. walleri*
     Lobes of lip 10–15 mm long; stigmas
        broadly club-shaped, 3–4 mm long . . . .
        . . . . *H. macruroides*

Habenaria altior Rendle

Plants 20–95 cm high, stem erect, rather stout, covered with leaves. Leaves 9–13, lower ones spreading, linear or lanceolate, the largest 7–22 cm long, 1–2 cm wide, upper ones appressed to the stem. Inflorescence 4–25 cm long, with 7–many flowers, dense, bracts usually shorter than the ovary. Flowers green and white; dorsal sepal reflexed, narrowly elliptic, convex, 6–9 mm long, 2–4 mm wide; lateral sepals obliquely obovate, 8–11 mm long, 4–7 mm wide; petals 2-lobed, ciliate or hairy, the upper lobe linear, 5–7 mm long, margin fringed, lower lobe lanceolate, 8–12 mm long, 1–3 mm wide; lip 3-lobed almost from the base,

midlobe linear, 10–17 mm long, side lobes a little wider, 6–13 mm long, spur swollen in the apical half, incurved, 15–22 mm long.

In grassland, especially near streams, and in forest glades; recorded from Mt Kenya, the Aberdare Mts, Namanga hill, and from several places west of the Rift Valley; 2000–3700 m; flowering May to December.

Also recorded from Tanzania and from Zaïre.

Habenaria armatissima Reichenbach f.

Plants 30–70 cm high, stem erect with 2 large basal leaves and several much smaller ones along its length. Basal leaves opposite, appressed to ground, ovate to reniform, cordate, 6–18 cm long, 7–22 cm wide, fleshy; cauline leaves 4–8, lanceolate, acuminate, to 5 cm long. Inflorescence 10–20 cm long, bearing 10–many flowers and short bracts. Flowers white; dorsal sepal erect, elliptic-ovate, convex, 11–16 mm long, 5–8 mm wide; lateral sepals reflexed, obliquely semi-orbicular, acuminate, 13–18 mm long, 4–8 mm wide; petals bilobed, upper lobe erect, linear, 11–15 mm long, only 1 mm wide, lower lobe filiform, 3–4 cm long; lip 3-lobed, basal part 2 mm long, midlobe 1.5–2 cm long, side lobes

Habenaria armatissima   ERIC LA CROIX

3–4.5 cm long, all lobes filiform, spur dependent, cylindric, 8–22 cm long.

Forest and bushland near the coast; only known from the Sokoke forest in Kenya; sea level to 100 m; flowering July.

Widespread in tropical Africa from Eritrea and Ethiopia westwards to Mali and south to Mozambique and Namibia.

Habenaria attenuata Hooker f.

Plants rather slender, up to 50 cm high. Leaves 4–7, very unequal, largest lanceolate-oblong, acute, up to 13 cm long, 2.5 cm wide. Inflorescence narrow, with up to 20 yellowish-green flowers arranged in a single spiral row. Flowers green, small, with minutely hairy sepals; dorsal sepal incurved, convex, 2.7–3.7 mm long; lateral sepals slightly longer; petals entire, lanceolate, forming a hood with the dorsal sepal; lip 3-lobed nearly to the base, 3.5–4.5 mm long, lobes narrowly oblong, midlobe longer and wider than the spreading side lobes, spur slender, 10–16 mm long.

Upland grassland among bracken and in conifer plantations; only known from Londiani district; 2100–2600 m; flowered July 1951.

Also known in similar habitats on Mt Cameroon, and in Uganda, Ethiopia and Zaïre.

Habenaria bracteosa A. Richard

Plants robust, 15–95 cm high. Leaves 5–10, the middle 3–5 lanceolate or broadly lanceolate, acute, up to 30 cm long and 3 cm wide. Inflorescence rather densely many-flowered, 5–50 cm long. Flowers small, green or yellowish green; dorsal sepal ovate, 2.5–4.5 mm long; lateral sepals oblique and broadly oblong-lanceolate, slightly longer than dorsal; petals similar to the dorsal sepal but a little wider; lip 3-lobed from a short broad base, 3–8 mm long, lobes oblong or ligulate, obtuse, side lobes as long as or a little longer than the midlobe, spur slender, 15–30 mm long.

Grassy glades in mountain forest, especially by streams, and in damp places in heath and grassland above the forest; 2200–3600 m; flowering April to August.

Also known in Uganda and in similar habitats in Fernando Po, Cameroon, Sudan and Ethiopia.

Habenaria cavatibrachia Summerhayes

Plants robust, 15–60 cm high. Leaves 4–7, broadly lanceolate, acute, the largest 5–12 cm long, 2–3.5 cm wide. Inflorescence up to 10 cm long, with 2–6 flowers. Flowers curving outwards, green with side lobes of lip whitish, column brown; dorsal sepal erect, convex, broadly elliptic, 10–20 mm long, 11–13 mm wide; lateral sepals obliquely lanceolate, subacute, 15–25 mm long, c. 10 mm wide; petals oblique, elliptic, 11–16 mm long, 6.5–8 mm wide, outer margins hairy; lip deflexed, 3-lobed, basal part 9 mm long, midlobe ligulate, 14 mm long, side lobes 16–22 mm long with 3–8 threads 12 mm long on the outer margins, spur pendent, swollen in the apical half, 10–14 cm long.

Upland grassland; Aberdare Mts and west of Rift Valley; 2100–2700 m; flowering May to July.

Also recorded in Uganda and Ethiopia.

Habenaria chirensis Reichenbach f.

Plants 20–100 cm high, stem erect, slender or stout, covered with leaves. Leaves 7–13, the lower ones spreading, linear or lanceolate-linear, acute, 8–30 cm long, 5–15 mm wide, the upper ones appressed to the stem. Inflorescence 6–30 cm long, 12–many flowers, dense, bracts usually much shorter than the ovary. Flowers white, with an unpleasant smell; dorsal sepal reflexed, narrowly elliptic, convex, 4.5–6 mm long; lateral sepals deflexed, obliquely obovate, 6–9 mm long, 3–5 mm wide; petals 2-lobed, papillose and ciliolate, upper lobe reflexed, linear, 4–6 mm long, lower lobe narrowly lanceolate 5–9 mm long, twice the width of upper lobe; lip 3-lobed from near the base, midlobe linear, 9–12 mm long, side lobes narrower than midlobe, 6–8 mm long, spur parallel to ovary, straight, cylindric, truncate at apex, 1–2 cm long.

In damp grasslands and swamps and in wet places among rocks; widely collected from medium altitudes including around Nairobi; 1850–2300 m; flowering May to August.

Also recorded from Tanzania, westwards through Uganda to Nigeria, and Ethiopia.

Habenaria chlorotica Reichenbach f.

Syn. *Habenaria filicornis* Lindley var. *chlorotica* (Reichenbach f.) Geerinck

Plants slender, 20–80 cm high. Leaves 5–11, suberect, narrow, linear or linear-lanceolate, up to 19 cm long, 11 mm wide, upper ones smaller. Inflorescence narrow, lax, with 7–many flowers. Flowers green, suberect with a curved ovary; dorsal sepal elliptic-ovate, up to 4 mm long; lateral sepals deflexed, curved, lanceolate, adhering to the edge of the dorsal sepal to form a hood; lip 3-lobed from a short undivided basal part, 6–9 mm long, lobes narrow and equal in length or the midlobe slightly longer than the side lobes, spur slender, 2–3 cm long.

Damp grassland, especially in poorly drained

areas over rocks; in areas west of the Rift Valley; 1200–2850 m; flowering May to November.

Widespread throughout Africa in tropical grasslands.

Habenaria cirrhata (Lindley) Reichenbach f.
Rather stout plants, 50–120 cm high. Leaves 9–14, the middle ones spreading, almost orbicular to lanceolate, obtuse or acute, 7–22 cm long, 3–9 cm wide. Inflorescence 4–30 cm long, bearing 3–11 or many flowers, laxly arranged, bracts leaf-like, short. Flowers curved upwards, green with white central parts; dorsal sepal erect, convex, elliptic-lanceolate, acute, 2–2.5 cm long, 7–10 mm wide; lateral sepals deflexed, rolled up lengthwise, obliquely obovate, 2–3 cm long, 10–15 mm wide; petals 2-lobed nearly to the base, upper lobe linear, adhering to the dorsal sepal, 2–2.5 cm long, lower lobe curving forwards and upwards like a horn, linear below, subulate above, 5–9 cm long; lip 3-lobed from the undivided basal part 2–4 mm long, midlobe linear, obtuse, 3–4 cm long, side lobes tapering and narrower, 2–3 cm long, spur often coiled with the apex caught up in the bracts, 13–22 cm long.

In woodland with scattered trees, and in grassland with scattered bushes; only recorded west of the Rift Valley; 2500–2700 m; flowering May and June.

Widespread in Africa from Kenya westwards through Uganda to Guinee Republic, north to Sudan and Ethiopia, southwards through Tanzania to Malawi and Zambia and also in Madagascar.

Habenaria clavata (Lindley) Reichenbach f.
Syn. *Habenaria holubii* Rolfe
Stout plants 20–80 cm high. Leaves 7–13, the middle ones spreading, ovate to narrowly lanceolate, the largest 7–15 cm long, 2–4.5 cm wide. Inflorescence 4–20 cm long, with 5–20 flowers rather laxly arranged, bracts short. Flowers green with white central parts; dorsal sepal erect, convex, elliptic-lanceolate, acute, 1.5–2 cm long, 6–10 mm wide; lateral sepals deflexed, rolled up lengthwise, obliquely oblanceolate, acute, 12–24 mm long, 6–15 mm wide; petals 2-lobed, upper lobe erect, adhering to the dorsal sepal, narrowly linear, 9–20 mm long, lower lobe curving upwards and outwards like a horn, linear, fleshy and tapering towards the tip, 2–4 cm long; lip 3-lobed from an undivided basal part *c.* 2 mm long, midlobe, deflexed, linear, 2–3.5 cm long, side lobes projecting upward and forward on each side of column,

narrowly lanceolate or linear, 6–18 mm long, 1.5–3 mm wide, spur swollen at apex, 3–7 cm long.

In swampy grassland, often by streams, rarely in dry woodlands; only recorded west of the Rift Valley; 1200–2300 m; flowering June to August.

Also recorded from Uganda and Tanzania; widespread in Africa from Kenya westwards to Nigeria, in Ethiopia, and southwards to South Africa (Transvaal, Natal and Cape Province).

Habenaria clavata   JOYCE STEWART

Habenaria cornuta Lindley
Plants 20–80 cm high, stem erect, slender or stout, leafy throughout its length. Leaves 9–15, middle ones spreading, linear-lanceolate to ovate, acute, the largest 2–10 cm long and up to 5 cm wide, upper ones decreasing in size. Inflorescence 5–19 cm, 4 – many flowers, lax or dense, bracts leafy, mostly shorter than the ovary. Flowers pale green or yellowish green; dorsal sepal erect, very convex, 5–16 mm long, 4–8 mm wide; lateral sepals deflexed, semiorbicular, rolled up lengthwise, 6–16 mm long, 5–10 mm wide; petals 2-lobed, upper lobe erect, linear, adhering to dorsal sepal, 6–14 mm long, lower lobe long and narrow, curling

upwards like a horn, 2–4.5 cm long; lip 3-lobed almost from the base, midlobe linear, 10–20 mm long, side lobes diverging, narrowly lanceolate, often with short teeth on the outer margin, 8–18 mm long, 1–3 mm wide, spur swollen in the apical half or third, 14–27 mm long.

In open grassland, often where drainage is poor; widespread, including the Chyulu hills and west of the Rift Valley; 850–2400 m; flowering April to July.

Also recorded from Tanzania and Uganda and widespread throughout the eastern side of Africa, westwards to Nigeria and south to South Africa (Transvaal, Natal, eastern Cape Province).

Habenaria cornuta   ERIC LA CROIX

Habenaria decorata A. Richard

Short, stout plants, 10–45 cm high. Leaves 3–7, suberect or spreading, broadly lanceolate, acute, the largest 5–12 cm long, 1.5–4 cm wide. Inflorescence up to 15 cm long, rather lax, bearing 1–11 flowers. Flowers suberect, the sepals pale green, petals and lip white; dorsal sepal erect, elliptic-ovate, convex, 8–12 mm long, 5–8 mm wide; lateral sepals spreading, acute, as long as dorsal but narrower; petals adhering to dorsal sepal and forming a hood with it, semiovate, 8–13 mm long, 4–8 mm wide; lip 3-lobed, basal part 3–5 mm long, midlobe projecting forward, narrowly triangular or lanceolate, 10–18 mm long, up to 6 mm wide at base, side lobes divergent or curving upwards, 16–22 mm long with 4–6 slender threads on the outer margins, spur pendent, somewhat swollen in the apical half, *c.* 3 cm long.

In rocky places in upland moor, with *Erica arborea* and other montane shrubs; only known in Kenya from the western side of the Aberdare Mts; 2200–3300 m; flowering in June.

Also known from high altitudes in eastern Uganda and Ethiopia.

Habenaria eggelingii Summerhayes

Syn. *Habenaria tenuispica* Rendle var. *eggelingii* (Summerhayes) Geerinck

Plants robust, up to 120 cm high. Leaves 6–12, lanceolate or narrowly lanceolate, acute, up to 35 cm long and 3 cm wide. Inflorescence densely many-flowered, up to 50 cm long. Flowers small, green; dorsal sepal elliptic or ovate, 3.5–5.5 mm long, very convex; lateral sepals of equal size, spreading, obliquely lanceolate; petals a little shorter than the sepals but broader; lip deflexed, 3-lobed from the middle, 4–6 mm long, lobes narrow, midlobe longer and wider than the side lobes, spur pendent, swollen in the apical part, 5–6.5 mm long.

In damp shady places in upland rain forest and moor, often in gullies and at the edge of lava flows; 2400–3800 m; flowering January and April.

Only known from the high mountains of Kenya, Uganda and eastern Zaïre.

Habenaria egregia Summerhayes

Robust but slender plants up to 100 cm high. Leaves 6–8, erect, broadly lanceolate, acute, the largest 9–15 cm long, 3.5–5 cm wide. Inflorescence lax, with 2–4 large flowers. Flowers spreading, the sepals green, petals and lip white; dorsal sepal erect, broadly lanceolate, 3.5–4 cm long, 1.5–2 cm wide; lateral sepals spreading, curved, 3.5–4.5 cm long, narrower than dorsal; petals curved, semiovate and spirally twisted upwards, *c.* 4.5 cm long, 1 cm wide, minutely hairy; lip deeply 3-lobed, basal part 1.5–2 cm long, midlobe broadly linear, obtuse, 3–4 cm long, 2 mm wide, side lobes widely divergent, *c.* 3 cm long with *c.* 14 long slender threads 1–2 cm long on the outer margins, spur pendent, cylindrical, swollen in the apical third, 13–19 cm long.

Grassland; only known in Kenya from a few collections in Kakamega district; 1500 m; flowering June and July.

Also recorded in Cameroon.

Habenaria epipactidea Reichenbach f.
Plants robust, 15–55 cm high. Leaves 8–15, suberect, lanceolate, broadly lanceolate, or oblong, rounded or acute at the apex, the largest up to 12 cm long, 2.5 cm wide, gradually decreasing in size up the stem. Inflorescence dense, with numerous greenish-cream flowers, sweetly scented. Flowers rather thick, opaque; dorsal sepal green, broadly ovate, hooded, 9–14 mm long; lateral sepals green, longer and narrower than dorsal,

Habenaria epipactidea   JOYCE STEWART

spreading or reflexed; petals pale green or cream with darker venation, rounded or ovate, 9–14 mm long, 6–12 mm wide; lip 3-lobed but side lobes reduced to small narrow processes, midlobe straight and thick, 10–16 mm long, spur 17–30 mm long, rarely longer; column broad.

Short grassland, especially where it is seasonally damp; only recorded at Langata and near Machakos; 1250–2000 m; flowering May to June and December.

Widely distributed at medium altitudes in eastern Africa, from Uganda and Kenya southwards to South Africa (eastern Cape Province); also in Angola and Namibia.

Habenaria helicoplectrum Summerhayes
Plant 25–55 cm high, stem erect with 2 large basal leaves and several much smaller ones along its length. Basal leaves appressed to the ground, broadly ovate to reniform or orbicular, 5–11 cm long, 5–16 cm wide, rather fleshy; cauline leaves 5–7, lanceolate, acuminate, up to 3 cm long. Inflorescence 8–22 cm long with many flowers, bracts small. Flowers white to greenish cream; dorsal sepal erect, elliptic-lanceolate, acute, very convex, 9–12 mm long, 4–6 mm wide; lateral sepals reflexed or deflexed, semi-ovate, acuminate, 10–14 mm long, 4–5 mm wide; petals bilobed, upper lobe erect, curved lanceolate, acute, 9–12 mm long, 1–2 mm wide, lower lobe filiform, 2–3 cm long; lip 3-lobed nearly to the base, midlobe linear, 8–15 mm long, side lobes filiform or narrowly linear, 2–2.5 cm long, spur incurved in the middle to form a complete loop, 3.5 cm long.

In grassland and scrub in the dry parts of the country; Northern Frontier, Kitui and Masai districts; 950–1150 m; flowering May to June, and in December.

Also recorded from Tanzania.

Habenaria hologlossa Summerhayes
Plants slender, 30–80 cm high. Leaves 6–9, linear or ligulate-linear, acute, up to 16 cm long, 12 mm wide, upper ones grading into the bracts. Inflorescence rather densely many-flowered, 7–30 cm long. Flowers small, green; dorsal sepal elliptic or ovate, obtuse, 3.5 mm long; lateral sepals deflexed, semiovate, slightly longer; petals equal to the dorsal sepal and forming a hood with it; lip entire, 6 mm long, ligulate, spur cylindric, 10–12 mm long.

Among grass in damp places in open bushland; only known from the southern slopes of Mt Elgon; *c.* 2000 m; flowering August.

Also recorded in Angola.

Habenaria huillensis Reichenbach f.
Syn. *Habenaria humilior* Reichenbach f.
Plants 15–100 cm high, stem erect, rather stout, leafy throughout. Leaves 7–16, lowermost ones white with green venation, middle ones erect,

Habenaria hologlossa   ERIC LA CROIX

Habenaria huillensis   BOB CAMPBELL

Habenaria ichneumonea (Swartz) Lindley

Plants 20–85 cm high, stem erect slender, leafy throughout. Leaves 5–12, erect or suberect, largest 7–20 cm long, 5–10 mm wide, upper ones smaller, appressed to stem. Inflorescence 6–22 cm long, 7 – many flowers, lax, bracts lanceolate, usually much shorter than the ovary. Flowers green with white centre; dorsal sepal reflexed, narrowly elliptic, convex, 3–5 mm long, 1–3 mm wide; lateral sepals deflexed, obliquely obovate, 5–8 mm long, 1–3 mm wide; petals 2-lobed, upper lobe linear, reflexed, 3–4 mm long, lower lobe spreading forward, narrowly lanceolate, curved, 6–11 mm long; lip 3-lobed from undivided base 1–4 mm long, lobes linear, midlobe 7–13 mm long, side lobes a little shorter, spur incurved, apex much swollen, 10–25 mm long.

Damp grassland and swamps; recorded in Kenya by Geerinck (1984) but I have not seen any specimens.

Also recorded from Tanzania and Uganda; widespread throughout Africa, from Ethiopia westwards to Guinee Republic and south to Angola and Zimbabwe.

Habenaria keniensis Summerhayes

Robust but slender plants, 20–60 cm high. Leaves 5–7, lanceolate or elliptic-lanceolate, acute, the largest 5–15 cm long, 2–6 cm wide. Inflorescence 10–27 cm long, with 6–32 rather widely spaced flowers. Flowers suberect, yellowish green and white; dorsal sepal erect, broadly lanceolate, very acute, 13–19 mm long, 7–9 mm wide; lateral sepals spreading or deflexed, obliquely lanceolate, 16–

linear, largest 6–35 cm long, 1–2 cm wide, upper ones smaller appressed to the stem. Inflorescence 6–27 cm long, 6–many flowers, dense, bracts thin, the lower ones longer than the pedicel and ovary. Flowers green with white centre; dorsal sepal reflexed, narrowly elliptic, convex, 4–7 mm long, 2–3 mm wide; lateral sepals deflexed, obliquely oblong-elliptic, 6–10 mm long, 3–5 mm wide; petals 2-lobed, upper lobe reflexed, linear, 4–7 mm long, glabrous or ciliolate, lower lobe spreading forward and upward, lanceolate, acute, 9–14 mm long, 1–3 mm wide, glabrous or papillose; lip 3-lobed nearly from the base, lobes linear, midlobe 6–14 mm long, side lobes 6–12 mm long, spur swollen in the apical half 1.5–3 cm long.

Grassland, often on shallow soil over rocks where it is usually wet; widespread in highlands, around Nairobi, and in Teita hills; 1200–2700 m; flowering May to July, also recorded in January.

Also recorded in Tanzania and Uganda; widespread throughout Africa, westwards to Ghana, south to Angola, and in Sudan and Ethiopia.

23 mm long, narrower than the dorsal; petals adhering to the dorsal sepal and equalling it in length but narrower; lip deflexed, basal part 5–6 mm long, then 3-lobed, midlobe linear or ligulate, obtuse, 12–18 mm long, side lobes widely divergent, 15–20 mm long, bearing 6–10 narrow threads on the outer margin, spur pendent, curving forward or S-shaped, 2–3 cm long; stigmatic arms on the front of the column long and conspicuous.

Forest margins in many parts of the Kenya highlands; 1950–2650 m; flowering May to July.

Not known elsewhere.

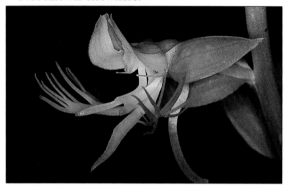

Habenaria keniensis   HERMANN MEYER

Habenaria kilimanjari Reichenbach f.

Plants 15–90 cm high, stem erect, slender or rather stout, leafy throughout. Leaves 7–13, spreading, linear or narrowly lanceolate, the largest 8–23 cm long, 1–2.5 cm wide, the upper ones smaller. Inflorescence 4–37 cm long, many-flowered, lax or dense, bracts lanceolate, the lowest nearly as long as the ovary. Flowers white with tip of spur green; dorsal sepal reflexed, elliptic, 5–7.5 mm long, 2–3 mm wide; lateral sepals deflexed, obliquely semiorbicular, 6–8 mm long, 2–4 mm wide; petals 2-lobed, lobes oblanceolate and toothed in the upper part, upper lobe 5–7 mm long, 1–2 mm wide, lower lobe 3–5 mm long, narrower than upper lobe; lip 3-lobed from near the base, lobes linear, midlobe 5–11 mm long, side lobes 3–6 mm long, spur swollen in the apical half, 13–17 mm long.

Grasslands which are seasonally flooded, near the coast; sea level to 200 m; flowering July and August.

Also recorded from Tanzania; widespread in tropical Africa westwards to Zaïre and south to Zambia, Malawi, Mozambique and Angola.

Habenaria laurentii De Wildeman

Plants 25–75 cm high, stem erect. Leaves 6–11, spreading, the largest ovate, or elliptic, acute, 7–22 cm long, 2.5–7 cm wide, upper ones smaller.

Inflorescence 6–22 cm long, with 3–15 flowers, laxly arranged, bracts short. Flowers white or pale green with white central parts; dorsal sepal erect, convex, elliptic-lanceolate, *c.* 2 cm long, 1 cm wide; lateral sepals deflexed, rolled up lengthwise, obliquely semi-obovate, *c.* 2.5 cm long, 1 cm wide; petals 2-lobed, upper lobe erect, linear, adhering to the dorsal sepal, *c.* 2 cm long, lower lobe curved upwards and outwards like a horn, linear and then subulate above, 4–8.5 cm long; lip 3-lobed, all lobes linear, projecting forward, midlobe 2.5–3.5 cm long, side lobes 2–3 cm long, spur curved backwards, 5.5–8 cm long.

Grassland, often among rocks or scattered bushes; only recorded west of the Rift Valley; 2000–2300 m; flowering May to August.

Also recorded throughout tropical Africa from Zaïre to Guinee Republic and in Zambia and Zimbabwe, but not in Uganda and Tanzania.

Habenaria laurentii   ERIC LA CROIX

Habenaria lindblomii Schlechter
   Syn. *Habenaria verdickii* (De Wildeman)
      Schlechter var. *lindblomii* (Schlechter)
                                    Geerinck

Plants 20–65 cm high, stem erect with 2 large unequal basal leaves and several smaller ones along its length. Basal leaves appressed to the ground, opposite, ovate to transversely elliptic, 3–6.5 cm long, 3.5–9 cm wide, fleshy; cauline leaves 5–10, lanceolate or ovate, acute, up to 5 cm long. Inflorescence 7–20 cm long, with 7–20 flowers, bracts small. Flowers green and white, fragrant; dorsal sepal erect, broadly lanceolate, acute, convex, 8–16 mm long, *c.* 8 mm wide, with 3 keels on the outer surface; lateral sepals deflexed, obliquely lanceolate, acuminate, 9–18 mm long, 4–6 mm wide, with one toothed keel on the outer surface; petals bilobed, upper lobe erect, linear, 8–16 mm long, lower lobe curved upwards, horn-like, 10–25 mm long; lip 3-lobed nearly to the base, lobes linear, midlobe 9–19 mm long, side lobes slightly shorter and narrower, spur much swollen in apical half, 14–23 mm long.

Grassland and woodland with scattered trees; only known in Kenya from the highlands near Kitale and Eldoret; 1850–2200 m; flowering June to August.

Also recorded from Tanzania, eastern Zaïre and Zambia.

Habenaria linderi Summerhayes
Plants 30–55 cm high, stem erect slender to rather stout, leafy throughout. Leaves 7–12, mostly lanceolate-linear, largest 6–25 cm long, 1–1.5 cm wide, upper ones smaller and appressed to stem. Inflorescence 10–20 cm long, 10–35 flowers, lax or dense, bracts mostly shorter than the ovary with pedicel. Flowers green; dorsal sepal reflexed, elliptic, convex, 8 mm long, 3 mm wide; lateral sepals deflexed, obliquely obovate, 9–10 mm long, 4–6 mm wide; petals 2-lobed from *c.* 2.5 mm above the base, lobes linear, equal, 5–9 mm long; lip 3-lobed from the base, midlobe linear, 8–12 mm long, side lobes a little shorter, spur cylindric or slightly swollen at apex, 10–14 mm long.

Grassland at high altitudes and in open glades in forest; 2350–3000 m; flowering October and November.

Also recorded from Uganda and Burundi.

Habenaria macrantha A. Richard
Stout but slender plants, 20–50 cm high. Leaves 5–7, lanceolate or ovate-lanceolate, acute, the largest 5–12 cm long and 1.5–5 cm wide. Inflorescence up to 12 cm long, lax, with 2–9 flowers. Flowers suberect, green or whitish green; dorsal sepal erect, ovate to narrowly lanceolate, 2–2.6 cm long, 7–11 mm wide; lateral sepals spreading, about as long and wide as the dorsal; petals adhering to the dorsal sepal, lanceolate, curved, 2–2.5 cm long, minutely

hairy; lip united with the base of the column for *c.* 6 mm, basal part 9–15 mm long, then 3-lobed, midlobe linear obtuse, 14–23 mm long, side lobes diverging but incurved, longer than the midlobe with 6–10 slender threads on the outer margins, spur incurved, often sharply bent in the middle, slightly swollen in the apical half, 2–3.5 cm long.

Upland grassland and moor, with *Erica arborea* and other montane shrubs; only known in Kenya from the western Aberdare Mts; 2500–3000 m; flowers in June.

Also recorded from high altitudes in eastern Uganda, Ethiopia and Arabia.

Habenaria macrura Kraenzlin
Plant 20–65 cm high, stem erect, with 2 basal leaves and appressed sheaths almost covering its entire length. Basal leaves appressed to the ground, ovate, elliptic or orbicular, 2.5–9.5 cm long, 2.5–7 cm wide; sheaths 3–9, lanceolate, up to 6 cm long.

Habenaria macrura   K.O.S.

Inflorescence up to 16 cm long, with up to 11 flowers, bracts short. Flowers large, white or cream with sepals green on outside, fragrant; dorsal sepal erect, ovate, convex, 8–13 mm long, 5–11 mm wide, venation distinct; lateral sepals reflexed or spreading, obliquely semiovate, acute, 9–17 mm long, 4–6 mm wide, venation distinct; petals bi-lobed, upper lobe erect, curved, lanceolate to semiovate, 7–11 mm long, 2–7 mm wide, lower lobe obliquely oblanceolate, 9–19 mm long, 2–6 mm wide; lip 3-lobed from a narrow base 2–6 mm long, midlobe lanceolate-ligulate, 10–19 mm long, 3–6 mm wide, side lobes similar to lower lobe of petals, 8–23 mm long, 3–8 mm wide, spur narrowly cylindric, 9–17 cm long, often caught up in the stem sheaths.

Grassland, or bush with scattered trees and grass; only recorded in Kenya in Kitale district; 1500–2200 m; flowering May.

Also recorded in Uganda and Tanzania, west-wards to Zaïre and Nigeria, south to Zambia, Malawi and Angola, as well as in Ethiopia.

Habenaria macruroides Summerhayes

Plants 35–50 cm high, stem stout, erect. Leaves 8–10, erect, clasping the stem, lanceolate, acute, the largest 6–7 cm long, grading into the bracts. Inflo-rescence 8–18 cm long, with 3–8 flowers, bracts short. Flowers white, fragrant; dorsal sepal erect, convex, ovate, 9–13 mm long, 6–8 mm wide; lateral sepals deflexed, obliquely ovate, 12–14 mm long, 5 mm wide; petals 2-lobed, upper lobe semiovate or lanceolate-ligulate, adhering to the dorsal sepal, 9–12 mm long, 3–5 mm wide, lower lobe curved, ligulate, obtuse, 9–12 mm long, 2–3 mm wide; lip 3-lobed from an undivided base 2–5 mm long, midlobe ligulate or lanceolate-ligulate, 10–15 mm long, 2–5 mm wide, side lobes similar but slightly shorter and narrower, spur slender, hidden among the bracts, 10–14 cm long.

Swampy grassland; only known from Kitale dis-trict; 1850–2200 m; flowers in June.

Also recorded from Uganda and from Cameroon.

Habenaria malacophylla Reichenbach f.

Plants 30–100 cm high, stem erect slender, leafy in the centre, bare below. Leaves 10–18, spreading, rather soft, middle ones oblanceolate or ovate, largest 7–20 cm long, 2–5 cm wide. Inflorescence 8–34 cm long, many-flowered, bracts shorter than the ovary. Flowers small, green; dorsal sepal erect, elliptic-ovate, convex, 3–6 mm long, 2–4 mm wide; lateral sepals deflexed, obliquely lanceolate, 4–7 mm long, 2–3 mm wide; petals 2-lobed, upper lobe ligulate, adhering to the dorsal sepal, 4–7 mm long, c. 1 mm wide, lower lobe linear, curved up-wards, 5–9 mm long; lip 3-lobed from near the base, lobes linear, midlobe 4.5–7 mm long, side

lobes a little longer, spur cylindric or enlarged in the middle, 9–18 mm long.

Usually in upland rain forest but also in grass-land that has replaced forest; widespread; 1350–2700 m; flowering August to October and in April.

Also recorded in Tanzania and Uganda; wide-spread throughout Africa, west to Sierra Leone, Ethiopia and south to South Africa (Transvaal, Natal, Cape Province).

Habenaria malacophylla   BOB CAMPBELL

Habenaria ndiana Rendle

Plants 30–90 high, stem erect slender to rather stout, leafy throughout. Leaves 10–16, spreading, linear-lanceolate, the largest 10–20 cm long, 1–2 cm wide, upper ones appressed to stem. Inflor-escence 10–24 cm long, with 10–many flowers, bracts rather thin, usually shorter than pedicel and ovary. Flowers green; dorsal sepal reflexed, nar-rowly elliptic, convex, 5–6 mm long, 2–3 mm wide; lateral sepals deflexed, obliquely obovate, 6–9 mm long, c. 4 mm wide; petals 2-lobed, upper lobe lin-ear, 4–6 mm long, lower lobe spreading, narrowly lanceolate, 7–12 mm long; lip 3-lobed from near the base, midlobe linear, 8–12 mm long, side lobes lanceolate-linear, tapering, 7–11 mm long, spur twisted once or twice in the middle, swollen in the apical half, 2–2.5 cm long.

Grasslands on poorly drained soils; around Mt Elgon, Chyulu hills and in Teita district; 1700–

3000 m; flowering mostly July to August.

Also recorded from Uganda and Tanzania.

Habenaria njamnjamica Kraenzlin
Plants 30–55 cm high, stem erect slender or rather stout. Leaves 11–17, erect, lanceolate, acute, the largest 3–7.5 cm long, 1–2 cm wide, the uppermost similar to the bracts. Inflorescence 8–17 cm long, 8–20 flowers, dense, bracts lanceolate, usually longer than the pedicel and ovary. Flowers green with white centre; dorsal sepal erect, ovate, convex, 6–10 mm long, 4–7 mm wide; lateral sepals deflexed, obliquely lanceolate, 8–13 mm long, 2–5 mm wide; petals 2-lobed, upper lobe erect, linear or lanceolate, curved, 7–10 mm long, 1–4 mm wide, lower lobe curved upwards linear or filiform, often twisted, 6–12 mm long; lip 3-lobed, from an undivided base 1–2 mm long, midlobe linear, 10–14 mm long, side lobes spreading, narrowly linear, 10–14 mm long, spur swollen in the apical half, 1–2 cm long.

Grassland; only recorded in a small area of west Kenya; 1500–2000 m; flowering July to August.

Also recorded from Tanzania, Sudan, west to Zaïre and south to Malawi, Zambia and Zimbabwe.

Habenaria peristyloides A. Richard
Slender to moderately robust plants, 10–80 cm high. Leaves 4–9, lanceolate or lanceolate-linear, gradually tapering to an acute point, the longest 6–24 cm long, 5–25 mm wide. Inflorescence cylindric, 5–30 cm long, 1–3 cm in diameter, densely many-flowered. Flowers small, green; dorsal sepal elliptic-lanceolate, convex, 4–6.5 mm long; lateral sepals spreading, longer and wider than the dorsal; petals curved, elliptic, similar to the dorsal sepal; lip 7–12 mm long, with a broad, cordate, undivided base, 3-lobed in the apical two thirds, lobes ligulate to linear, midlobe twice as long as the side lobes that are spreading or recurved, spur cylindric, 1.5–3 mm long.

Short upland grassland, marshes and open scrub, in areas west of the Rift Valley; 1800–2500 m; flowering May to September.

Widespread across tropical Africa from Kenya westwards to Nigeria and from Ethiopia south to Tanzania.

Habenaria perrieri Schlechter
Plants 30–60 cm high, stem erect slender, leafy throughout. Leaves 10–11, spreading, elliptic-lanceolate, acute, the largest 9–20 cm long, 3.5–4 cm wide, the upper 2 or 3 much smaller. Inflorescence 12–20 cm long, many-flowered, dense, bracts lanceolate, much shorter than the flowers. Flowers green, yellowish green or greenish white; dorsal sepal erect, elliptic or ovate, 4 mm long, 2–3 mm wide; lateral sepals deflexed, obliquely semiorbicular, 5–6 mm long, 3 mm wide; petals 2-lobed, upper lobe curved, ligulate, 4 mm long, lower lobe linear, 2 mm long, narrower than upper lobe; lip entire or minutely 3-lobed near the base, 6–8 mm long, midlobe linear, side lobes, if present, tooth-like or less than 2 mm long, spur slightly swollen in apical half, 11–14 mm long.

Forest margins and in coastal evergreen bush; sea level to 400 m; flowering August.

Also recorded from Zanzibar, Pemba and Madagascar.

Habenaria petitiana (A. Richard) Durand & Schinz
Syn. *Peristylus snowdenii* Rolfe
Peristylus ugandensis Rolfe
Slender or robust plants, 10–100 cm high. Leaves 7–14, ovate or broadly lanceolate, acute, the base clasping the stem, up to 8.5 cm long, 1.5–4.5 cm wide. Inflorescence slender, densely many-flowered, rarely more than 20 cm long. Flowers small, green or yellowish green; dorsal sepal ovate or ovate-lanceolate, 2.5–4 mm long; laterals spreading, a little longer but narrower than the dorsal; petals oblique and curved, obtuse, 2–3 mm long; lip broadly cuneate, or fan-like, 2.5–4 mm long and nearly as wide, almost equally 3-lobed in the apical half, spur almost globose, c. 1 mm long.

Rather frequently collected in short grassland, among scrub and at forest edges; widespread in west Kenya and around Nairobi; 2000–3000 m; flowering May to July and in December.

Also recorded in similar habitats in Uganda and Tanzania, Ethiopia and Zaïre.

Habenaria plectromaniaca Reichenbach f. & S. Moore
Robust plants 60–100 cm high, stem erect. Leaves 10–15, the middle ones suberect, linear or lanceolate-linear, acute, the largest 13–32 cm long, 5–20 mm wide. Inflorescence 10–30 cm long, 7–many flowers, bracts short, rather thin. Flowers white or greenish white; dorsal sepal reflexed away from the rest of the flower, narrowly elliptic, obtuse, convex, 8–9 mm long, c. 3 mm wide; lateral sepals deflexed, obliquely obovate, 11–13 mm long, 6–8 mm wide; petals 2-lobed, upper lobe upright or reflexed, linear, c. 8 mm long, lower lobe spreading forwards, lanceolate, 12–15 mm long, 2–

5 mm wide; lip 3-lobed from an undivided base *c.* 1 mm long, midlobe linear, 16–20 mm long, side lobes lanceolate-linear, 11–17 mm long, wider than the midlobe, spur swollen in the apical third or quarter, 4.5–7 cm long.

Marshy grassland at the forest edge; only known from the Shimba hills in Kwale district; sea level to 500 m; flowering July.

Also recorded from Tanzania.

Habenaria quartiniana A. Richard
Robust but slender plants, 25–70 cm high. Leaves 5–7, lanceolate or ovate-lanceolate, acute, the largest 6–10 cm long, 2–5 cm wide. Inflorescence 7–23 cm long, rather lax, with 6–20 widely spaced flowers. Flowers curved outwards, sepals green, petals and lip white; dorsal sepal erect, lanceolate or elliptic-lanceolate, acute, 4.5–9 mm long; lateral sepals spreading, curved, acuminate, 7–13 mm long, broader than the dorsal; petals obliquely tri-angular, equalling the dorsal sepal in length but wider; lip 3-lobed, the basal part 3–4.5 mm long, midlobe linear or ligulate, 7–14 mm long, side lobes divergent, 9–17 mm long with 6–11 slender threads on the outer margins, spur pendent, slightly curved, swollen towards the apex, 2.5–4 cm long.

Upland grassland, often among rocks, in thick bush and at forest margins; only known in Kenya from the northeast side of Mt Elgon; 2100–2600 m; flowers in June.

Also recorded from Uganda and Ethiopia.

Habenaria schimperiana A. Richard
Plants 30–100 cm high, stem erect slender to stout, leafy throughout. Leaves 6–10, suberect or spreading, linear or linear-lanceolate, the largest 7–28 cm long, 1–3 cm wide, the upper ones small, appressed to the stem. Inflorescence 6–35 cm long, 4–many flowers, lax or dense, bracts usually much shorter than the pedicel with ovary. Flowers green with white centre, smell unpleasant; dorsal sepal re-flexed, narrowly elliptic, convex, 6–8 mm long, nearly 4 mm wide; lateral sepals deflexed and twisted, obliquely obovate, 9–11 mm long, 5–8 mm wide; petals 2-lobed, both lobes ciliate, upper lobe linear or narrowly lanceolate, 5–8 mm long, lower lobe spreading downwards, lanceolate, 14–18 mm long, 2 mm wide; lip 3-lobed above an undivided base 2–3 mm long, midlobe linear, 13–17 mm long, side lobes narrowly lanceolate, 8–11 mm long, spur twisted several times in the middle, much swollen in the apical half, 10–16 mm long.

Grassland in swamps and on badly drained soils; 2500–2800 m; flowering June to August.

Also recorded from Tanzania, from Ethiopia, Sudan and Zaïre, and south to Malawi, Zambia and Zimbabwe.

Habenaria splendens Rendle
Plants robust, 30–75 cm high. Leaves 6–8, ovate or ovate-lanceolate, acute, the largest 6–20 cm long, 2.5–8 cm wide. Inflorescence 8–27 cm long, rather lax with 4–17 flowers. Flowers large and often fragrant, sepals green, petals and lip white; dorsal sepal erect, broadly lanceolate or elliptic, apiculate, 2–3 cm long, 9–15 mm wide; lateral sepals spreading, a little longer than the dorsal but narrower; petals adhering to the dorsal sepal, ligulate, often angled on the outside below the middle, as long as the dorsal sepal, 5–9 mm wide; lip with basal part narrow, 7–13 mm long, 3-lobed, midlobe often de-flexed, linear, 2–3 cm long, 1–2 mm wide, side lobes diverging, a little longer than the midlobe with 6–12 slender threads on the outer margin, spur incurved, swollen at the bluntly rounded tip, 3–4 cm long.

Upland grassland, often among bushes and at forest margins; only known in Kenya from Mt

Habenaria splendens   ERIC LA CROIX

Elgon and from the Chyulu hills; 1000–2400 m; flowering June (Mt Elgon) and December (Chyulu hills).

Also recorded from Uganda and Tanzania, and from Ethiopia, Malawi and Zambia.

Habenaria stylites Reichenbach f. & S. Moore

Plant 20–55 cm high, stem erect, slender, with 2 large basal leaves and several smaller ones scattered along its length. Basal leaves appressed to the ground, opposite, ovate to reniform, 2.5–6.5 cm long, 2–9 cm wide, fleshy; cauline leaves 4–9, appressed to the stem, lanceolate, acuminate, to 3 cm long. Inflorescence 3–16 cm long, with 3-many flowers, bracts short. Flowers white or cream; dorsal sepal erect, elliptic, convex, 10–15 mm long, 3–7 mm wide; lateral sepals spreading, obliquely semiovate, acuminate, 10–16 mm long, 4–8 mm wide; petals bilobed, upper lobe erect, curved, lanceolate, 8–12 mm long, 1–2 mm wide, lower lobe narrowly linear or filiform, 8–15 mm long; lip deflexed, 3-lobed from a narrow basal part 2–5 mm long, lobes linear or lanceolate-linear, midlobe 6–14 mm long, 1–5 mm wide, side lobes 6–19 mm long, 1–2 mm wide, spur slender, 3–6 cm long.

Grassland at edge of forest and in gaps in forest; only known in Kenya from Shimba hills in Kwale district and Namanga hill; 100–1600 m; flowers in July.

Also recorded from Tanzania; slightly smaller subspecies are recorded from Tanzania, Mozambique and Zimbabwe.

Habenaria subarmata Reichenbach f.

Plant 40–65 cm high, stem erect, slender, with 2 large leaves at the base and several much smaller ones along its length. Basal leaves opposite, appressed to the ground, broadly ovate to reniform or orbicular, cordate, 7–15 cm long, 7–19 cm wide, fleshy; cauline leaves 6–10, lanceolate, up to 5 cm long. Inflorescence 5–18 cm long, with many flowers close together, bracts short. Flowers white; dorsal sepal erect, elliptic-lanceolate, acute, convex, 7–11 mm long, 6–7 mm wide; lateral sepals spreading or reflexed, obliquely semiovate, 9–12 mm long, 4–6 mm wide; petals bilobed, upper lobe curved linear, 7–11 mm long, lower lobe curved upwards, linear-filiform, 2.5–4 cm long; lip 3-lobed from a short undivided base, midlobe linear, obtuse, 11–16 mm long, side lobes linear-filiform, 2.5–5 cm long, spur slender, 5–7.5 cm long.

Grassland or open woodland; only known in

Kenya from Lamu district; near sea level; flowering June.

Also recorded from Tanzania, Zambia, Zimbabwe and Mozambique.

Habenaria subarmata   ERIC LA CROIX

Habenaria thomsonii Reichenbach f.

Plants 30–55 cm high, stem erect slender to rather stout, leafy throughout. Leaves 7–10, erect, lanceolate, the largest 9–12 cm long, 1.5–2.5 cm wide, the upper ones smaller. Inflorescence 6–12 cm long, 12–35 flowers, dense, bracts lanceolate, often equalling or longer than the pedicel with ovary. Flowers green with white centre; dorsal sepal reflexed, elliptic, convex, at least 7 mm long, 3 mm wide; lateral sepals deflexed, obliquely obovate, 7–8 mm long, 5–6 mm wide; petals 2-lobed, upper lobe reflexed, linear, 6–7 mm long, lower lobe spreading forward, obliquely lanceolate, 6–7 mm long, 2–3 mm wide; lip 3-lobed from near the base, midlobe linear, 10–12 mm long, side lobes curved forward, linear-lanceolate, 6–7 mm long, spur swollen in the apical half 10–12 mm long.

Damp or swampy grasslands; only known from Mt Longonot and Londiani district; 2000–2700 m; flowering July and November.

Not known elsewhere.

Habenaria trilobulata Schlechter

Plant 15–35 cm high, stem erect, slender, with 2 large basal leaves and several much smaller sheath-like leaves scattered along its length. Basal leaves opposite, appressed to the ground, ovate or orbicular, 2.5–7.5 cm long, 2–6.5 cm wide; cauline leaves 5–8, lanceolate, up to 2 cm long. Inflorescence 3–11 cm long, bearing 4–10 flowers, bracts short. Flowers pale green or greenish white; dorsal sepal sloping forwards, broadly ovate, convex, 4–6.5 mm long, 5 mm wide; lateral sepals reflexed, obliquely semielliptic, 4.5–7 mm long, 2–3 mm wide; petals bilobed above an undivided basal part 3–4 mm long, upper lobe erect, curved, ovate, papillose, 3–4 mm long, 2 mm wide, lower lobe spreading upwards, filiform, 1.7–2.3 cm long; lip 3-lobed above an undivided basal part 2 mm long, midlobe linear, obtuse, 6.5–8 mm long, side lobes similar to lower petal lobe, 2–2.7 cm long, spur swollen in the apical half, 2–3 cm long.

Open woodland and dry bush; only known in Kenya near the coast in Kwale and Kilifi districts; sea level to 100 m; flowers in August.

Also recorded from Tanzania, Malawi, Mozambique and Zimbabwe.

Habenaria tweedieae Summerhayes

Plants 40–100 cm high, stem erect, stout, leafy throughout. Leaves 9–15, spreading, lanceolate or elliptic, the largest 8–25 cm long, 2–5 cm wide, upper ones smaller, appressed to the stem. Inflorescence 10–45 cm long, 15-many flowers, dense, bracts thin, the lower ones equalling the pedicel with ovary, hairy. Flowers green with whitish centre; dorsal sepal erect, narrowly elliptic, convex, 6–7 mm long, 2–4 mm wide; lateral sepals deflexed, obliquely semiorbicular, 8–10 mm long, 4–6 mm wide; petals 2-lobed, upper lobe erect, often adhering to the dorsal sepal, linear, 6–7 mm long, 1–2 mm wide, ciliolate and shortly hairy, lower lobe spreading forward, curved, lanceolate, 9–11 mm long, 1.5–3 mm wide, hairy towards the base; lip 3-lobed from a short base, midlobe curved, linear, 10–12 mm long, side lobes linear, 5–8 mm long, spur swollen in the apical half, c. 2.5 cm long.

In grassland and amongst scrub, often on rocky hills; 2200–2600 m; flowering August to November.

Also recorded from Uganda.

Habenaria vaginata A. Richard

Plant 10–50 cm high, stem erect, slender or stout, with 1 or 2 leaves at or near the base and several sheaths along the stem. Basal leaves appressed to the ground, the upper one 1–2 cm above the lower, reniform, orbicular or ovate, 2–10 cm long, 1.5–9 cm wide; sheaths appressed to stem, lanceolate, to 4 cm long. Inflorescence 4–20 cm long, with 6-many flowers, bracts sheath-like. Flowers small,

Habenaria vaginata   BOB CAMPBELL

Habenaria vaginata   BOB CAMPBELL

green or yellowish green; dorsal sepal erect, convex, elliptic, 3.5–5 mm long, 2.5 mm wide; lateral sepals deflexed, oblique, semiovate, 5–6.5 mm long, 2–3 mm wide; petals entire, erect, adhering to the dorsal sepal, lanceolate, 3.5–5 mm long, *c.* 1.5 mm wide; lip deflexed, 3-lobed from an undivided base 1 mm long, lobes incurved, linear, fleshy, midlobe 4.5–7 mm long, side lobes a little shorter and narrower, spur pendent, curving forwards, 17–27 mm long.

Widespread in short grassland especially where damp, at forest margins and in forest glades; common around Nairobi; 1300–3000 m; flowering April and May.

Also recorded from Tanzania and Ethiopia.

Habenaria walleri Reichenbach f.

Plants rather stout, 40–80 cm high, stem erect. Leaves 7–10, erect, close to the stem, lanceolate, acute, the largest 6–14 cm long, 1–3.5 cm wide, the upper ones similar to the bracts. Inflorescence 8–28 cm long, with 2–14 flowers, bracts short. Flowers with green sepals, the other parts white; dorsal sepal erect, convex, ovate, acuminate, 11–16 mm long, 10 mm wide; lateral sepals deflexed,

Habenaria walleri   ERIC LA CROIX

semi-orbicular, acute, 1.5–2 cm long, 6–9 mm wide; petals 2-lobed, upper lobe linear, adhering to the dorsal sepal, 11–15 mm long, lower lobe oblong-lanceolate, 2–3 cm long, 3–6 mm wide; lip 3-lobed from an undivided base 3–6 mm long, lobes diverging, oblong-lanceolate, acute, midlobe 15–30 mm long, 2.5–5 mm wide, side lobes 19–32 mm long, 4–6 mm wide, spur swollen in the apical third, 13–17 cm long.

Swampy grassland; only recorded west of the Rift Valley; 1200–2300 m; flowering May to June.

Also recorded from Uganda and Tanzania, westwards as far as Nigeria and Gabon, southwards to Malawi, and in Sudan.

Habenaria zambesina Reichenbach f.

Plants robust, 40–120 cm high. Leaves 9–14, the middle ones broadly lanceolate or elliptic-ovate, acute, the largest 4–23 cm long, 2–7.5 cm wide. Inflorescence cylindrical, up to 40 cm long, 4–6 cm in diameter. Flowers spreading, white; dorsal sepal broadly ovate, convex, 4–6 mm long and almost as broad; lateral sepals deflexed, obliquely semiorbicular, 5–7.5 mm long, a little wider than the dorsal; petals broadly ovate, 3.5–6 mm long; lip 6–9 mm long, projecting forwards, usually entire but sometimes angled or with short teeth on either side at the base, spur pendent, very slender, 3–6.5 cm long.

Grassy swamps; only known in Kenya from one collection near Lake Victoria; *c.* 1200 m; flowering in July.

Widespread throughout tropical Africa.

Holothrix Lindley

Syn. *Deroemera* Reichenbach f.

The small plants in this genus of orchids are rarely encountered because they appear above the ground, flower and die down within a short space of time. Reappearing each year, or each rainy season, from one or two underground tubers, they usually produce one or two round or ovate leaves that lie flat on the surface of the ground. Sometimes, however, these have died off by the time the slender flowering stem arises between them. The short inflorescence is usually less than 40 cm high and often difficult to see amongst the other vegetation nearby. The flowers are very small with petals and lip that are white, greenish or yellowish, and in one Kenya species the lip is lilac. Usually the flowers are secund, all facing the same direction.

The petals are much more conspicuous than the tiny sepals and both they and the lip are often finely divided into three or more lobes.

The name *Holothrix* was derived by John Lindley from two Greek words *holos* (whole) and *thrix* (hair), alluding to the overall hairiness of the plants and flowers in most of the species. More than 50 species have been described in all, from tropical Africa, South Africa and Arabia. Only six are so far recorded from Kenya.

CULTIVATION

There are no records of the Kenya species in cultivation, but they should not be any more difficult than other orchids that have underground tubers. Careful attention to the wetness or dryness of the compost in relation to the stage of growth or resting of the plant will be the key to success.

Key to the species of *Holothrix*

1 Flowering stem bearing a number of
    pointed sheaths   2
  Flowering stem without sheaths   4

2 Lip 3-lobed; petals 3-lobed at apex . . . .
  . . . . **H. aphylla**
  Lip with 5 or more lobes   3

3 Lip shortly 5–7-lobed; petals 5-lobed . . . .
  . . . . **H. pentadactyla**
  Lip 9–15-lobed, the lobes long and
    slender; petals 9–13-lobed . . . . . . **H. randii**

4 Petals entire, narrowed towards the apex. .   5
  Petals 2–4-lobed above, widened from the
    base upwards . . . . **H. elgonensis**

5 Flowers white; lip 3-lobed above; bracts
    hairy . . . . **H. arachnoidea**
  Flowers lilac or mauve; lip entire, or very
    shortly 2-lobed at the apex; bracts
    almost hairless . . . . **H. puberula**

Holothrix aphylla (Forsk.) Reichenbach f.
  Syn. *Deroemera acuminata* Rendle & Schlechter
Perennial herb 6–25 cm high, glabrous. Leaves 2, basal, round or ovate, to 3 cm long, 4 cm wide, usually shrivelled at flowering time. Inflorescence erect, with numerous erect sheaths in the lower part. Flowers secund, white, slightly tinged purplish or blueish; sepals lanceolate or ovate-lanceolate, acute, 2.5–4 mm long; petals narrowly ovate or oblong, 4–8 mm long, 3-lobed at apex, the

midlobe often longer than side lobes, papillose; lip narrow at base then orbicular or transversely elliptic, 4–8 mm long, 3-lobed, the midlobe longer and narrower than side lobes, spurred at the base, spur incurved, slender, 4–8 mm long.

Found in upland grassland; in western Kenya and in the Chyulu hills; 2300–2600 m; flowering in March to May.

Also recorded in Uganda, westwards to Rwanda, Zaïre, Cameroon and northern Nigeria, and northwards in Ethiopia and Yemen.

Holothrix arachnoidea (A. Richard)
                    Reichenbach f.
Perennial herb 10–27 cm high, hairy. Leaves 2, lanceolate, broadly ovate or orbicular, to 4 cm long and wide, with long, soft hairs. Inflorescence erect, hairy, lacking sheaths. Flowers white or greenish; sepals ovate, acute, the laterals oblique, 1–2 mm long, glabrous; petals lanceolate or ligulate, 2–3 mm long, fleshy above; lip narrowly ovate, 2–3 mm long, 3-lobed in the upper half, lobes nearly equal, spur conical, 1.5 mm long; ovary hairy.

Only recorded from grasslands near Nanyuki; 2200 m; flowering in September.

Also known from Tanzania and Ethiopia.

Holothrix elgonensis Summerhayes
Perennial herb 25–40 cm high. Leaves 2, unequal, basal, elliptic to reniform, 4 cm long, 6 cm wide, sparsely hairy on the upper surface and with more hairs along the margin. Inflorescence erect, hairy, lacking sheaths. Flowers white, tinged with rose or pale mauve, secund; sepals ovate or elliptic-ovate, acute, 4–5 mm long, slightly hairy; petals wedge-shaped, 10 mm long, 4–6-lobed in the upper half, glabrous; lip broadly fan-shaped, 10 mm long, 9–13-lobed in the upper third, glabrous, spur cylindrical, straight, 3 mm long.

Known only from the grasslands on the upper slopes of Mt Elgon; 3300–3700 m; flowering in December.

Also recorded from the Uganda side of Mt Elgon; not known elsewhere.

Holothrix pentadactyla (Summerhayes)
                    Summerhayes
  Syn. *Deroemera pentadactyla* Summerhayes
Perennial herb 12–35 cm high. Leaf 1, basal, reniform, cordate, to 3 cm long and slightly wider, glabrous, usually withered at flowering time. Inflorescence erect, with small scattered sheaths along its length, glabrous. Flowers white, secund; sepals broadly lanceolate or oblong-lanceolate, apiculate,

the laterals oblique, 2.5–4 mm long; petals cuneate, 6–7 mm long, 5-lobed in the upper quarter, central lobes longer than others, papillose; lip narrowly fan-shaped from a narrow base, 4–5 mm long, shortly 5–7-lobed at the apex, lobes finger-like, papillose, spur incurved, cylindric, 7–8 mm long.

Holothrix pentadactyla   K.O.S.

Upland grassland and open rocky ground; recorded from Mt Kenya, the Aberdare Mts, Cherangani hills and the Mau forest; 2300–2900 m; flowering in January and February.

Not known elsewhere.

Holothrix puberula Rendle
Perennial herb to 20 cm high. Leaves 2, close to the ground, reniform-orbicular, glabrous, 2.5 cm long, 3.5 cm wide. Inflorescence erect, lacking sheaths, hairy. Flowers few, lilac or pale mauve; sepals ovate or broadly lanceolate, the laterals oblique, acute, 2–4 mm long, almost glabrous; petals obliquely lanceolate, acute, 3–5 mm long; lip much longer than other flower parts, oblanceolate or narrowly elliptic from a narrow base, 7–10 mm long, rounded or shortly bilobed at the tip, spur narrowly incurved, 3–4 mm long.

Usually found among rocks in short upland grassland; 2300–3200 m; flowering in May and June.

Also known from Uganda, Tanzania, Malawi, Zambia and Ethiopia.

Holothrix randii Rendle
Perennial herb 8–35 cm high. Leaves 2, basal, reniform, up to 3 cm long, 4 cm wide, fleshy, glabrous, usually withered at time of flowering. Inflorescence erect, with one or two papery sheaths at the base and 3–6 lanceolate sheaths above. Flowers 5–18, secund, white; sepals oblique-lanceolate or broadly lanceolate, the laterals oblique, 3–4 mm long; petals fan-shaped in outline, 10–13 mm long, divided in the upper half into 9–13 thread-like lobes 6–9 mm long, glabrous; lip narrowly fan-shaped from a narrow base, a little longer than the petals, the upper half divided into 9–15 thread-like lobes, spur incurved, 4–6 mm long.

On stony slopes in grassland; only known in Kenya from Maparashu hills in Kajiado district.

Also known from Tanzania, Zimbabwe and South Africa (Transvaal).

Malaxis Swartz

This is a large genus of small, usually terrestrial orchids with about 300 species in tropical Asia. Seven species are known from Africa of which only one has been collected in Kenya.

The Greek word *malaxis* (softening) has been used to coin this generic name, in an allusion to the soft texture of the leaves and stems. All the species have rather small flowers in which the sepals and petals are similar. The lip is broad and flat and often has toothed margins. It is held on the upper side of the flower. However, since the flowers are often carried in an umbel-like group at the apex of the flowering stem, whether the flowers are resupinate or not may be hard to determine. The column is short and carries 4 pollinia in 2 pairs at its apex.

This genus is related to *Liparis* (see page 48), and the stems and foliage of the two genera are somewhat similar. *Malaxis* species are easily recognised by the different flowers, especially the short column and the rounded lip with auricles at its base.

CULTIVATION

The plants are unknown in cultivation but should not be difficult to maintain in shallow pots or pans of well-drained compost. They will grow best in intermediate conditions where the temperature drops to *c.* 15 °C at night but is considerably warmer during the day. They need to be kept moist in the period of active growth. After flowering the plants should be allowed to dry off while the leaves become thin, turn brown and eventually shrivel or fall. After a further rest, watering and feeding should begin again when new shoots begin to develop on the rhizome.

Malaxis weberbaueriana (Kraenzlin) Summerhayes

A small terrestrial plant, up to 25 cm high, often growing in colonies. Secondary stems arising from the slender creeping rhizome, 2.5–8 cm tall, bearing 3–5 leaves near the apex. Leaves thin, ovate or elliptic-ovate, up to 5.5 cm long and 3 cm wide, shortly petiolate. Inflorescence erect, laxly many-flowered. Flowers small, flat, purple or green; dorsal sepal ovate, 2–3 mm long, lateral sepals similar but oblique, shortly united at the base; petals obliquely linear-lanceolate, rounded, 2–3 mm long; lip subcircular to subquadrate, 2 mm long and wide, bearing 2 lateral, lunate, pubescent calli.

Forest and woodland floor, only recorded in Kakamega forest; *c.* 1700 m; flowering in June.

Also recorded from Zaïre, Cameroon, Bioko, Tanzania, Zambia, Malawi and Zimbabwe.

Nervilia Gaudichaud-Beaupré

This is a curious genus in which the single leaf appears at a different season from the inflorescence which arises from the same underground tuber. Thus two collections are necessary from the same locality in order to describe the complete plant. Alternatively, the plants are often collected when in leaf and then brought into flower in cultivation. Sometimes a plant is collected in flower and grown until the leaf appears. Unfortunately the tubers often perish in cultivation, so this is not easy. The leaves are easily recognisable from their attractive shape and the name of the genus refers to their distinctive and characteristic venation (from the Latin, *nervus*, vein).

About 80 species have been described so far. They extend from tropical Africa, through Madagascar, to India, Southeast Asia and Australia. Sixteen species have been recorded from Africa

(Pettersson, 1990) but only two species had been collected in Kenya prior to 1994. Recently, extensive searching in the forests near the coast has revealed the presence of two more species which are mentioned briefly below.

CULTIVATION

Plants can be maintained in cultivation provided great attention is paid to the need for a dormant period after the leaf matures, and a further dry period after flowering. The leaves are more attractive subjects for cultivation than the flowers. The tubers should be planted in a well-drained but moisture-retentive compost, and the pans kept in a suitable place depending on the origin of the tubers – grassland species usually require less shade than those collected from thicket or forest.

Key to the species of *Nervilia*

Inflorescence with 2 or more flowers; leaf
    more than 4 cm wide, green on the lower
    surface . . . . *N. kotschyi*
Inflorescence 1 – flowered; leaf less than 2.5 cm
    wide, purple below . . . . *N. petraea*

Nervilia kotschyi (Reichenbach f.) Schlechter

A slender terrestrial herb, 10–30 cm high, arising from an ovoid, tomentose tuber. Leaf solitary, usually appearing after the inflorescence has set seed, broadly ovate, cordate, acute to apiculate, 3–

Nervilia kotschyi   ERIC LA CROIX

8 cm long, 4–13 cm wide, petiole slender, 0.5–5 cm long. Inflorescence erect, up to 28 cm long, bearing 2–7 pale olive-green flowers with a white lip lined on the veins with purple. Flowers pendent or suberect, not opening widely; sepals and petals linear-lanceolate, acute, 1.4–2 cm long, 3 mm wide; lip elliptic in outline, 10–19 mm long, 7–12 mm wide, obscurely 3-lobed in the apical half, side lobes shortly triangular, acute or subacute, bearing 2 longitudinal fleshy ridges, hairy within; column clavate, slightly curved, 7–9 mm long.

In short grassland and amongst bushes and scrub, usually on poor sandy soils, near the coast and also in west Kenya; near sea level to 2000 m; plants collected in flower in March and April.

A very variable species that appears to be widespread across tropical Africa and south to Zimbabwe.

Nervilia bicarinata (Blume) Schlechter has been reported recently from Diani forest in Kwale district. It is similar to *Nervilia kotschyi* but with slightly larger flowers.

Nervilia petraea (Afzelius ex Swartz)
Summerhayes

A small terrestrial herb, 2–10 cm high, arising from a globose tuber. Leaf solitary, reniform or cordate, more or less prostrate on the surface of the soil, dark green above and purple below. Inflorescence erect, bearing a single, small white flower, elongating after pollination. Flower erect at first then pendent, white or greenish, sometimes tinged with purple; sepals subsimilar, ligulate, 10 mm long; petals similar to the sepals but narrower; lip obovate, cuneate, 3-lobed at the apex, to 12 mm long, 8 mm wide, margins erose, bearing numerous thick hairs on its upper surface and a yellow central line in the throat.

In swampy ground or moist grassland, usually growing in small colonies; only recorded twice in Kenya, in the Shimba hills and in the Rabai hills near the coast; 15–350 m; flowering between April and June but the flowers only last for a day.

Widespread in tropical Africa but rarely collected. It has been recorded from Kenya to Sierra Leone and south to Mozambique, extending to Madagascar and Mauritius.

Nervilia crociformis (Zollinger & Moritzi) Seidenfaden has been reported recently from the Shimba hills near Kwale. It is similar to *Nervilia petraea* but has larger leaves and flowers, and the outgrowths on the lip are very thin and hair-like, sometimes lacking.

Oeceoclades Lindley

Syn. *Eulophidium* Pfitzer

This genus is relatively rare in cultivation, but it comprises a number of species that are very easy and rewarding to grow. They are easy because the pseudobulbs are borne close together above the ground and their moisture requirements can be judged according to their stage of growth. Every season one or more new pseudobulbs arises, bearing its terminal leaf or leaves, and the inflorescence arises alongside the new growth. They are rewarding because they seem to flower easily, without fail, on long inflorescences. The flowers themselves are of medium size and immediately recognisable by the 4-lobed lip. Technically, the lip is often described as 3-lobed, with the median lobe apically divided or with two lobes. This feature distinguishes species of *Oeceoclades* from *Eulophia* whose flowers always have a 3-lobed lip. The name is derived from two Greek words *oikeios* (private) and *klados* (branch), perhaps referring to the separation of these species into a genus separate from *Eulophia*.

About 30 species of *Oeceoclades* have been described, mostly from Africa and Madagascar. However several species have become widespread in tropical regions, *Oeceoclades maculata* extending westwards throughout the American continent and Caribbean, and *Oeceoclades pulchra* extending eastwards as far as northern Australia.

CULTIVATION

An open sandy compost with plenty of humus is the best growing medium for the Kenya species of *Oeceoclades*. They like warm conditions and high humidity, but the compost needs to dry out thoroughly between waterings except when the new pseudobulb and inflorescence are actively growing when it should be kept moist.

Key to the species of *Oeceoclades*

1 Pseudobulbs always 1-leaved   2
   Pseudobulbs usually 2- or 3-leaved   3

2 Leaves greyish green with darker green
      banding and mottling, usually
      12–25 cm long; pseudobulbs 2–4 cm
      long . . . .   *O. maculata*
   Leaves entirely green, usually 30–45 cm
      long; pseudobulbs 5–8 cm long . . . .
      . . . .   *O. zanzibarica*

3   Leaves bluish grey, mottled; lateral sepals
         spathulate, 14–20 mm long . **O. decaryana**
     Leaves dark green, uniform; lateral sepals
         narrowly oblong or obovate, 9–14 mm
         long . . . . **O. saundersiana**

Oeceoclades decaryana (H. Perrier)
Garay & Taylor

Syn. *Eulophia decaryana* Perrier
Eulophidium decaryanum (Perrier) Summerhayes
Terrestrial herb 50–60 cm high. Pseudobulbs
ovoid, 2–4 cm long, 2 cm wide, bearing 2–3 leaves.
Leaves linear-ligulate, acute, 15–23 cm long, 1–
2 cm wide, greyish green and attractively mottled
with white and dark bluish green, sometimes suffused with brown, persistent for several seasons.
Inflorescence erect, simple or branched, 20–60 cm
long and bearing 12–30 flowers, bracts small.

Oeceoclades decaryana   BOB CAMPBELL

Flowers olive green with red or purplish brown
markings, lip and column with some yellow
patches; dorsal sepal erect, oblanceolate to spathulate, 12–20 mm long, 3–4 mm wide; lateral sepals
spathulate, somewhat falcate, deflexed, 14–20 mm
long, 3–4 mm wide; petals oblong-elliptic, sometimes oblique, 7–10 mm long, 4–7 mm wide; lip
projecting forward, distinctly 3-lobed or obscurely
4-lobed, 12–16 mm long, 13–18 mm wide, callus of
2 raised lobes at the base that decrease forwards,
spur stout, 4–6 mm long; column erect 4–5 mm
long.
    In leaf mould under bushes on a rocky outcrop;

known in Kenya from a collection on Sagala hill in
Teita district; 960 m; flowering in June.
    Also recorded in Mozambique, Zimbabwe and
Madagascar.

Oeceoclades maculata (Lindley) Lindley

Syn. *Angraecum maculatum* Lindley
Eulophidium maculatum (Lindley) Pfitzer
Terrestrial herb 15–30 cm high, with thick white
roots. Pseudobulbs ovoid or cylindric, 2–4 cm long,
bearing a single leaf that is shortly petiolate. Leaf
oblong-lanceolate or elliptic, narrow at the base,
15–25 cm long, 2–4 cm wide, dark green with paler
green and whitish mottling and banding, peristent
for several seasons, petiole 1–8 cm long. Inflorescence simple or with few short branches, erect,
5–20 cm long, bearing 6–20 flowers, bracts
lanceolate, acuminate. Flowers cream or greenish
pink, lip darker with two rose pink blotches at the
base, callus and column white; dorsal sepal linear
elliptic, obtuse to acute, 10–12 mm long, 2–3 mm
wide; lateral sepals similar but shorter; petals oblong elliptic, acute, wider than sepals; lip projecting
forwards, distinctly 3-lobed with the midlobe
sometimes bilobed at the tip, *c.* 4 mm long, 7–8 mm
wide, callus of 2 short white keels, spur stout, 4–
5 mm long with bulbous tip; column erect, 4–5 mm.

Oeceoclades maculata   JOYCE STEWART

Amongst leaf mould in shady forests and rocky scrub near the sea; sea level to 300 m; flowering in February to May.

Also recorded in Tanzania and Uganda and widespread throughout tropical Africa westwards as far as Liberia and southwards to Angola and South Africa (Natal). Widely distributed in South America, the Caribbean and recently recorded as spreading throughout Florida (U.S.A.).

Oeceoclades saundersiana (Reichenbach f.)
                                    Garay & Taylor

Syn. *Eulophidium saundersianum*
     (Reichenbach f.) Summerhayes

Terrestrial herb 50–80 cm high with thick white fleshy roots. Pseudobulbs narrowly ovoid or cylindric, sometimes slightly compressed, 8–15 cm long, 2.5 cm wide at widest part, dark glossy green, bearing 1–3 petiolate leaves. Leaves ovate elliptic, margins flat or gently undulate, lamina erect or spreading 12–18 cm long, 4–6 cm wide, dark glossy green, petiole 6–15 cm long. Inflorescence erect, simple or with up to 2 short branches, 16–45 cm long, bearing 15–40 large flowers, bracts ovate-elliptic. Flowers cream or pale greenish yellow but heavily overlaid with dark purplish brown so that they appear almost black; dorsal sepal narrowly oblong, obtuse or mucronate, 8–15 mm long, 3–5 mm wide; lateral sepals similar but longer; petals ovate, 9–13 mm long, 5–7 mm wide; lip projecting forward, distinctly 3-lobed or 4-lobed, 12–15 mm long, callus of 2 fleshy keels in front of the spur opening, spur cylindrical 4–6 mm long; column erect 3–6 mm long.

Damp, shady places in forest and thickets, sometimes at the edge of streams; only known in Kenya from several coastal sites and along streams on the southeast side of Mt Kenya; sea level to 1200 m; flowering in September to November.

Also recorded from Tanzania and Uganda; widespread across tropical Africa as far west as Sierra Leone and south to Zambia and Angola.

Oeceoclades zanzibarica (Summerhayes)
                                    Garay & Taylor

Syn. *Eulophidium zanzibaricum* Summerhayes

Terrestrial herb 25–45 cm high with smooth fleshy white roots. Pseudobulbs cylindrical, 5–8 cm long, 1.5–2 cm wide, bearing 1 petiolate leaf. Leaf linear-lanceolate to broadly lanceolate, lamina 30–45 cm long, 2–5 cm wide, petiole 5–10 cm long, dark dull green. Inflorescence erect, paniculate, 8–40 cm long, bearing many flowers, bracts elliptic or linear. Flowers with green sepals and petals and white lip with reddish veins and two purple blotches at the base; dorsal sepal oblong-elliptic, 8–10 mm long, 3–4 mm wide; lateral sepals oblique or falcate, lanceolate, 8–10 mm long, 3–5 mm wide; petals oblong-elliptic, 7–9 mm long, 3–5 mm wide; lip 4-lobed, 8–10 mm long, 8–12 mm wide, callus of 2 parallel basal keels, spur straight, obtuse, 3–4 mm long; column erect, 2 mm long.

In dense shade in forest and bush near sea level; flowering in December.

Also recorded from Tanzania, including Zanzibar.

Platycoryne
Reichenbach f.

The Kenya species of these small grassland orchids are immediately recognised by their bright orange flowers. The inflorescences are small, with the flowers close together at the apex of the slender stem, but the colour is so vivid that they show up

Oeceoclades saundersiana   JOYCE STEWART

rather easily among the grasses with which they grow. The name is derived from two Greek words *platys* (wide, broad) and *coryne* (club), and refers to the shape of the stigmatic processes that are quite distinctive, decurved and thick with rounded, knob-like apices. Other features of the flower that are distinctive are the large dorsal sepal, the petals cohering to its outer margins on each side to form a shallow hood and the rather small, slender lip.

Plants of this genus are usually found in damp grasslands, often those that are burnt over in the dry season and flooded during the rains. Some have a rosette of leaves at the base from among which the slender inflorescence arises, while others have leaves scattered along the length of the stem. About 17 species have been described, mostly from central Africa. One species is known from Madagascar and two, one of them with two distinct subspecies, occur in Kenya.

Platycoryne crocea   BOB CAMPBELL

CULTIVATION

None of the species of *Platycoryne* is known in cultivation as yet.

Key to the species of *Platycoryne*
Plants with a basal tuft of leaves and several
    more leaves scattered all along the stem;
    lip with short tooth-like side lobes at the
    base, curving downwards . . . . ***P. crocea***
Plants lacking a basal tuft, leaves all along the
    stem; lip entire, curving forwards and
    upwards in front . . . . ***P. pervillei***

Platycoryne crocea (Reichenbach f.) Rolfe
Terrestrial herb 10–40 cm high, arising from ellipsoid or globose tubers. Stem erect, slender, with a tuft of leaves at the base and several others along the stem. Leaves 5–12, the lowermost reduced to sheaths, 3–8 forming a tuft, linear or linear-lanceolate, the largest 2–6 cm long, 2–8 mm wide, the upper ones smaller. Inflorescence short, apical with 2–8 flowers close together, bracts leafy, shorter than the pedicel with ovary. Flowers curving outwards, bright yellow or orange; dorsal sepal erect or curved forwards, ovate, 6–12 mm long, 4–8 mm wide; lateral sepals deflexed, obliquely oblong-lanceolate, acute, 5–11 mm long, 2–3 mm wide; petals erect, adhering to the margins of the dorsal sepal, obliquely ligulate-lanceolate, 4–10 mm long, 2 mm wide; lip deflexed, 3-lobed at the base, 5–12 mm long, midlobe fleshy, 1–2 mm wide, side lobes tooth-like, spur dependent, swollen towards the tip, 9–15 mm long.

The plants at the coast are much smaller than those around Mt Elgon which have been recognised as a distinct species in the past. Two subspecies are currently accepted. They can be distinguished by the following key:

Basal leaves 3, similar to cauline ones; dorsal
    sepal 6–7 mm long . . . . ssp. *crocea*
Basal leaves 3–6, distinctly longer than cauline
    ones; dorsal sepal 7.5–11 mm
    long . . . . ssp. *montis-elgon*

ssp. *crocea*
The small flowered plants have been collected in grasslands on the Shimba hills in Kwale district; sea level to 360 m; flowering in June and July.
    Also known from Sudan.

ssp. *montis-elgon* (Schlechter) Summerhayes
    Syn. *Habenaria montis-elgon* Schlechter
    Platycoryne montis-elgon (Schlechter)
                    Summerhayes
The large flowered plants have been collected from several places in the western highlands of Kenya, usually in shallow grassland over rocks or pavements where it is seasonally moist; 2000–2350 m; flowering in May to July.
    Also recorded from Uganda, Ethiopia and Sudan.

Platycoryne pervillei Reichenbach f.
Terrestrial herb 30–70 cm high arising from ellipsoid tubers. Stem erect, slender, with leaves scattered along its length. Leaves 5–8, lanceolate, acute, the largest 2.5–8 cm long, 5–10 mm wide. Inflorescence apical, rather closely 2–8 flowered, bracts lanceolate. Flowers yellow to deep orange; dorsal sepal erect, convex, broadly ovate, 10–14 mm long, 7–9 mm wide; lateral sepals deflexed, obliquely lanceolate, acute, 10–12 mm long, *c.* 3 mm wide; petals erect, curved, lanceolate-linear, adhering to the margins of the dorsal sepal, 8–12 mm long, 2 mm wide; lip projecting forwards and upcurved in front, ligulate, fleshy, 7–11 mm long, 2 mm wide, spur dependent, swollen in the apical half, 12–20 mm long.

In damp or swampy grassland near the coast, rarely recorded in Kenya; sea level to 100 m; flowering in March to May.

Also recorded from Tanzania, Malawi, Mozambique, Zimbabwe and Madagascar.

Platycoryne pervillei   ERIC LA CROIX

Platylepis A. Richard

This is a small genus of creeping forest herbs that are mostly found in the warm shaded forests of Madagascar and the islands of the Mascarenes group. One species is widespread in tropical Africa and has been found on one or two occasions in Kenya.

The plants have creeping stems that are usually horizontal above the surface of the ground to which they are anchored by hairy roots. The somewhat glaucous stems and broad leaves superficially resemble those of some members of the family Commelinaceae. The flowers are small and usually held close together in a dense terminal inflorescence. The elongate column bears four pollinia attached to a single small viscidium on its upper surface.

CULTIVATION

Easily maintained in a shallow pan of rich soil with leaf litter that is kept moist. A group of plants makes an attractive addition to a collection of orchids or pot plants. The pan should be kept in a well-shaded position where the night temperature does not fall below 15 °C. The day time temperatures can be much higher, but shade and high humidity must also be maintained.

Platylepis glandulosa (Lindley) Reichenbach f.
Perennial herb 15–50 cm high, stems creeping at the base. Leaves close together on the lower part of the stem, ovate, acute, 4–16 cm long, 2–5.5 cm wide, petiole sheathing at the base, 2–9 cm long.

Platylepis glandulosa   JOYCE STEWART

Inflorescence a dense, glandular-hairy raceme, 5–12 cm long. Flowers small, mostly white; sepals pinkish brown or yellowish green, subsimilar, ovate-oblong, 7–9 mm long; petals white, connivent with the dorsal sepal to form a hood, spathulate, 7.5–8.5 mm long; lip white, adnate to the column for half its length, 6.5–8.5 mm long, 2–2.5 mm wide, saccate at the base with 2 rounded calli within, apex rounded and reflexed.

In shaded, marshy places and on river banks in forest, only found so far in Kenya in the Teita hills; c. 1200 m; flowering in February.

Widespread in tropical Africa and southwards to South Africa (Natal).

Pteroglossaspis
Reichenbach f.

This small genus of terrestrial orchids is closely related to *Eulophia* and in many ways resembles that genus. However, in all the species of *Pteroglossaspis* the flowers have a flat lip without a spur or mentum at the base. They also have a very short column that lacks a foot. The flowers are somewhat hidden by the long chaffy sheaths that cover the inflorescence stalk and grade into the bracts.

Although widespread, the species of *Pteroglossaspis* are not often collected because of their rather dull flowers. About seven species are now recognised, one of which (*Pteroglossaspis ruwenzoriensis*) occurs in Kenya and elsewhere in Africa and also in Brazil and Argentina. It is curious that the genera *Eulophia* and *Oeceoclades*, also each have one species that occurs both in Africa and in the American continent.

CULTIVATION

The species of *Pteroglossaspis* are not known in cultivation.

Key to the species of *Pteroglossaspis*
Lip velvety hairy, with 3–7 raised veins . . . . *P. eustachya*
Lip warty but not hairy, veins indistinct . . . . *P. ruwenzoriensis*

Pteroglossaspis eustachya Reichenbach f.
Syn. *Pteroglossaspis engleriana* Kraenzlin
Terrestrial herb arising from a chain of lobed fleshy underground pseudobulbs. Leaves 1–3, linear-lanceolate, long petiolate, plicate, enclosed in sheaths towards the base, arising with inflorescence of current year, petiole 12–18 cm long, lamina 30–40 cm long. Inflorescence on a long peduncle 22–65 cm long, covered with scarious sheaths, the terminal 2–8 cm bearing many flowers close together, bracts scarious. Flowers variable in colour, white or dull yellow suffused with dark purple maroon or entirely purple maroon; sepals obtuse, mucronate, oblong-elliptic, c. 10 mm long; petals similar; lip 3-lobed, 7–9 mm long, 12–14 mm wide, midlobe bearing 3–7 raised or lacerate keeled veins; column 1.5–2 mm long.

Damp grassland among trees and in the open or over rocks; 1650–2000 m; flowering in May to August.

Also recorded from Uganda and Tanzania, Ethiopia, Mozambique and Zimbabwe.

Pteroglossaspis ruwenzoriensis (Rendle) Rolfe
Syn. *Eulophia ruwenzoriensis* Rendle
Pteroglossaspis carsonii Rolfe
Terrestrial herb arising from a chain of lobed fleshy underground pseudobulbs. Leaves 1–3, linear-lanceolate, long petiolate, plicate, enclosed in sheaths towards the base, arising with inflorescence of current year, petiole 15–25 cm long, lamina 23–30 cm long. Inflorescence on a long peduncle 30–60 cm long, covered with scarious sheaths, the terminal 3–6 cm bearing many flowers close together, bracts scarious. Flowers variable in colour, white with dark purple maroon blotch on the lip or entirely purple maroon, sometimes flushed pale lilac or greenish on the outer surface; sepals obtuse, mucronate, oblong-elliptic, 8–14 mm long; petals narrowly oblong-elliptic 11–12 mm long; lip 3-lobed, 8–12 mm long, 8–12 mm wide, midlobe bearing a few raised warts, the veins not pilose; column 3–5 mm long.

Upland grassland and seasonally moist grassland; widespread in suitable areas in Kenya; 1650–2530 m; flowering in June to September.

Also recorded from Uganda and Tanzania as well as Zambia, Brazil and Argentina.

Roeperocharis
Reichenbach f.

Superficially, the plants of *Roeperocharis* resemble those of *Habenaria* and they also have green flowers. However, the flowers are immediately distinctive, not only by their deep green sepals and petals that are almost leafy in appearance, but in particular by the bilobed stigmas, one lobe vertical and the other pendent, which almost cover the surface of the column. When the furled petals are folded back to view the column, the two stigmas are large and conspicuous.

This genus was proposed by the younger Reichenbach to honour Herr Roeper 'a man of great merit and pious spirit' and the name is derived from his surname with the Greek word *charis* (grace) added to it. Five species have been described from eastern Africa only one of which has ever been collected in Kenya and that on only one occasion in 1935.

CULTIVATION

The species of *Roeperocharis* are not known in cultivation.

Roeperocharis bennettiana Reichenbach f.

Terrestrial herb to 80 cm high, glabrous, arising from ellipsoid or globose tubers. Stem erect, robust, up to 1 cm in diameter, leafy throughout. Leaves 5–10, linear or narrowly lanceolate, the largest 11–25 cm long, 1–2.5 cm wide, decreasing in size up the stem and merging into the bracts. Inflorescence narrow, cylindrical, 9–27 cm long, 2–3 cm in diameter, rather densely flowered. Flowers green, suberect; dorsal sepal erect, broadly lanceolate, acuminate, convex, 6–10 mm long, 4–6 mm wide; lateral sepals spreading or almost reflexed, curving upwards, obliquely lanceolate-ovate, lower margin rounded, 6–12 mm long, 4–6 mm wide; petals almost S-shaped, folded forward over the column, obliquely lanceolate, fleshy, 5–11 mm long, 2–5 mm wide; lip pendent, 3-lobed, all the lobes linear, the midlobe longer than the divergent side lobes, up to 20 mm long, spur cylindrical, 8–15 mm long, shorter than the lip.

Only known to date from a single collection in damp grassland in the Cherangani hills; 2850 m; flowering in September.

Also recorded in southern Tanzania, and in Ethiopia, Malawi and Zambia.

Satyrium Swartz

The Swedish botanist Olof Swartz established the name *Satyrium* for a genus of orchids from South Africa in 1800. In the early Greek herbals the name *Satyrion* had been used for various plants that were thought to excite lust. A number of different orchids with paired underground tubers were reputed to have this property. Accordingly, several of them were associated with the lascivious satyrs.

The South African plants that Swartz named had very distinctive tubers together with a number of roots arising from the base of the stem.

About 100 species of the genus *Satyrium* are now recognised in various parts of Africa, together with a few in Madagascar and two in Asia. They are all easily recognised by the enlarged, helmet shaped lip on the upper side of the flower. At its base the lip bears two elongated spurs, although these are sometimes absent and occasionally they are duplicated. Although all the plants are terrestrial, a few are sometimes found on tree trunks in mossy forests. Their tall spikes of small flowers show up from a distance and many of them are brightly coloured. In undisturbed grasslands and marshes they may make a very conspicuous feature easily visible from afar. Eleven species have been recorded in Kenya.

Satyrium fimbriatum   BOB CAMPBELL

CULTIVATION

None of the Kenya species of *Satyrium* has been maintained in cultivation for more than one or two seasons. The chief difficulty seems to be maintaining the roots or tubers during the season when the plants are dormant. They are easily lost by some kind of rot brought about by over-watering or eaten by small predators. The Himalayan species, *Satyrium nepalense*, seems to be much easier to keep in cultivation and is a very attractive plant. At the Royal Botanic Gardens, Kew it is grown in the Alpine collection where it is treated like other terrestrial orchids from temperate regions.

Key to the species of *Satyrium*

1 Flowers green 2
  Flowers pink, yellow, red or white, never
    entirely green 3

2 Foliage leaves on lower part of flowering
    stem; spurs 5–8 mm long ... *S. schimperi*
  Foliage leaves on a separate shoot at base
    of flowering stem; spurs 11–23 mm
    long .... *S. volkensii*

3 Leaves round or ovate, appressed to the
    ground at base of flowering stem..... 4
  Leaves not round or ovate, erect or
    spreading, not appressed to the
    ground 5

4 Spurs over 2 cm long ...... *S. fimbriatum*
  Spurs under 2 cm long .... *S. carsonii*

5 Foliage leaves borne on lower part of
    flowering stem 6
  Foliage leaves borne on a separate,
    non-flowering shoot adjacent to
    flowering stem 9

6 Flowering stem with two almost equal
    broad leaves near the base, the rest
    sheath-like; sepals and petals narrow-
    oblong, much longer than the lip ....
    .... *S. macrophyllum*
  Flowering stem with several leaves either
    along the stem or towards its base;
    sepals oblong, only slightly longer
    than lip 7

7 Flowers white with pink markings; spurs
    2.5 mm long or absent ... *S. paludosum*
  Flowers pink, crimson or mauve; spurs
    8–18 mm long 8

8 Lip 5–6.5 mm long, joined to sepals
    for about half its length; spurs
    8–13 mm long; leaves spaced out
    along stem, narrow, sometimes
    ribbed .... *S. crassicaule*
  Lip 7–10 mm long, joined to sepals for
    one third its length; spurs 12–18 mm
    long; leaves bunched at base of stem,
    usually ovate or broadly lanceolate,
    shiny .... *S. robustum*

9 Flowers white or greenish flushed pink,
    sometimes crimson ... *S. coriophoroides*
  Flowers yellow-orange, flame coloured
    or dark red 9

10 Lip with two additional short spurs at
    the base .... *S. sacculatum*
  Lip never with additional spurs .. *S. woodii*

Satyrium carsonii Rolfe

Terrestrial herb, 25–90 cm high, arising from ovoid, tomentose tubers, roots slender, pubescent. Stem erect, with two basal leaves and several leaf-like sheaths. Leaves opposite, appressed to the ground, broadly ovate to reniform, 1.5–6 cm long, 1–9 cm wide. Inflorescence rather dense, erect, 4–15 cm long with 2–18 flowers each supported by a conspicuous leafy bract; ovary not twisted. Flowers erect, white, sepals united to the petals and lip;

Satyrium carsonii   ERIC LA CROIX

dorsal sepal oblanceolate or oblong, free part 7–17 mm long; lateral sepals obliquely lanceolate, free part 9–19 mm long; petals oblanceolate, rounded at apex, free part 8–15 mm long; lip erect, on upperside of flower, hooded, with a broad mouth, apex recurved, 9–16.5 mm long with 2 spurs at the base, spurs tapering, 6–14 mm long; column erect and incurved, included within the lip.

Found in grassland that is kept short by grazing; only known west of the Rift Valley on Mt Elgon and the Cherangani hills; 2000–2330 m; flowering in June to August.

Also known from Uganda and southern Tanzania southwards to Zambia and Malawi, and westwards to Burundi, Zaïre, Cameroon and Nigeria.

Satyrium coriophoroides A. Richard

Terrestrial herb 40–100 cm high, arising from an ellipsoid, tomentose tuber. Stem erect, densely covered with leaf-like sheaths. Leaves 4–5 on a separate non-flowering shoot immediately adjacent to the flowering stem, the upper 2 lanceolate to elliptic-lanceolate, 7–16 cm long, 2.5–4.5 cm wide. Inflorescence a narrow, erect raceme, 8–23 cm long, each flower supported by a conspicuous leafy bract; ovary not twisted. Flowers curved outwards, not resupinate, white, pink, to crimson red; sepals united to the petals and lip, dorsal sepal oblong-elliptic, free part 5–6 mm long; lateral sepals obliquely elliptic-oblong, obtuse, free part 5–6 mm long; petals oblong-lanceolate, rounded, margins hairy, free part 4–6 mm long; lip erect, on upperside of flower, almost globular, with a narrow mouth, apex shortly reflexed, 5–7 mm long, with 2 spurs at the base, spurs 11–17 mm long; column erect and incurved, included within the lip.

Only known from damp places in highland grasslands and on rocky slopes west of the Rift Valley; 2150–2300 m; flowering in May to July.

Also recorded from Ethiopia and Cameroon.

Satyrium crassicaule Rendle

Syn. *Satyrium niloticum* Rendle

Terrestrial herb 30–120 cm high, arising from a short thick rootstock with a dense mass of hairy roots. Stem erect, leafy along its entire length. Leaves 8–13, spreading or erect in a tuft towards the base of the stem, the upper ones smaller and spaced, ligulate, acute, somewhat ribbed, 8–50 cm long, 2–8 cm wide. Inflorescence a dense erect raceme 5–40 cm long, each flower supported by a conspicuous leafy bract; ovary not twisted. Flowers spreading or curved outwards, not resupinate, pink to mauve or rarely white; sepals united to the petals

Satyrium crassicaule   BOB CAMPBELL

and lip, dorsal sepal narrowly oblanceolate-elliptic, obtuse, free part 4–8 mm long; lateral sepals obliquely oblong-elliptic, free part 4–8 mm long; petals similar to sepals, free part 4–7 mm long; lip erect, on upperside of flower, hooded, with a broad mouth, apex shortly pointed, with 2 spurs at the base, spurs slender, 8–13 mm long; column erect and incurved, included within the lip.

Damp grassland or swamps, often by streams and sometimes in running water, also in forest glades especially in the bamboo zone; widespread in western Kenya and also on the Aberdare Mts and Mt Kenya; 1850–3300 m; recorded in flower throughout the year but mostly in June.

Also recorded from Ethiopia, Uganda and Tanzania, southwards to Zambia and Malawi, and westwards to Rwanda, Burundi, Zaïre, Cameroon and Nigeria.

Satyrium fimbriatum Summerhayes

Terrestrial herb 15–40 cm high, arising from 1–2 ovoid or ellipsoid tubers. Stem erect, with few leaf-like sheaths spaced along its length. Leaves 2, basal, appressed to the ground, broadly ovate or reniform, 2–10 cm long and wide. Inflorescence a raceme of 6–12 flowers each supported by a conspicuous leafy bract; ovary not twisted. Flowers erect, not resupinate, rose pink to deep pink or, rarely, white; sepals united to the petals and lip at the base, dorsal sepal oblanceolate, obtuse, free part 8–12 mm long; lateral sepals obliquely elliptic-oblanceolate, obtuse or oblong, free part 8–12 mm long; petals broadly oblanceolate, obtuse, margins

Satyrium crassicaule: terrestrial orchid in a highland swamp.

BOB CAMPBELL

fimbriate, free part 8–11 mm long; lip erect, on upperside of flower, convex in the lower part, upper part flattened and recurved with fimbriate margins resembling the petals, with 2 spurs at the base, spurs slender, 2.5–6.5 cm long; column erect and incurved, included within the lip.

Open grassland near streams and forest edges, also on stony slopes and even on rock ledges; mostly from the highlands west of the Rift Valley but also north of Maralal and on the Aberdare Mts from where it was first described; 2000–3300 m; flowering from May to August.

Also recorded from Uganda and Tanzania and from Sudan.

Satyrium fimbriatum   BOB CAMPBELL

Satyrium macrophyllum Lindley
Syn. *Satyrium cheirophorum* Rolfe
Satyrium speciosum Rolfe

Terrestrial herb 15–100 cm high arising from a pair of round or ellipsoid tubers. Stem erect, leafy along its entire length. Leaves 6–10, towards the base of the stem, the largest 2–3 elliptic, ovate or lanceolate, acute, 4–20 cm long, 3–11 cm wide, the others much smaller. Inflorescence 5–30 cm long, a dense erect raceme of 10–many flowers each supported by a conspicuous leafy bract; ovary not twisted. Flowers erect, not resupinate, pale to bright pink; sepals united to the petals and lip in the lower third, dorsal sepal ligulate or narrowly elliptic, obtuse, free part 10–15 mm long; lateral sepals obliquely oblong-elliptic, obtuse, free part 10–15 mm long, broader than the dorsal sepal; petals

lanceolate, free part 8–12 mm long; lip erect, on upperside of flower, convex and hooded, with a short reflexed apex, with 2 spurs at the base, spurs slender, 10–18 mm long; column erect and incurved, included within the lip.

Found in damp grasslands and at the edges of scrub; in several areas west of the Rift Valley and near Nairobi; 1700–2850 m; flowering May and June.

Also recorded from Tanzania and southwards to Malawi, Zimbabwe, Mozambique, Swaziland and South Africa (Transkei and Natal).

Satyrium macrophyllum   ERIC LA CROIX

Satyrium paludosum Reichenbach f.
Terrestrial herb 30–80 cm high, arising from ellipsoid tubers. Stem erect, leafy along its length. Leaves 2–11, the largest towards the base of the stem, narrowly lanceolate, acute, 12–22 cm long, 1.5–3.5 cm wide. Inflorescence pyramidal, an erect raceme of many flowers each supported by a con-

spicuous leafy bract; ovary not twisted. Flowers spreading horizontally, white with pink markings; sepals united to the petals and lip in the lower half, dorsal sepal oblong-ligulate, free part 9–11 mm long; lateral sepals oblong-ligulate, free part 9–13 mm long; petals spathulate, oblanceolate, free part 7–9 mm long; lip erect, on upperside of flower, very convex with a broad mouth, and erect, narrowed apex, with 2 spurs at the base, spurs broad and rounded, up to 2 mm long but sometimes scarcely developed; column erect and incurved, included within the lip.

Satyrium paludosum   ERIC LA CROIX

Only known in Kenya from swamps and grasslands around Gilgil and surroundings; 2700–2850 m; flowering in June.

Also recorded from Zambia, Zimbabwe and Angola.

Satyrium robustum Schlechter

Terrestrial herb 25–70 cm high, arising from small ovoid or ellipsoid tubers. Stem erect, leafy or covered with leaf-like sheaths along its length. Leaves 7–11, mostly bunched towards the base of the stem, the largest lanceolate to broadly ovate, acute, 8–28 cm long, 3–5 cm wide. Inflorescence a dense erect cylindrical raceme to 24 cm long with 10–many flowers each supported by a conspicuous leafy bract; ovary not twisted. Flowers spreading, not resupinate, usually bright pink to crimson; sepals united to the petals and lip in the basal fifth only, dorsal sepal oblanceolate, obtuse, free part 8–

12 mm long; lateral sepals obliquely oblanceolate-oblong, similar to the dorsal but wider; petals similar to the dorsal sepal; lip erect, on upperside of flower, very convex, hooded, with a broad mouth, apex shortly recurved, 7–10 mm long, with 2 spurs at the base, spurs slender, 12–18 mm long; column erect and incurved, included within the lip.

Satyrium robustum   K.O.S.

Swampy grassland or bogs, especially near streams; only known from the Kinangop, Mt Kenya, Mt Elgon and the Cherangani hills in Kenya; 2700–3000 m; flowering in September to October.

Also recorded from the Uganda side of Mt Elgon and from southern Tanzania.

Satyrium sacculatum (Rendle) Rolfe

Terrestrial herb 30–120 cm high, arising from an ellipsoid tuber. Stem erect, covered with leaf-like sheaths. Leaves 3–6, borne on a separate non-flowering shoot immediately adjacent to the flowering stem, the largest lanceolate to elliptic, 6–24 cm long, 1–7 cm wide. Inflorescence a dense erect raceme of many small flowers each supported by a conspicuous leafy bract; ovary not twisted. Flowers erect, not resupinate, dark cherry red or brownish; sepals united to the petals and lip in the basal third, deflexed and sometimes rolled up, dorsal sepal elliptic-oblong, rounded, free part 4–7 mm long; lateral sepals obliquely oblong-oblanceolate, free part 5–8 mm long; petals oblong-oblanceolate, rounded, free part 4–6 mm long; lip erect, on upperside of flower, almost spherical with a very narrow mouth, apex shortly recurved, only 2 mm wide, with 2 spurs at the base and two rounded or vestigial spurs just below them, spurs 8–10 mm long; column erect and incurved, included within the lip.

In short grassland, often on rocky slopes and at the edge of bush; widespread in western Kenya and on the Aberdare Mts; 1700–2800 m; flowering in June to August.

Also recorded from Uganda and Tanzania; widespread in tropical Africa westwards through Rwanda, Burundi, Zaïre to Cameroon, north to Ethiopia and Sudan, and south to Zambia and Malawi.

Geerinck (1984) considers that the name *Satyrium sacculatum* should be treated as synonymous with *Satyrium coriophoroides*, but I have followed Summerhayes (1968) in keeping the two species separate. In Kenya specimens it is easy to see the extra pair of spurs below the usual slender pair at the base of the lip.

Satyrium schimperi A. Richard

Terrestrial herb 15–60 cm high, arising from ellipsoid tubers. Stem erect, leafy. Leaves 5–7, a large pair towards the base of the stem elliptic to elliptic-lanceolate, acute, 4–16 cm long, 2–5 cm wide, the others smaller. Inflorescence a narrowly cylindrical, erect raceme of 9–many flowers each supported by a conspicuous leafy bract; ovary not twisted. Flowers half spreading or horizontal, not resupinate, green or yellowish green; sepals united to the petals and lip in their basal half or third, dorsal sepal oblong-lanceolate, rounded, free part 4–5 mm long; lateral sepals obliquely oblong-oblanceolate, twisted, free part 5 mm long; petals similar to sepals but shorter; lip on upperside of flower, fleshy, hooded, with a narrow mouth, apex shortly recurved, 5–6 mm long, with 2 spurs at the base, spurs slender, 5–8 mm long; column erect and incurved, included within the lip.

Highland grasslands, often among rocks; mainly recorded from western Kenya but also known from the Aberdare Mts; 2330–3200 m; flowering in July to August.

Also recorded from Ethiopia, Rwanda, Burundi and Zaïre.

Satyrium volkensii Schlechter

Syn. *Satyrium dizygoceras* Summerhayes

Terrestrial herb 20–110 cm high, arising from globose tubers. Stem erect, covered with leaf-like sheaths. Leaves 3–4, on a separate non-flowering shoot immediately adjacent to the flowering stem, the upper 3 largest, oblong-elliptical, acute, 2–11 cm long, 1–3 cm wide. Inflorescence a narrowly cylindrical raceme of 10–50 flowers each supported by a conspicuous leafy bract; ovary not twisted. Flowers erect, not resupinate, green to yellowish green, often tinged brown; sepals united to the petals and lip in the lower third, dorsal sepal oblanceolate, free part 3–5 mm long; lateral sepals obliquely elliptic or oblong, curved or twisted, free part 4–6 mm long; petals oblanceolate, rounded, hairy, free part 3–4 mm long; lip erect, on upperside of flower, much hooded, with a narrow mouth, apex shortly recurved, 4–5 mm long, with 2 spurs at the base and sometimes two additional short spurs, spurs very slender, 11–23 mm long; column erect and incurved, included within the lip.

Grassland at higher altitudes, also amongst bushes and trees in grassland; mostly west of the Aberdare Mts; 2200–2700 m; flowering in April to June.

Also known from Tanzania; widespread in tropical Africa westwards to Zaïre, Cameroon and Nigeria and southwards to Malawi, Zambia, Mozambique and Zimbabwe.

Satyrium woodii Schlechter

Syn. *Satyrium sceptrum* Schlechter

Satyrium acutirostrum Summerhayes

Terrestrial herb 30–100 cm high, arising from ellipsoid tubers. Stem erect, covered with leaf-like sheaths. Leaves 2–5, on a separate non-flowering shoot immediately adjacent to the flowering stem, the upper 2 larger, lanceolate, oblong-lanceolate or elliptic, acute, 10–45 cm long, 2–7 cm wide. Inflorescence a cylindrical erect raceme of many flowers each supported by a conspicuous leafy bract; ovary not twisted. Flowers erect, not resupinate, yellow or yellow-orange, sometimes flame coloured; sepals united to the petals and lip in their basal quarter, dorsal sepal oblong-elliptical, obtuse or rounded, free part 6–10 mm long; lateral sepals obliquely elliptic-oblong, free part 7–12 mm long; petals similar to dorsal sepal; lip erect, on upperside of flower, somewhat hooded, with a broad mouth, apex shortly reflexed, 6–9 mm long and wide, with 2 spurs at the base, spurs slender, 10–15 mm long; column erect and incurved, included within the lip.

Upland grassland, often in damp places; throughout Kenya in suitable habitats; 2150–3000 m; flowering in April to August but mainly in June.

Also recorded from Uganda and Tanzania; widespread in tropical Africa from Sudan and Zaïre southwards to Malawi, Zambia, Zimbabwe and South Africa (Natal and Transkei).

Satyrium woodii   BOB CAMPBELL

Zeuxine Lindley

More than 70 species are known in this genus of small plants which often have long creeping rhizomes. They occur throughout the tropics and subtropics of the old world and one species seems to have spread to the warmer parts of North America. Four species occur in Africa of which only one has so far been discovered in Kenya.

The name is derived from the Greek word *zeuxis* (yoked), perhaps referrring to the partial union of the column and lip or to the way the pollinia are borne on a broad viscidium.

CULTIVATION

Not known in cultivation, but should not be more difficult than *Platylepis glandulosa* which the author maintained for several seasons.

Zeuxine elongata Rolfe

Perennial herb up to 40 cm high, stems creeping and rooting at the base. Leaves close together at the base of the erect part of the stem, petiole sheathing at the base, lamina ovate-lanceolate, acute, rounded at the base, up to 7 cm long, 3 cm wide. Inflorescence a slender raceme, up to 13 cm long, with many tiny flowers. Flowers green and white; dorsal sepal ovate, obtuse, 2 mm long; lateral sepals elliptic-oblong, obtuse, 2 mm long; petals linear, acute, connivent with the dorsal sepal, 1.75 mm long, apices free; lip equalling the sepals, narrowly saccate at the base with 2 hooked calli within, midlobe reniform, entire; column short with 2 semicircular flaps at the base.

In dense shade, in humus and on rocks of the forest floor, by rivers and waterfalls, only recorded in Kenya from near the Yala river, north of Kaptiki; *c.* 1500 m; flowering in January.

Widespread in tropical Africa from west Africa south to Angola, east to Zambia, and in Tanzania and Uganda.

Part IV Orchid Conservation in Kenya

Benny Bytebier and Tim Pearce★

Introduction

Areas with high plant and animal diversity are generally also those with a high agricultural potential often leading to a conflict of land use priorities between farmers and conservationists. Nowhere is this better illustrated than in Kenya, where 80 per cent of the population as well as 80 per cent of the remaining closed canopy forests occur in just 20 per cent of the total land area. Kenya has a large rural population relying more and more on subsistence farming. With low agricultural inputs, the subsequent demand for fresh and fertile soil is very high. Consequently, forests and virgin lands will increasingly be turned into agricultural land. Indeed, the current demographic trend can only exacerbate this pressure on the natural resources of the country: in 1992 the population of Kenya stood at 25 million; it is expected to reach 37 million by the end of the century.

Following a number of national workshops on endangered plant genetic resources, the National Museums of Kenya was given the mandate of identifying endangered species and proposing action for their conservation. In 1992 the Plant Conservation and Propagation Unit (PCPU) was established as a part of the East African Herbarium with bilateral assistance from the UK Overseas Development Administration.

Its broad mission is to: *Ensure the survival and proliferation of Kenya's endemic and threatened flora* by

> assessing conservation priorities through compiling and analysing our current knowledge of species and important sites for plant diversity;
> carrying out extensive field investigations for monitoring known populations of rare plants and identifying new wild populations;
> compiling a database of all the rare, threatened and endemic plants of conservation importance;
> securing germplasm for long-term storage *ex-situ*;
> developing a propagation research programme; and
> producing conservation plans and providing advice to land managers on appropriate conservation measures through site-based protection, sustainable species utilisation and reintroduction programmes.

Today, other national institutions such as the Kenya Wildlife Service and the Forestry Department are continuing to develop and implement sound site-based management programmes. It is generally recognised, however, that this approach needs to be complemented by targeted species conservation efforts. Many species, either occurring outside protected areas or even within our Forest Reserves and National Parks, are threatened by degradation or loss of habitat. With an enormous list of potentially threatened plants in Kenya and the limited resources available to such species conservation initiatives, prioritisation is inevitable.

The East African Herbarium has always had a vested interest in the Orchidaceae and after the PCPU was established this family was highlighted as a plant group for priority conservation study. Elsewhere the orchids are important horticultural plants, both as appealing house plants and as cut flowers. They are often a flagship group useful as material for introducing concepts of plant conservation and species management to a wide range of

★ Plant Conservation and Propagation Unit, East African Herbarium, National Museums of Kenya, P.O. Box 40658, Nairobi.

people. The opportunity to tap into the wealth of horticultural expertise and knowledge of wild populations through the Kenya Orchid Society also influenced our decision to make an early start on the conservation of these beautiful plants. Having encouraged the establishment of an *ad hoc* Indigenous Orchid Group through the Society, our conservation programme got off to a good start early in 1993.

The National Museums of Kenya Orchid Conservation Programme

Databasing
The East African Herbarium at the National Museums of Kenya in Nairobi is the second largest herbarium in Africa containing more than 750,000 specimens of which more than 6000 are orchids. Plant specimens in herbaria are arranged according to a phylogenetic system that physically arranges supposedly closely related families together in cupboards. Within a plant family, like the Orchidaceae, specimens are arranged by genus and within each genus, by species. As such, it is fairly easy to trace specimens of a particular species for confirmation of a provisional identification for example.

In addition to being an essential tool for plant identification, a herbarium specimen is a mine of additional information. With detailed data on the label we can establish where it was collected and by whom, at what time of the year and from what kind of environment it was collected, how the plant was growing, what colour the flowers were when it was collected, and often many more useful anecdotes depending on the keenness of the original collector. This wealth of information is absolutely vital in our quest for a better understanding of orchids in the wild and a prerequisite for any conservation work.

Valuable though this information is, questions are more often asked about species that are widely separated in the herbarium cupboards: 'Which epiphytic orchids can be found in Saiwa Swamp National Park, flowering in May?' Historically, this would have meant first sifting through 6000 specimens looking for those that had been collected in Saiwa Swamp, then filtering out those with open

flowers that were collected in May, a rather extensive and impractical task. Part of any conservation work requires all the available data about these specimens to be immediately 'on line' and easily manageable. The advent of modern computerised databasing systems has given us tremendous flexibility in querying the wealth of data stored on herbarium systems. A further advantage of having access to the data in an electronic form is that the actual specimens no longer need to be physically manipulated, which ensures that they will still be there, in good condition, for future generations of botanists.

We currently use a well-tested database application called BRAHMS (Botanical Research And Herbarium Management System), developed especially for this type of work at the Department of Plant Sciences, University of Oxford. The very task of computerising this sort of specimen data should not be underestimated. Three university graduates took a total of 18 person months to enter information from 6105 specimens at the East African Herbarium. This was further added to by data from an additional 410 specimens (from species of high conservation priority) at Kew giving our database a current holding of 6515 records, mostly from East Africa but covering a wide geographical area.

Orchid Red Data Book
One of the first outputs of any databasing activity is the production of a species list. How many species of orchids are there in Kenya, what are their correct names and where can they be found? The distribution and the number of times it has been collected give us an indication of the 'rarity' of a particular species. To develop a comprehensive list of those orchids that are in need of protection there are other aspects of the biology of a plant that have to be taken into consideration.

To decide whether an orchid is 'rare' or not we try to judge the following parameters.

Geographic range
Angraecum decipiens is only known from the floral regions K4 (Central Province, Kenya) and T2 (Northern Province, Tanzania). If we compare this with *Ansellia africana*, which occurs throughout sub-Saharan Africa and is widespread in Kenya as well, we can say that the geographic range of *A. decipiens* is very restricted.

Habitat specificity

Diaphananthe tenuicalcar is only found in, and at the edge of, montane forest and wooded grassland, between 2100 and 2400 m. This is a rather specific habitat requirement if we compare it with *Diaphananthe pulchella*, which grows in riverine forest, bushland, woodland and forest between 1500 and 2500 m.

Local population size

Here we judge if a species is locally abundant or constantly sparse where it occurs. This is difficult as it demands either good field notes on the specimen and/or a detailed knowledge of the species over the whole of its range.

Using these criteria we produced a 'candidate list' of the rare orchids of Kenya. Two things should be kept in mind when looking at this list.

1   The horticultural value of a plant has no direct influence on its priority classification. To us, as conservationists, every species matters, whether it has showy flowers or not. Indeed, even every population matters, because every population carries its own unique set of genes.

However, horticultural value can have an indirect effect on the rarity classification. For example, *Ansellia africana* is picked off the trees at the coast for sale to tourists and hotels because of its beautiful flowers. Because of this, the number of plants in the wild has been dramatically reduced; so that *A. africana* now becomes 'rare' at the coast.

2   Although a particular plant might be scarce in Kenya, its geographic range might be so wide that it is in no immediate danger of extinction. Here we should consider whether this particular plant was once abundant in Kenya and is now becoming rare, or whether it has always been rare. If it has always been rare in Kenya but can be found (in larger numbers) in other countries, it might not be of the highest priority to us. The orchids found in Kakamega forest are a good example. We recognise that with the general health of the forest in decline, definitely the orchids are threatened. However, most of the orchids found there also occur in the rain forests in other parts of Africa.

Ansellia africana: variety from coastal Kenya.   BOB CAMPBELL

Having established a 'candidate list' of plants likely to be in need of active conservation measures, an extensive investigative process on this narrow band of species can begin. The available specimen data is added to from literature sources, from comments by experts both local and international and from our own observations in the field. For example, several members of the Kenya Orchid Society have passed on extremely valuable information about our candidate species and have advised us accordingly on whether special attention should be paid to particular species. Often there are populations of candidate species known by 'amateur' botanists from where no herbarium specimens have been collected. All this information is held in our database and can be prepared into a variety of species reports.

This major output of the project will be a fully annotated list of about 70 species of Kenya orchids out of the total of some 280. Data availability on most of the terrestrial species is still very scanty in Kenya and hence we have erred on the side of caution. With extensive field work and careful scrutiny by field workers our understanding of terrestrial species will improve over the years, and many species currently ranked with high priority will be moved to a lower priority or indeed taken off the rare list altogether.

Field surveys

The large number of species contained in our Red Data Book merely reflects the lack of necessary

Ansellia africana: plant in cultivation.

BOB CAMPBELL

extensive field data required to make decisions about the current status of a species in the wild. The challenge at this particular stage of the project is to add value to our list by beginning a monitoring programme of field populations. Firstly, a visit to the known localities of each rare species (derived from both herbarium specimens and information passed to us from our colleagues in the Kenya Orchid Society) will tell us if these plants still exist. Consider for instance the case of *Polystachya bella*, a plant known only from the Kericho area, highly prized for cultivation both at home and abroad, and a species of high priority in our Red Data Book. The last time it was collected for the East African Herbarium was in 1942! We have no idea how many wild populations of this species are left, what numbers of plants exist in each and to what extent they are threatened.

Our field surveys have the following objectives to:

> verify the existence of previously reported wild populations of priority species;
>
> establish the size of the existing populations in terms of habitat extent and potential breeding stock (the local genepool);
>
> identify those populations with the immediate threat of genetic erosion; and
>
> collect sufficient germplasm for propagation and seed production *ex-situ* (at least two plants required per population).

In addition we are able to observe a number of biological characters of the plants in the wild such as pollinating agents, microhabitat requirements and the interactions with animals (including use of the plant by the local human population). We will normally collect plants for herbarium specimens and, equally importantly, for our living collection in the PCPU nursery.

With 70 high priority species, the number of localities to visit is very high. However, with the help of our database we can easily plot orchid distribution maps and extract those areas in Kenya which are 'orchid hot spots'. It is paramount that an assessment of these areas should be made as a matter of priority. We soon hope to integrate a thorough field investigation programme using the Indigenous Orchid Group members as well as M.Sc. students to assist in gathering this type of information.

The living collection
Whilst we will concentrate our activities on the high priority species identified in our Red Data Book, we are also working towards gathering a representative living collection, with a specimen from each recognised species occurring in Kenya.

This living collection is housed in three newly built greenhouses on the NMK grounds. The houses cater for plants from different climatic zones. There is a hothouse for the coastal plants, an intermediate house for plants from the warmer forests or lower altitude zones and a shade house for the cooler forest species.

The living collection serves several purposes.

Ex-situ germplasm collection

First and foremost, it holds the stock material, *ex situ*, for propagation and seed production. Should certain species disappear from their natural environment then this material can be used for breeding and reintroduction in the same or similar habitats. Therefore, every living plant is fully documented just as if it were a herbarium specimen with a unique accession number on its label that refers back to all the information on this particular plant stored in our database.

Taxonomy

In effect the collection is a living herbarium, complementing the pressed material in the cupboards. It provides a readily available source of material for our taxonomic colleagues around the world who may need living material for a whole variety of analyses; simple morphological studies and the modern molecular systematic techniques can all benefit from the availability of this material.

Education and display

While two of the three greenhouses are reserved for scientific use, the bigger shadehouse will, in future, be open to the general public. The living collection will be used to educate the many parties of school children that visit the museum every year, as well as the general public, on matters of nature and plant conservation.

In addition, we hope to be able to keep confidential notes on the variety of Kenyan material held in other collections both locally and worldwide. This will ultimately give us the ability to pinpoint the whereabouts of living material for study and breeding without needing to deplete wild populations. Many conservation programmes around the world consider selling orchid plants to the albeit limited international market, a valuable and justifiable scenario in the combat against collection of wild plants. In addition to providing a ready supply of local species plants, the profit from these activities will be able to contribute to the funding of the conservation programme.

In vitro *propagation*
When an *Ansellia* seed pod bursts and the tiny yellow seeds are released from the pod everything is set for a new generation of leopard orchids to start life. Evolution has geared up orchid seeds for wind dispersal. An *Ansellia* pod contains hundreds

of thousands of seeds that will spread on the wind like tiny yellow dust particles. Because the seeds are so small they have no reserves for independent germination. Indeed, they need an intimate association with certain fungi before germination can take place. The chance that seed and fungus land in the same spot is slight and in nature very few seeds will actually find the right conditions for germination. In the laboratory, however, the right conditions for germination of orchid seeds can be created rather easily. If the seeds are placed on a nutrient medium that contains a source of energy like sugar, then the fungus can be omitted. In fact, the germination percentage can be dramatically

Polystachya caespitifica ssp. *latilabris*

BOB CAMPBELL

increased using this technique of *in vitro* asymbiotic germination. Where few seeds would find the right conditions in nature to germinate, in tissue culture all seeds are given ideal conditions. In some cases more than 99 per cent of the seeds will germinate and given the high number of seeds per pod, one pod will provide us with more plants than we need for our purposes.

Within the PCPU we use this approach to propagate rare and endangered Kenyan orchids. The unit has a tissue culture laboratory and a culture room where the germinating seeds and the small plants are kept. Whilst the techniques for *in vitro* orchid seed germination are rather standard, little work has been done on African species. Usually, a trial and error approach is necessary to find the right conditions to propagate a particular species.

Our general approach is as follows:

1 Ripe, but not yet burst, pods are brought to the laboratory where they are pre-sterilised. This can be done by simply dipping them in 20 per cent bleach for 20 minutes (for smaller pods) or by dipping them in alcohol and putting the alcohol on fire (for larger pods). In this way most of the microorganisms on the outside of the pod are destroyed.

2 Seed pods are then dried in an hermetically closed cabinet. Inside the cabinet a jar with anhydrous calcium chloride will absorb all the moisture.

3 After a while the seed pod will burst and the seeds can be separated from the pod. They are stored in small vials in a refrigerator at 4 °C for later use.

4 Before being sown on nutrient medium the seeds have to be sterilised. If any microorganisms are present when the seeds are distributed on the nutrient medium, these microorganisms will quickly overgrow the germinating seeds and the latter will be killed quite fast. Therefore, the tiny seeds are wrapped in a small filter paper packet which is submersed in a 10 per cent bleach solution for 10 minutes. From this point onwards all manipulations have to be done under sterile conditions. A laminar air flow cabinet provides us with such a sterile environment. Basically it is a bench with plastic walls on the sides and at the top. At the opposite end from the worker is an engine that pulls air through a very fine filter. Because the pores of the filter are smaller than any of the microorganisms, the air that passes over the bench is sterile. Furthermore, non-sterile air cannot enter the cabinet because the air flow is in one direction.

5 Once the seeds are sterilised, they are washed in sterile water and plated on to three different media. As standard media we use Murashige & Skoog, Knudson C and Phytamax™. There is no way to establish before hand which medium is going to support germination, but usually at least one of the media will give good results. Different species will also give different results, so for each new species we will have to test which of the media will support germination and growth.

6 Once plated, the petri dishes are incubated in a culture room at around 25 °C under a 10 hour day/14 hour night cycle. Progress is observed and notes are made.

7 Once the plants start developing leaves, they are transferred to fresh medium. Because the seeds are so small it is usually very difficult to spread them evenly over the medium. Sometimes there are too many seeds on a plate and once they start growing the medium can get depleted quite quickly. Therefore the plants are transferred onto fresh medium after a certain time. They are then brought back to the culture room where they are left until they are big enough for weaning.

8 Plants are carefully removed from the flasks and all remnants of the medium are washed off. The roots are dipped in an antifungal solution, before the plants are potted. Depending on the habit of the plant, whether it is an epiphyte or a terrestrial, a suitable substrate will be selected. Locally available substrates like pumice, lava, vermiculite, compost and elephant manure are used in different mixtures.

9 The whole process, starting from the seed to the weaned plant, may easily take a year or more.

Study of the fungi associated with Kenyan terrestrial orchids

The technique described above is called asymbiotic seed germination because the fungi, known as mycorrhizal fungi, that naturally have an important role in the germination process are omitted. The role of the fungi is taken over by the nutrients and the sugar in the medium. This technique works well with most epiphytic orchids, however it is not always successful with terrestrial orchids. Temperate terrestrials, especially, do not always respond to asymbiotic germination. It seems that in their case the role of the fungus is much more important. They can only be propagated using a symbiotic germination technique, whereby seeds are sown on medium in the presence of a particular fungus, so that the natural infection process can take place. The symbiotic technique was developed early this century, but was more or less abandoned when Knudson developed his asymbiotic technique in 1922. However, it was revived in the 1970s and has since been used successfully to propagate hardy Australian, European and North American terrestrial orchid species.

As is the case for temperate terrestrial orchids, seeds of a number of Kenyan terrestrials do not respond to the asymbiotic germination. If we are to propagate these, symbiotic techniques will have to be developed. A prerequisite for this is to have the right fungi for symbiotic germination.

The majority of the fungi associated with orchids are considered to be members of the genus *Rhizoctonia*. Although many species have been described, very little information is available on the fungi associated with African orchids. Initially it was believed that symbiosis between orchids and their fungi was always highly specific. These days a degree of fungal specificity is suspected in certain orchid species while some seem to be capable of utilising a wider range of fungi for germination. It seems unlikely, however, that the fungi which are used in the symbiotic germination of temperate terrestrials will give equally good results with tropical terrestrials.

We have, therefore, initiated a research project on the isolation and description of fungi from Kenyan terrestrial orchids and will attempt to establish their role in orchid seed germination. The project is carried out in collaboration with the Botany Department of the University of Nairobi.

To date we have isolated 15 fungal strains from 8 terrestrial orchid species belonging to 5 genera. Having described them, they will be used in symbiotic germination experiments. They will be scored for their ability to improve the germination of seeds of terrestrial orchids that do not respond to the symbiotic germination technique. With this project we hope to lay a foundation for the propagation of Kenya's terrestrial orchids.

Conclusion

With these initiatives in orchid conservation, we hope to continue to draw together the expertise within the East African Herbarium, the Kenya Orchid Society and the various Universities in the country to address the many issues so important to species conservation planning. Conservation must not be viewed solely as a job for the research scientist in professional institutions. Indeed, most of the important new information about our rarer species is the result of a keen horticultural eye or a strong pair of legs to reach the mist forest at the top of dry country hills.

The next decade will see whether or not these early initiatives will bear fruit in terms of protecting some of our most beautiful plant resources from the many inevitable pressures that modern Kenya puts on our natural habitats. Orchid enthusiasts worldwide have a responsibility to promote and encourage studies of the very subjects of their enthusiasm. We must all work hard to pool resources, information and expertise to ensure that our children can still marvel at the tremendous variety of these very special elements of our natural plant heritage.

Glossary

The definitions of botanical terms that are given below are limited to the sense in which the words have been used in this book. Many of them would have slightly different or broader meanings in a wider botanical context.

Acumen a long slender sharp point.
Acuminate gradually tapering to a long slender point or acumen.
Acute sharply pointed.
Adnate attached throughout its whole length to another structure of the same kind.
Anther the pollen-bearing part of a stamen.
Anther cap the outer, deciduous cap, or case which covers the pollinia.
Anthesis the opening of the flower.
Apex the tip of a leaf, bract or stem.
Apical at the tip.
Apiculate ending abruptly in a sharp point.
Apiculus a short point.
Appendage a part, usually small, that is attached to another part.
Arcuate curved like a bow.
Auricle a small lobe or appendage, sometimes shaped like an ear lobe.
Auricled having an auricle or pair of auricles.
Auriculate eared, auricled.
Axil the angle between the upper side of a leaf, branch or bract and the stem, or axis, from which it grows.
Axillary growing in an axil.
Axis the central or main stem of a plant or inflorescence.

Bifid divided halfway into two.
Bilabiate with two lips.
Bipartite divided nearly to the base into two, usually unequal parts.
Bract a small leaf, or leaf-like structure, in the axil of which a flower is borne.

Calcarate carrying a spur.
Callus (singular) **calli** (plural) a solid protuberance caused by a mass of cells.
Capitate growing close together in a head.
Capsule a dry fruit that splits open at maturity to release its seeds.

Caudicle a stalk connecting the pollen masses to the viscidium, or gland, or uniting them.
Cauline belonging to the stem, or arising from it.
Chloroplast the granule, or plastid, that contains green pigments.
Ciliate fringed with short hairs, like eyelashes, on the margin.
Ciliolate ciliate but with very short fine hairs.
Claw the narrow, stalk-like base of the petal or lip.
Clavate thickened at the end, club-shaped.
Column the central part of the orchid flower, formed by the union of the stamen, style and stigma.
Conduplicate folded lengthwise, V-shaped in cross-section.
Connate when the bases of two opposite parts are joined together.
Convolute when one part is rolled up inside another.
Cordate heart-shaped.
Coriaceous leathery.
Corymb an inflorescence that appears flat – the flowers are borne on pedicels of different lengths so that they lie all in one plane.
Corymbose like a corymb.
Crenulate scalloped, but the individual scallops or teeth small.
Crest a ridge, usually on one of the tepals, often decorated or fringed.
Crispate having an irregular, curly margin.
Crisped irregular and curling, usually applied to the margin of a leaf or tepal.
Cuneate wedge shaped.
Cuspidate tipped with a cusp, a sharp rigid point.

Deciduous falling off at some stage in the life of the flower or plant; not evergreen.
Deflexed bent or turned sharply downwards.
Dentate having a row of tooth-like outgrowths along the margin.
Denticulate toothed, but the teeth small.
Disc the upper surface of the lip; usually used for the central part of the upper surface.
Distichous arranged in 2 vertical ranks or rows on opposite sides of an axis.
Dormant applied to parts which are not in active growth.

Dorsal relating to the back or outer surface.

Dorsal sepal the intermediate, or odd sepal, usually at the back or upper side of the flower.

Elliptic shaped like an ellipse, narrowly oblong with regular, rounded ends.

Emarginate having a notch cut out, usually at the apical margin.

Endemic confined to a region, or country, and not occurring naturally anywhere else.

Entire with an even margin, without teeth or divisions.

Epichile the terminal part of the lip, used when this is distinct from the basal part.

Epidermis the cellular skin or covering of a plant, often protected by a waxy outer covering or cuticle.

Epilithic growing on rocks.

Epiphyte a plant that grows on other plants, but not as a parasite.

Epiphytic relating to epiphytes.

Equitant folded lengthwise so that the base of each leaf enfolds the next.

Erose as though bitten or gnawed at the edge.

Falcate sickle-shaped.

Filiform thread-like.

Fimbriate having the margin fringed with long, narrow processes or appendages.

Flabellate fan-shaped.

Flexuose, flexuous zig-zag, bent alternately in opposite directions.

Floriferous producing many flowers.

Foot a basal extension of the column.

Fungus (singular) **fungi** (plural) a living organism that lacks chlorophyll and obtains its nutrients by digesting dead or living organic matter.

Galea a sepal or petal shaped like a helmet.

Galeate hollow and vaulted, like a helmet.

Geniculate abruptly bent so as to resemble a knee joint.

Genus (singular) **Genera** (plural) the smallest natural group containing distinct species.

Generic the name of a genus.

Glabrous smooth, completely lacking hairs, spines or other projections.

Glandular possessing glands, secreting structures on the outer surface of an organ, often hair-like.

Glaucous blueish green.

Globose spherical, or nearly so.

Habit the general appearance of a plant, whether prostrate, erect, climbing, etc.

Herbaceous describing plants of small size whose stems are not woody, often plants with annual stems from a perennial root.

Hypochile the basal portion of the lip.

Imbricate overlapping like the tiles on a roof.

Inflorescence the part of the plant bearing flowers; the arrangement of flowers on the flowering stem.

Intermediate sepal the dorsal, or odd sepal, usually uppermost in the flower.

Internode the space or portion of stem between two adjacent nodes.

Keel a median, lengthwise ridge.

Keikei a small plant arising from the stem or inflorescence, rarely from a root of a mature plant.

Labellum the lip, or lowest petal of an orchid flower; usually held on the lower side of the flower and different in form from the two lateral petals.

Lacerate torn.

Lamella (singular) **lamellae** (plural) a thin, plate-like elevation.

Lamina part of a leaf or petal that is expanded, usually thin and flat; the blade of a leaf.

Lanceolate lance or spear-shaped; much longer than wide and tapering to a point at both ends.

Lateral sepals the pair of similar sepals arranged at the sides of an orchid flower.

Lax loose or distant, as opposed to tightly or densely arranged.

Liane a very elongated climber, usually with a woody stem.

Ligulate strap-shaped.

Limb the broad or expanded part of a petal or leaf.

Linear narrow, many times longer than wide, sides more or less parallel.

Lip the labellum, or odd petal of an orchid flower; usually held on the lower side of the flower and different in shape, colour and size from the two lateral petals.

Lithophyte, lithophytic living on a rock.

Lobe a division of an organ, often round but may be of any shape.

Lunulate half-moon shaped, but very small.

Mentum a chin-like projection formed at the base of the lip or by the united bases of the lateral sepals.

Mesochile the intermediate part of the lip, in those orchid flowers where three parts are clearly discernible.

Moniliform like a string of beads.

Monocotyledons plants characterised by one seed-leaf in the embryo, and other associated features.

Monopodial a stem with a single continuous axis.

Monotypic having only one example, as in a genus with only one species.

Mucro a sharp terminal point.

Mucronate having a short sharp point, usually at the apex.

Mycelium the vegetative growth of a fungus, made up of many hyphae.

Mycorrhiza, mycorrhizal the symbiotic union of a fungus with the roots of a plant.

Node a point on a stem where a leaf is attached.

Obconic, obconical conical, but attached at the narrower end.

Obcordate heart-shaped, with the widest part at the apex.

Oblanceolate lanceolate, with the widest part near the apex.

Oblong much longer than broad, with nearly parallel sides.

Obovate reversed ovate, wider at the apical end.

Obtuse blunt or rounded at the end.

Orbicular round and flat.

Ovary that part of the flower which contains the ovules; in orchids it is always below the flower;

Ovate egg-shaped in outline, usually pointed at the apex, wider towards the base.

Ovoid egg-shaped.

Pandurate fiddle-shaped.

Panicle a branching inflorescence in which all the branches bear flowers.

Papilla (singular) **Papillae** (plural) small fleshy protuberance on the surface of the leaf or flower.

Papillose bearing papillae.

Pedicel the stalk of an individual flower.

Peduncle the stalk of an inflorescence.

Perianth the colourful parts of an orchid flower, consisting of 6 tepals usually distinguished as 3 sepals, 2 petals and the lip.

Petals in orchid flowers, 2 of the 3 inner members of the perianth.

Petiole the stalk of a leaf.

Petiolate having a petiole.

Plicate folded like a fan; pleated.

Pollinium (singular) **Pollinia** (plural) a body composed of many pollen grains cohering together.

Pollinarium the structure consisting of pollinia, stipe and viscidium which is the unit of pollination in many orchids.

Pseudobulb the thickened stem or stem-base of many orchid plants.

Pubescent hairy.

Quadrate square.

Raceme an unbranched inflorescence in which the flowers are borne on short pedicels and usually open in succession from the base upwards.

Rachis the flower-bearing portion of an inflorescence.

Radical describing leaves which arise so close to the base of the stem as to appear to be proceeding from the root.

Recurved curved downwards or back upon itself.

Reniform kidney-shaped.

Resupinate having the lip lowermost because the pedicel or ovary is twisted through 180°.

Reticulate net-veined; the smallest visible veins are connected together like the meshes of a net.

Retuse a rounded end the centre of which is depressed or shorter than the sides.

Revolute rolled back from the edges.

Rhizome a root-like stem that creeps under or over the ground or other surface, sending roots downwards and branches, leaves or flowering shoots upwards; always distinguished from a root by the presence of leaves or scales and buds.

Rostellum a projection from the upper edge of the stigma in front of the anther.

Rugose covered with wrinkles.

Rugulose somewhat wrinkled.

Saccate pouched or bag-shaped.

Saprophyte a living organism that obtains its nourishment from dead organic matter.

Scabrid rough to the touch.

Scandent climbing.

Scape a leafless flower-stalk arising from the ground.

Scarious thin, dry and membranous, not green.

Secund having the flowers arranged apparently in one row along the side of an inflorescence.

Sepals the 3 outermost tepals of the perianth in the flower.

Serrate with forward-pointing teeth along the margin.

Serrulate serrate, but with minute teeth.

Sessile without a stalk.

Sheath the lower portion of the leaf, clasping the stem; also used for bracts which enclose the flowering stem below those which support the flowers.

Spathulate oblong, with the apical end rounded like a spatula.

Species a group of individuals that exhibit the same distinctive characters; the unit which provides the basis for classification.

Spike an unbranched inflorescence bearing sessile flowers; sometimes used, in orchids, for long slender racemes of many flowers.

Spreading arranged so that the tips of the parts are directed outwards, more or less horizontally.

Spur a tubular projection from one of the floral parts, usually the lip or the dorsal sepal.

Stelidium (singular) **Stelidia** (plural) a term used to describe 2 small teeth at the apex of the column in certain genera of orchids.

Stigma, Stigmatic surface the sticky area on the column that receives the pollen or pollinarium.

Stipe the stalk that connects the viscidium with the caudicles of the pollinia.

Stolon a branch which, because it roots at a node, often gives rise to a new individual at some distance from the parent plant.

Subspecies (ssp.) a subdivision of a species, usually confined to one geographical area and recognised by one or more characteristic features.

Subtribe a small group of genera that have certain characteristics in common; a smaller unit of classification than the tribe.

Subulate with a fine sharp point; awl-shaped.

Superposed arranged vertically, each somewhat above the preceding.

Symbiosis the living together of dissimilar organisms with benefit to one or both.

Symbiotic relating to symbiosis.

Sympodial a stem made up of a series of superposed branches; each branch terminates in a leaf or flower and a new branch arises below it to extend the body of the plant.

Synonym another name for the same species or genus, but one which is no longer in general use.

Taxonomist one who is skilled in classification.

Taxonomic pertaining to classification.

Tepal a division of the perianth; usually used collectively or when the perianth is not markedly differentiated into sepals and petals.

Terete cylindrical, circular in cross-section.

Terrestrial on or in the ground.

Tomentose densely hairy, either with many short hairs or with a matted, wool-like outgrowth of hairs.

Tribe a group of several genera that have certain characteristics in common.

Truncate straight-ended, as though cut off across the end.

Tuber (i) a thickened branch of an underground stem that produces buds; (ii) a swollen root or branch of a root that serves as a store of reserve food.

Tuberous (i) resembling a tuber; (ii) producing tubers.

Tufted a group of leaves or stems arising very close together.

Type specimen the original specimen from which a description was drawn up.

Umbel, Umbellate an inflorescence in which the diverging pedicels, all of the same length, arise from the same point at the apex of the peduncle.

Undulate with a wavy margin or surface.

Vandaceous with a habit of growth similar to that of the genus *Vanda*, i.e. monopodial with the leaves in two ranks.

Variety (var.) a subdivision of a species that is easily recognised by its different size, colour, or other minor modification.

Velamen the absorbent epidermis of the roots of many orchids.

Venation the arrangement of the veins in a leaf, bract or flower.

Verrucose warty.

Viscidium (singular) **viscidia** (plural) the sticky gland attached to the pollinium, usually produced by the rostellum.

Whorl the arrangement of leaves or flowers in a circle around an axis.

Bibliography

References to the original publication of plant names are not given here because they would make the bibliography so long. Also, there is so much detailed information on taxonomic and nomenclatural matters in the *Flora of Tropical East Africa* that it seemed unnecessary to repeat it in a book of this kind.

Agnew, A.D.Q. & Agnew, S., 1994. *Upland Kenya Wild Flowers*, 2nd edn. East Africa Natural History Society, Nairobi.

Ball, J.S., 1978. *Southern African Epiphytic Orchids*. Conservation Press, Johannesburg.

Bechtel, H., Cribb, P.J. & Launert, E., 1992. *The Manual of Cultivated Orchid Species*, 3rd edn. Blandford Press, London.

Blundell, M., 1987. *Collins Guide to the Wild Flowers of East Africa*. Collins, London.

Copley, G.C., Tweedie, E.M. & Carroll, E.W., 1964. A key and checklist to Kenya orchids. *Journal of the East African Natural History Society*, 24: 1–59, 85–91.

Cribb, P.J., 1979. The orchids of Arabia. *Kew Bulletin*, 33: 651–78.

Cribb, P.J., 1984. Orchidaceae, Part 2. In *Flora of Tropical East Africa*, ed. R.M. Polhill, pp. 237–412 A.A. Balkema, Rotterdam.

Cribb, P.J., 1989. Orchidaceae (Part 3). In *Flora of Tropical East Africa*, ed. R.M. Polhill, pp. 413–652. A.A. Balkema, Rotterdam.

Dressler, R.L., 1974. Classification of the orchid family. In *Proceedings, 7th World Orchid Conference*, ed. H. Mariano Ospina, pp. 259–79. Medellin.

Geerinck, D., 1984. Orchidaceae (premiere partie). In *Flore d'Afrique Centrale*, pp. 1–296. Jardin botanique national de Belgique.

Geerinck, D., 1988. Orchidaceae. In *Flore du Rwanda*: Spermatophytes, Vol. IV, ed. G. Troupin, pp. 505-629. Tervuren, Belgium.

Geerinck, D., 1992. Orchidaceae (seconde partie). In *Flore d'Afrique Centrale*, pp. 297–780. Jardin botanique national de Belgique.

Hall, A.V., 1965. Studies of the South African species of *Eulophia*. *Journal of South African Botany*, Suppl. Vol. no. V.

Hall, A.V., 1982. A revision of the Southern African species of *Satyrium*. *Contributions from the Bolus Herbarium*, 10: 1-137.

Johannson, D., 1974. Ecology of vascular epiphytes in West African rain forest. *Acta Phytogeographica Suecica*, Uppsala, 59.

Jonsson, L., 1981. A monograph of the genus *Microcoelia*. *Symbolae Botanicae Uppsalienses*, 23 (4).

la Croix, I.F., la Croix, E.A.S., & la Croix, T.M., 1991. *Orchids of Malawi*. A.A. Balkema, Rotterdam.

Lind, E.M. & Morrison, M.E.S., 1974. *East African Vegetation*. Longman, London.

Linder, H.P., 1981. Taxonomic studies on the Disinae. III A revision of *Disa* Berg. excluding sect. Micranthae Lindl. *Contributions from the Bolus Herbarium*, 9.

Linder, H.P., 1981. Taxonomic studies on the Disinae. IV A revision of *Disa* Berg. sect. Micranthae Lindl. *Bulletin du Jardin botanique national Belgique*, 51: 255–346.

Moreau, W.M. & Moreau, R.E., 1943. An introduction to the epiphytic orchids of East Africa. *Journal of the East African Natural History Society*, 17: 1–32.

Pettersson, B., 1990. Studies in the genus *Nervilia* (Orchidaceae) in Africa. Ph.D. thesis, Uppsala.

Piers, F., 1968. *Orchids of East Africa*. J. Cramer, Lehre.

Rolfe, R.A., 1897–8. Orchideae. In *Flora of Tropical Africa*, Vol. 7, ed. W.T. Thiselton-Dyer, pp. 12–292. Reeve, Ashford.

Schelpe, E.A.C.L.E., 1966. *An Introduction to the South African Orchids*. Macdonald, London.

Segerback, L.B., 1983. *Orchids of Nigeria*. Balkema, Rotterdam.

Stewart, J., 1973. A second checklist of the orchids of Kenya. *American Orchid Society Bulletin*, 42: 525–31.

Stewart, J., 1979. A revision of the African species of *Aerangis* (Orchidaceae). *Kew Bulletin*, 34: 239–319.

Stewart, J. & Campbell, B., 1970. *Orchids of Tropical Africa*. W.H. Allen, London.

Stewart, J. & Griffiths, M. (eds.) 1995. *The RHS Manual of Orchids*. Macmillan Press, London.

Stewart, J. & Hennessy, E.F., 1982. *Orchids of Africa: a Select Review*. Macmillan South Africa, Johannesburg.

Stewart, J. & la Croix, I.F., 1987. Notes on the orchids of southern tropical Africa III: Aerangis. *Kew Bulletin*, 42: 215–19.

Stewart, J., Linder, H.P., Schelpe, E.A. & Hall. A.V., 1982. *Wild Orchids of Southern Africa*. Macmillan South Africa, Johannesburg.

Summerhayes, V.S., 1968. Orchidaceae, Part 1. In *Flora of Tropical East Africa*, eds. E. Milne-Redhead & R.M. Polhill, pp. 1–236. Crown Agents, London.

Vermeulen, J.J., 1987. *Orchid Monographs*, Vol. 2: *A Taxonomic Revision of the Continental African Bulbophyllinae*. E.J. Brill, Leiden.

Williamson, G., 1977. *The Orchids of South Central Africa*. Dent, London.

Index

In this index the names printed in roman type are those which are in current use. Synonyms are printed in italics. Page numbers in bold type refer to illustrations.

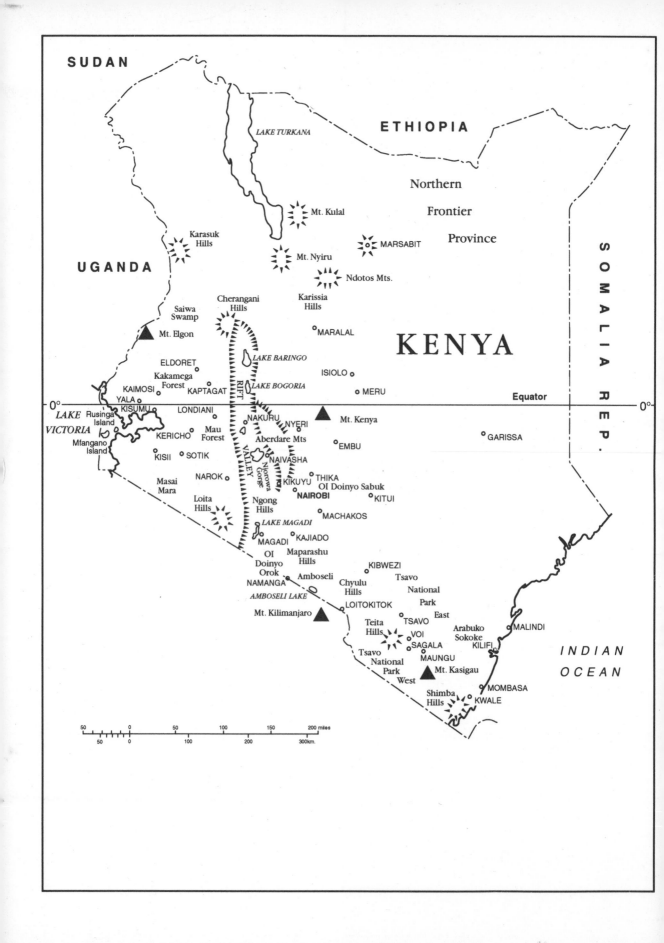